Susan Uetrok
1505 Bonnie Drive
Bethlehem Penna. 18018.

868-2280

Introduction
to Mathematics

SECOND EDITION

INTRODUCTION

Bruce E. Meserve
Professor of Mathematics
University of Vermont

Max A. Sobel
Professor of Mathematics
Montclair State College

TO MATHEMATICS

Prentice-Hall, Inc., Englewood Cliffs, New Jersey

Introduction to Mathematics, *Second Edition*

BRUCE E. MESERVE

MAX A. SOBEL

Current printing (last digit): 10 9 8 7 6

13-487322-X

Library of Congress Catalog Card Number 75-77849

Printed in the United States of America

PRENTICE-HALL INTERNATIONAL, INC., *London*
PRENTICE-HALL OF AUSTRALIA, PTY. LTD., *Sydney*
PRENTICE-HALL OF CANADA, LTD., *Toronto*
PRENTICE-HALL OF INDIA PRIVATE LTD., *New Delhi*
PRENTICE-HALL OF JAPAN, INC., *Tokyo*

PREFACE

Mathematics can be fun! The authors have embarked with this idea
and have gone ahead to introduce a variety of interesting and timely
topics without a major emphasis upon the so-called practical applications. This point of view, it is felt, will leave the reader with a better
picture of the true meaning and beauty of mathematics as opposed
to a traditional approach with a major emphasis on abstract manipulations.

Very little mathematical background is required of the reader.
It is expected that he will have had some secondary school introduction to algebra and geometry, but no working knowledge of any of
the skills normally taught in these subjects is presupposed. Maturity,
on the other hand, is expected; and interest in the subject is antici-
pated.

The topics considered in this book are used throughout many of the activities of citizens in our technological society. Accordingly, this book has been written with a number of different audiences in mind. The subject matter is suitable for the undergraduate college student who has had moderate secondary school training in mathematics, one who is not a mathematics major but who wishes to acquire a basic understanding of the nature of mathematics. Many students seeking a knowledge of basic mathematics are so included. Frequently, prospective elementary-school teachers will be among such students. This book is also appropriate for inservice courses for elementary school and many junior high school teachers. To this end, the emphasis throughout the book is on key concepts and the structure of mathematics, without undue concern over the mechanical procedures.

The famous French mathematician René Descartes concluded his famous *La Géométrie* with the statement: "I hope that posterity will judge me kindly, not only as to the things which I have explained, but also as to those which I have intentionally omitted so as to leave to others the pleasure of discovery." The authors have attempted to provide a great deal of exposition in this text. They have, however, left a great deal for the reader so that he may experience the true beauty of mathematics through discovery.

Finally, the authors wish to express their appreciation to the editors of Prentice-Hall, Inc. for all of their efforts in behalf of the publication of this text. In particular the authors wish to thank Mr. James Walsh for his constant faith in them, and Miss Dorothy Crouch for her patience and skill in editing the manuscript.

Bruce E. Meserve
Max A. Sobel

CONTENTS

GLOSSARY OF SYMBOLS

$=$	is equal to	$\parallel$	is parallel to
$\neq$	is not equal to	$\perp$	is perpendicular to
$>$	is greater than	$\cong$	is congruent to
$\ngtr$	is not greater than	$\sim$	is similar to
$<$	is less than	$\angle ABC$	angle ABC
$\nless$	is not less than	$f(x)$	a function of x
$\geq$	is greater than or equal to	$|x|$	the absolute value of x
$\leq$	is less than or equal to	$\wedge$	and (conjunction)
$\in$	is a member of	$\vee$	or (disjunction)
$\notin$	is not a member of	$\sim p$	not p (negation)
$\varnothing$, { }	the empty set	$p \rightarrow q$	if p, then q (conditional)
$\{1, 2\}$	the set one, two		
$\{x \,|\, \ldots\}$	the set of all x such that . . .	$p \leftrightarrow q$	p if and only if q (biconditional)
$\subseteq$	subset	$P(A)$	the probability of A
$\subset$	proper subset		
$\cap$	intersection	$n!$	$1 \times 2 \times 3 \times \ldots \times n$
$\cup$	union	$_nP_r$	the number of permutations of n things taken r at a time
$\overset{\leftrightarrow}{AB}$	the line AB		
$\overset{\circ\rightarrow}{AB}$	the half-line AB	$_nC_r$, $\binom{n}{r}$	the number of combinations of n things taken r at a time
$\overline{AB}$	the line segment AB		
$\overset{\rightarrow}{AB}$	the ray AB	$\forall_x$	for all x
$\overset{\circ-\circ}{AB}$	the open line segment AB	$\exists_x$	there exists an x such that

chapter 1

FUN WITH MATHEMATICS

Mathematics has numerous practical applications ranging from everyday household usage to the charting of astronauts through outer space. Many people study the subject because of such applications as they relate to their particular fields of interest. Mathematics may also be considered as part of our great cultural heritage, for it has a history that dates back many thousands of years. As such, it should be studied by the average citizen who wishes to be literate in this twentieth century.

Mathematics also interests many just by the sheer beauty of its structure. We hope in this text to examine some of this beauty without unduly emphasizing the practical values. Thus we hope to show that mathematics can be studied just for one's interest in it—that is, just for fun. Accordingly, this chapter contains a smorgasbord variety of items served up to whet the reader's appetite for the main course that follows. The material contained in this chapter is not sequential, nor is it necessary for an understanding of the later chapters in this text, although some of the topics presented here will be presented in greater detail in later chapters.

1-1 MATHEMATICAL PATTERNS

Mathematicians love to search for patterns and generalizations in all branches of their subjects—in arithmetic, in algebra, and in geometry. A search for such patterns may not only be interesting but may also help one develop insight into mathematics as a whole.

MULTIPLES OF NINE

Many patterns that often escape notice may be found in the structure of arithmetic. For example, consider the multiples of 9:

$$1 \times 9 = 9$$
$$2 \times 9 = 18$$
$$3 \times 9 = 27$$
$$4 \times 9 = 36$$
$$5 \times 9 = 45$$
$$6 \times 9 = 54$$
$$7 \times 9 = 63$$
$$8 \times 9 = 72$$
$$9 \times 9 = 81$$

What patterns do you notice in the column of multiples on the right? You may note that the sum of the digits in each case is always 9. You should also see that the units digit decreases (9, 8, 7, . . .), whereas the tens digit increases (1, 2, 3, . . .). What lies behind this pattern?

Consider the product

$$5 \times 9 = 45.$$

To find 6×9 we need to add 9 to 45. Instead of adding 9, we may add 10 and subtract 1.

$$
\begin{array}{ll}
45 & 55 \\
+10 & -1 \\
\hline
55 & 54 = 6 \times 9
\end{array}
$$

That is, by adding 1 to the tens digit, 4, of 45, we are really adding 10 to 45. We then subtract 1 from the units digit, 5, of 45 to obtain 54 as our product.

FINGER MULTIPLICATION

The number 9, incidentally, has other fascinating properties. Of special interest is a procedure for multiplying by 9 on one's fingers. For example, to multiply 9 by 3, place both hands together as in the figure, and bend the third finger from the left. The result is read as 27.

The next figure shows the procedure for finding the product 7×9. Note that the seventh finger from the left is bent, and the result is read in terms of the tens digit, to the left, and the units digit to the right of the bent finger. (Note that a thumb is considered to be a finger.)

What number fact is shown in the next figure?

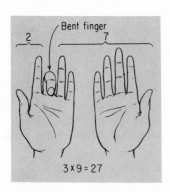
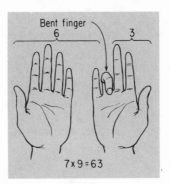
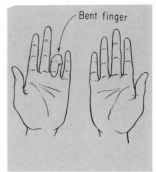

PATTERNS OF NUMBERS

Here is one more pattern related to the number 9. You may, if you wish, verify that each of the following is correct:

$$1 \times 9 + 2 = 11$$
$$12 \times 9 + 3 = 111$$
$$123 \times 9 + 4 = 1{,}111$$
$$1{,}234 \times 9 + 5 = 11{,}111$$
$$12{,}345 \times 9 + 6 = 111{,}111$$

Try to find a correspondence of the number of 1's in the number symbol on the right with one of the numbers used on the left. Now,

see if you can supply the answers, without computation, to the
following:

$$123,456 \times 9 + 7 = ?$$
$$1,234,567 \times 9 + 8 = ?$$

Let us see *why* this pattern works. To do so we shall examine just
one of the statements. A similar explanation can be offered for each
of the other statements. Consider the statement:

$$12,345 \times 9 + 6 = 111,111$$

We can express 12,345 as a sum of five numbers as follows:

$$
\begin{array}{r}
11,111 \\
1,111 \\
111 \\
11 \\
1 \\
\hline
12,345
\end{array}
$$

Next we multiply each of the five numbers by 9:

$$
\begin{aligned}
11,111 \times 9 &= 99,999 \\
1,111 \times 9 &= 9,999 \\
111 \times 9 &= 999 \\
11 \times 9 &= 99 \\
1 \times 9 &= 9
\end{aligned}
$$

Finally, we add 6 by adding six ones as in the following array, and
find the total sum:

$$
\begin{array}{r}
99,999 + 1 = 100,000 \\
9,999 + 1 = 10,000 \\
999 + 1 = 1,000 \\
99 + 1 = 100 \\
9 + 1 = 10 \\
1 = 1 \\
\hline
111,111
\end{array}
$$

Here is another interesting pattern. After studying the pattern,
see if you can add the next four lines to the table.

$$
\begin{aligned}
1 \times 1 &= 1 \\
11 \times 11 &= 121 \\
111 \times 111 &= 12,321 \\
1,111 \times 1,111 &= 1,234,321 \\
11,111 \times 11,111 &= 123,454,321
\end{aligned}
$$

Do you think that the pattern displayed will continue indefinitely? Compute the product 1,111,111,111 × 1,111,111,111 to help you answer this question.

GEOMETRIC PATTERNS

In the study of geometry we frequently form conclusions on the basis of a small number of examples, together with an exhibited pattern. Consider, for example, the problem of determining the number of triangles that can be formed from a given polygon by drawing diagonals from a given vertex P. First we draw several figures and consider the results in tabular form as follows.

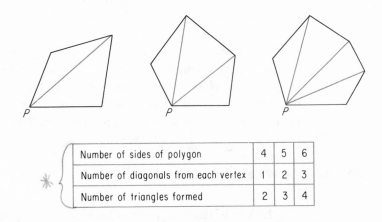

Number of sides of polygon	4	5	6
Number of diagonals from each vertex	1	2	3
Number of triangles formed	2	3	4

From the pattern of entries in the table it appears that the number of triangles formed is two less than the number of sides of the polygon. Thus we expect that we can form 10 triangles for a dodecagon, a polygon with 12 sides, from a given vertex. In general, then, for a polygon with n sides, called an n-gon, we can form $n - 2$ triangles.

This is reasoning by *induction*. We formed a generalization on the basis of several specific examples and an obvious pattern. This procedure does not, however, constitute a proof. In order to *prove* that $n - 2$ triangles can be formed in this way for a polygon with n sides, we must observe that two of the n sides intersect at the common point of the diagonals and that each of the other $n - 2$ sides is used to form a different triangle.

It is important to recognize that not all patterns lead to valid generalizations. Patterns offer an opportunity to make reasonable guesses, but these need to be proved before they can be accepted with certainty. Consider, for example, the maximum number of regions into which a circular region can be divided by line segments joining given points on a circle in all possible ways.

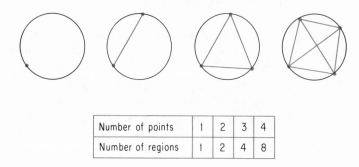

Number of points	1	2	3	4
Number of regions	1	2	4	8

Would you agree that a reasonable guess for the number of regions derived from five points is 16? Draw a figure to confirm your conjecture. What is your guess for the maximum number of regions that can be derived from six points? Again, draw a figure to confirm your conjecture. You may be in for a surprise!

EXERCISES FOR SECTION 1-1

1. Verify that the process for finger multiplication shown in this section will work for each of the multiples of nine from 1×9 through 9×9.

2. Follow the procedure outlined in this section and show that $1234 \times 9 + 5 = 11,111$.

3. Study the following pattern and use it to express the squares of 6, 7, 8, and 9 in the same manner.

$$1^2 = 1$$
$$2^2 = 1 + 2 + 1$$
$$3^2 = 1 + 2 + 3 + 2 + 1$$
$$4^2 = 1 + 2 + 3 + 4 + 3 + 2 + 1$$
$$5^2 = 1 + 2 + 3 + 4 + 5 + 4 + 3 + 2 + 1$$

4. Study the entries that follow and use the pattern that is exhibited to complete the last four rows.

$$1 + 3 = 4 \text{ or } 2^2$$
$$1 + 3 + 5 = 9 \text{ or } 3^2$$
$$1 + 3 + 5 + 7 = 16 \text{ or } 4^2$$
$$1 + 3 + 5 + 7 + 9 = ?$$
$$1 + 3 + 5 + 7 + 9 + 11 = ?$$
$$1 + 3 + 5 + 7 + 9 + 11 + 13 = ?$$
$$1 + 3 + 5 + \cdots + (2n - 1) = ?$$

5. An addition problem can be checked by a process called "casting out nines." To do this, you first find the sum of the digits of each of the addends (that is, numbers that are added), divide by 9, and record the remainder. Digits may be added again and again until a one-digit remainder is obtained. The sum of these remainders is then divided by 9 to find a final remainder. This should be equal to the remainder found by considering the sum of the addends (that is, the answer), adding its digits, dividing the sum of these digits by 9, and finding the remainder. Here is an example:

Addends	Sum of digits	Remainders
4,378	22	4
2,160	9	0
3,872	20	2
1,085	14	5
11,495		11

When the sum of the remainders is divided by 9, the final remainder is 2. This corresponds to the remainder obtained by dividing the sum of the digits in the answer $(1 + 1 + 4 + 9 + 5 = 20)$ by 9.

Try this procedure for several other examples and verify that it works in each case.

6. Try to discover a procedure for checking multiplication by casting out nines. Verify that this procedure works for several cases.

7. There is a procedure for multiplying a two-digit number by 9 on one's fingers provided that the tens digit is smaller than the ones digit. The accompanying diagram shows how to multiply 28 by 9.

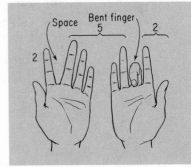

Reading from the left, put a space after the second finger and bend the eighth finger. Read the product in groups of fingers as 252.

Use this procedure to find: (**a**) 9 × 47; (**b**) 9 × 39; (**c**) 9 × 18; (**d**) 9 × 27. Check each of the answers you have obtained.

8. Take a piece of notebook paper and fold it in half. Then fold it in half again and cut off a corner that does not involve an edge of the original piece of paper.

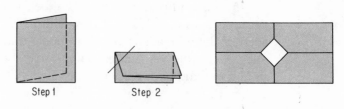

Step 1   Step 2

Your paper, when unfolded, should look like the accompanying sketch.

That is, with two folds we produced one hole. Repeat the same process but this time make three folds before cutting off an edge. Try to predict the number of holes that will be produced. How many holes will be produced with four folds? With *n* folds?

9. A famous mathematician named Gauss is said to have found the sum of the first 100 counting numbers at a very early age by the following procedure:

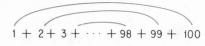

$$1 + 2 + 3 + \cdots + 98 + 99 + 100$$

He reasoned that there would be 50 pairs of numbers, each with a sum of 101 (100 + 1, 99 + 2, 98 + 3, etc.). Thus, the sum would be 50 × 101 or 5050. Use this procedure to find:

(**a**) The sum of the first 80 counting numbers.

(**b**) The sum of the first 200 counting numbers.

(**c**) The sum of all the odd numbers from 1 through 49.

(**d**) The sum of all the odd numbers from 1 through 199.

(**e**) The sum of all the even numbers from 2 through 400.

10. Use the results obtained in Exercise 9 and try to find a formula for the sum of:

(a) The first n counting numbers [that is, $1 + 2 + 3 + \cdots + (n - 1) + n$].

(b) The first n odd numbers [that is, $1 + 3 + 5 + \cdots + (2n - 3) + (2n - 1)$].

11. Find the sum:

$$\frac{1}{2} + \frac{1}{2^2} + \frac{1}{2^3} + \frac{1}{2^4} + \cdots + \frac{1}{2^n}$$

To help you discover this sum, complete these partial sums and search for a pattern.

(a) $\dfrac{1}{2} + \dfrac{1}{2^2} = \dfrac{1}{2} + \dfrac{1}{4} = ?$

(b) $\dfrac{1}{2} + \dfrac{1}{2^2} + \dfrac{1}{2^3} = \dfrac{1}{2} + \dfrac{1}{4} + \dfrac{1}{8} = ?$

(c) $\dfrac{1}{2} + \dfrac{1}{2^2} + \dfrac{1}{2^3} + \dfrac{1}{2^4} = \dfrac{1}{2} + \dfrac{1}{4} + \dfrac{1}{8} + \dfrac{1}{16} = ?$

***12.** Try to discover the rule that is being used in each case to obtain the answer given. For example, the given information

$$2, 5 \to 6; \qquad 3, 10 \to 12; \qquad 7, 8 \to 14; \qquad 5, 3 \to 7$$

should lead you to the rule $x, y \to x + y - 1$.

(a) $3, 4 \to 8$; $3, 3 \to 7$; $1, 5 \to 7$; $2, 8 \to 11$.
(b) $2, 4 \to 8$; $3, 5 \to 15$; $1, 7 \to 7$; $3, 9 \to 27$.
(c) $1, 5 \to 1$; $5, 2 \to 2$; $3, 9 \to 3$; $6, 5 \to 5$.
(d) $4, 8 \to 4$; $5, 1 \to 5$; $6, 6 \to 6$; $8, 2 \to 8$.
(e) $3, 4 \to 5$; $4, 4 \to 4$; $5, 7 \to 0$; $9, 2 \to 1$.

1-2 MATHEMATICAL RECREATIONS

The popularity of mathematics as a means of recreation and pleasure is evidenced by the frequency with which it is found in popular magazines and newspapers. In this section we shall explore several of these recreational aspects of mathematics.

---

* An asterisk preceding an exercise indicates that the exercise is more difficult or challenging than the others.

MAGIC SQUARES

How many of us have ever failed to be impressed by a magic square? The magic square shown here is arranged so that the sum of the numbers in any row, column, or diagonal is always 34.

Use Gauss Theory to figure out

1	12	7	14
8	13	2	11
10	3	16	5
15	6	9	4

Although there are formal methods to complete such an array, we will not go into them here. Suffice it to say that such arrangements have fascinated man for many centuries. Indeed, the first known example of a magic square is said to have been found on the back of a tortoise by the Emperor Yu in about 2200 B.C.! This was called the "lo-shu" and appeared as an array of numerals indicated by knots in strings as in the figure on the left below. Black knots were used for even numbers and white ones for odd numbers. In modern times this appears as a magic square of third order. The sum along any row, column, or diagonal is 15 as in the figure below.

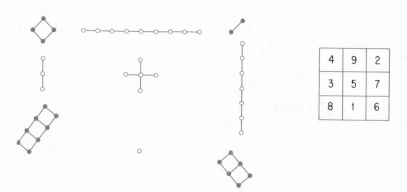

4	9	2
3	5	7
8	1	6

MATHEMATICAL TRICKS

Closely akin to magic squares are square arrays of numbers useful in "mathemagic." Let us "build" a trick together. We begin by forming a square array and placing any six numerals in the surrounding spaces as in the figure. The numbers 3, 4, 1, 7, 2, and 5 are chosen arbitrarily. Next find the sum of each pair of numbers as in a regular addition table.

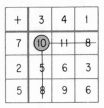

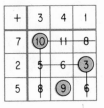

+	3	4	1
7			
2			
5			

Now we are ready to perform the trick. Have someone circle any one of the nine numerals in the box, say 10, and then cross out all the other numerals in the same row and column as 10.

Next circle one of the remaining numerals, say 3, and repeat the process. Circle the only remaining numeral, 9. The sum of the circled numbers is $10 + 3 + 9 = 22$.

+	3	4	1
7	(10)	11	8
2	5	6	3
5	8	9	6

+	3	4	1
7	(10)	11	8
2	5	6	(3)
5	8	(9)	6

The interesting item here is that the sum of the three circled numbers will always be equal to 22, regardless of where you start on the first row! Furthermore, note that 22 is the sum of the six numbers outside the square. Try to explain why this trick works, and build a table with 16 entries.

Another type of mathematical trick that is quite popular is the "think of a number" type. Follow these instructions:

> Think of a number.
> Add 3 to this number.
> Multiply your answer by 2.
> Subtract 4 from your answer.
> Divide by 2.
> Subtract the number with which you started.

If you follow these instructions carefully, your answer will always be 1, regardless of the number with which you start. We can explain why this trick works by using algebraic symbols or by drawing pictures, as shown below.

Try to make up a similar trick of your own.

Think of a number:	n	☐	(Number of coins in a box)
Add 3:	$n+3$	☐ ○ ○ ○	(Number of original coins plus three)
Multiply by 2:	$2n+6$	☐ ○ ○ ○ ☐ ○ ○ ○	(Two boxes of coins plus six)
Subtract 4:	$2n+2$	☐ ○ ☐ ○	(Two boxes of coins plus two)
Divide by 2:	$n+1$	☐ ○	(One box of coins plus one)
Subtract the original number, n:	$(n+1)-n=1$	○	(One coin is left)

OPTICAL ILLUSIONS

Optical illusions are vivid reminders of the fact that we can not always trust our eyes. Can you trust yours? Test yourself and see.

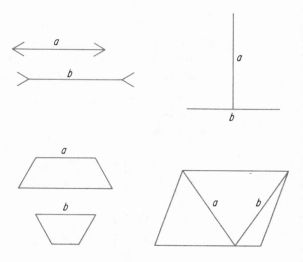

First guess which of the line segments, *a* or *b*, appears to be the longer
in the four parts of the figure at the bottom of p. 12. Then use a ruler
and check your estimate.

Now see whether you can guess which line segments are parallel,
if any, in the three parts of the next figure.

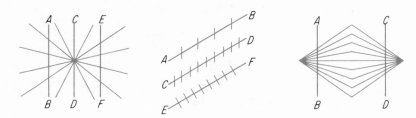

You should have found, in both cases, that looks can be deceiving.
In each of the first four drawings, the segments are equal in length;
in each of the last three they are parallel!

Here are two other optical illusions that were recently created and
that appear most startling at first glance.

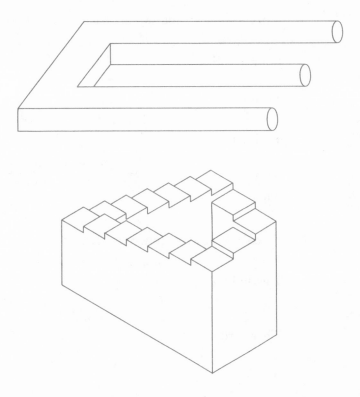

FALLACIES

Mathematical fallacies have always intrigued both professional and amateur mathematicians alike. Here is an arithmetic fallacy to puzzle you. You might even consider trying this on your local banker. First you need to deposit $50 in the bank and then make withdrawals in the following manner:

[handwritten: Fallacy - you don't Add balances.]

Withdraw $20, leaving a balance of $30.	
Withdraw $15, leaving a balance of $15.	
Withdraw $ 9, leaving a balance of $ 6.	
Withdraw $ 6, leaving a balance of $ 0.	

Adding, we have: $50 $51

The total withdrawal is $50, whereas the total of the balances is $51. Can you therefore go to the bank to demand an extra dollar?

Here is a ".proof" that 1 = 2. Even though you may have forgotten the algebra you need to follow this, don't let it stop you; see if you can discover the fallacy.

Let $a = b$. Then

$$a^2 = b^2 = b \cdot b.$$

Since $a = b$, we may write $b \cdot b$ as $a \cdot b$. Thus

$$a^2 = a \cdot b.$$

Subtract b^2:

$$a^2 - b^2 = a \cdot b - b^2.$$

Factor:

$$(a + b)(a - b) = b(a - b)$$

Divide by $a - b$:

$$\frac{(a + b)(a - b)}{(a - b)} = \frac{b(a - b)}{(a - b)} \quad ⟵ \quad ✳$$

Thus

$$a + b = b.$$

Since $a = b$, we may write this as

$$b + b = b \quad \text{or} \quad 2b = b.$$

Divide by b:

$$\frac{2b}{b} = \frac{b}{b}$$

Therefore

$$2 = 1.$$

[handwritten: ✳ Fallacy because you divided by zero]

Many people enjoy solving interesting or amusing puzzles. A variety of these, many of which are old-timers, appear in the exercises that follow.

EXERCISES FOR SECTION 1-2

1. All of the following puzzles have logical answers, but they are not strictly mathematical. See how many you can answer.

(**a**) How many two-cent stamps are there in a dozen?

(**b**) How many telephone poles are needed in order to reach the moon?

(**c**) How far can you walk into a forest?

(**d**) Two United States coins total 55¢ in value, yet one of them is not a nickel. Can you explain this?

(**e**) How much dirt is there in a hole which is 3 feet wide, 4 feet long, and 2 feet deep?

(**f**) There was a blind beggar who had a brother, but this brother had no brothers. What was the relationship between the two?

2. A farmer has to get a fox, a goose, and a bag of corn across a river in a boat which is only large enough for him and one of these three items. Now if he leaves the fox alone with the goose, the fox will eat the goose. If he leaves the goose alone with the corn, the goose will eat the corn. How does he get all items across the river?

3. Three Indians and three missionaries need to cross a river in a boat big enough only for two. The Indians are fine if they are left alone or if they are with the same number or with a larger number of missionaries. They are dangerous if they are left alone in a situation where they outnumber the missionaries. How do they all get across the river without harm?

4. A bottle and cork cost $1.50 together. The bottle costs one dollar more than the cork. How much does each cost?

5. A cat is at the bottom of a 30-foot well. Each day she climbs up three feet; each night she slides back two feet. How long will it take for the cat to get out of the well?

6. If a cat and a half eats a rat and a half in a day and a half, how many days will it take for 100 cats to eat 100 rats?

7. Ten coins are arranged to form a triangle as shown in the figure. By rearranging only three of the coins, form a new triangle that points in the opposite direction from the one shown.

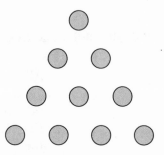

8. Rearrange the eight segments shown so as to form three congruent squares; that is, three squares that are exactly the same size. Each of the four smaller segments is one-half of the length of one of the larger segments.

9. Use six match sticks, all of the same size, to form four equilateral triangles. (An equilateral triangle has all three sides the same length.)

10. Four match sticks are arranged to form a "cup" with a coin contained within three of the segments, as shown in the figure. By rearranging only two of the match sticks, form a new figure that is congruent to the original one (that is, exactly the same in shape but possibly different in position) but with the coin no longer contained within any of the segments.

11. A sailor lands on an island inhabited by two types of people. The A's always lie, and the B's always tell the truth. The sailor meets three inhabitants on the beach and asks the first of these: "Are you an A or a B?" The man answers, but the sailor doesn't understand him and asks the second person what he had said. The man replies: "He said that he was a B. He is, and so am I." The third inhabitant then says: "That's not true. The first man is an A and I'm a B." Can you tell who was lying and who was telling the truth?

12. A man goes to a well with three cans whose capacities are 3 gallons, 5 gallons, and 8 gallons. Explain how he can obtain exactly 4 gallons of water from the well.

13. Here is a mathematical trick you can try on a friend. Ask someone to place a penny in one of his hands, and a dime in the other. Then tell him to multiply the value of the coin in the right hand by 6, multiply the value of the coin held in the left hand by 3, and add. Ask for the result. If the number given is even, you then announce that the penny is in the right hand; if the result is an odd number, then the penny is in the left hand and the dime is in the right hand. Can you figure out why this trick works?

14. Consider a house with six rooms and furniture arranged as in the accompanying figure. We wish to interchange the desk and the bookcase, but in such a way that there is never more than one piece of furniture in a room at a time. The other three pieces of furniture do not need to return to their original places. Can you do this? Try it using coins or other objects to represent the furniture.

Cabinet		Desk
Television set	Sofa	Bookcase

15. Three men enter a hotel and rent a suite of rooms for $30. After they are taken to their rooms the manager discovers he overcharged them; the suite rents for only $25. He thereupon sends a bellhop upstairs with the $5 change. The dishonest bellhop decides to keep $2 and returns only $3 to the men. Now the rooms originally cost $30, but the men had $3 returned to them. This means that they paid only $27 for the room. The bellhop kept $2. $27 + $2 = $29. What happened to the extra dollar?

16. Write the numbers from 1 through 10 using four 4's for each. Here are the first three completed for you:

$$\frac{44}{44} = 1; \qquad \frac{4}{4} + \frac{4}{4} = 2; \qquad \frac{4+4+4}{4} = 3.$$

17. Arrange two pennies and two dimes as shown below. Try to interchange the coins so that the pennies are at the right and the dimes at the left. You may move only one coin at a time, you may jump over only one coin, and pennies may be moved only to the right while dimes may be moved only to the left. No two coins may occupy the same space at the same time. What is the minimum number of moves required to complete the game?

18. Repeat Exercise 17 for three pennies and three dimes, using seven blocks. What is the minimum number of moves required to complete the game?

1-3 BEYOND THE GOOGOL

In modern times all of us have become familiar with very large numbers merely by observing the national budget and the national debt. The number "one million" no longer seems exceptionally large, but have you ever stopped to consider just how big this number really is?

Just for fun, can you estimate how long it would take you to count to a million? Assume that you count at the rate of one number per second with no time off to eat, rest, or sleep. (Don't do any computation yet; merely estimate.) Would you guess that it would take you less than an hour? A few hours? A day? A few days? More than a week? A month?

Let's find out how long it would take to count to a million. At the rate we suggested it would take a million seconds. There are 3,600 seconds in an hour, so it would take 1,000,000 ÷ 3,600 or approximately 278 hours. This is equivalent to about $11\frac{1}{2}$ days, counting night and day without rest, to reach one million!

Yes, one million is a large number, but it is **finite**; that is, it is countable. In this sense we also consider the number "one billion" as finite even though we would not want to actually count to it. Can you guess how long it would take to count to a billion?

Is there a largest number? The answer is clearly "no," for if someone claimed to be in possession of the world's largest number, you would merely have to add one to this number and then you would be in possession of a larger number.

One of the largest numbers ever named is a **googol**. This has been defined as 1 followed by one hundred zeros:

10000000000000000000000000000000000000000000000000000
00000000000000000000000000000000000000000000000

This number is larger than what is considered to be the total number of protons or electrons in the universe! A googol can be expressed, using exponents, as

$$10^{100}.$$

Even larger than a googol is a **googolplex**, defined as 1 followed by a googol of zeros. One famous mathematician claimed that there would not even be room between the earth and the moon to write all the zeros in a googolplex! $10^{10^{100}}$

Although large beyond human comprehension, these numbers are still finite. The question one might well ask is whether or not there are numbers that are **infinite**—that is, beyond the finite. To answer this we turn to the procedure used by man in ancient times.

When ancient man wished to count the number of animals he owned he did so by placing a pebble on the ground for each animal. Then the number of pebbles was the same as the number of animals. He had established a **one-to-one correspondence** between the set of animals that he owned and a set of pebbles; for each pebble there was an animal, and for each animal there was a pebble.

When we wish to count today, we make use of the set of numbers 1, 2, 3, 4, 5, and so on. We place the things that we count in a one-to-one correspondence with members of this set of numbers. The last number used tells the size of the collection. For example, to count the numbers of letters in the word "Thursday" we proceed as follows:

We say that the **cardinality** of the set of letters in the word is 8. A number used to denote the size of a collection is called a **cardinal number**. (Actually when we write "8" we are writing a **numeral** and not a number. Numbers are abstract concepts, which cannot be written on paper. However, here, and in later work, we shall distinguish between a number and a numeral only when it proves helpful to do so.)

Whenever two sets are such that their members may be placed in a one-to-one correspondence with each other we say that the two sets are **equivalent**. Thus the set of letters in the word "Thursday" is equivalent to the set of the first eight counting numbers. In a similar manner, the following two sets are equivalent.

$$
\begin{array}{ccccc}
1 & 2 & 3 & 4 & 5 \\
\updownarrow & \updownarrow & \updownarrow & \updownarrow & \updownarrow \\
2 & 4 & 6 & 8 & 10
\end{array}
$$

Also, the set of even numbers greater than zero is equivalent to the set of counting numbers.

$$
\begin{array}{ccccccccc}
1 & 2 & 3 & 4 & 5 & 6 & \cdots & n & \cdots \\
\updownarrow & \updownarrow & \updownarrow & \updownarrow & \updownarrow & \updownarrow & & \updownarrow & \\
2 & 4 & 6 & 8 & 10 & 12 & \cdots & 2n & \cdots
\end{array}
$$

Each counting number n can be matched with an even counting number $2n$.

It appears strange to be able to say that these two sets are equivalent. We are really saying that there are just as many even counting numbers as there are counting numbers altogether! This puzzled mathematicians for centuries until, at the turn of the twentieth century, a German mathematician named Georg Cantor developed an entire theory of infinite sets of numbers.

This is essentially what he did. He assigned a cardinal number to the set of counting numbers, namely, $\aleph_0$. This is read **"aleph-null"** and is really a **transfinite** (beyond the finite) **cardinal number**. It is correct then to say that there are $\aleph_0$ counting numbers, just as you might say that there are 7 days of the week or 10 fingers on your hands. Furthermore, any set that can be matched in a one-to-one correspondence with the set of counting numbers is also of size $\aleph_0$.

The discussion of transfinite numbers gives rise to some very interesting apparent paradoxes. One of the most famous of these is the story of the infinite house. This is a house that contains an infinite number of rooms, numbered 1, 2, 3, 4, 5, and so on. Each room is occupied by a single tenant. That is, there is a one-to-one correspondence between rooms and occupants. There are $\aleph_0$ rooms, and $\aleph_0$ occupants. One day a stranger arrived at the house and asked to be admitted. The caretaker was an amateur mathematician and was able to accommodate this visitor in the following manner. He asked the occupant of room 1 to move to room 2, the occupant of room 2 to move to room 3, the occupant of room 3 to move to room 4, and in general the occupant of room n to move to room $n + 1$. Now everyone had a room and room number 1 was available for the visitor! In other words, we have demonstrated this interesting fact:

$$\aleph_0 + 1 = \aleph_0$$

Several days later an infinite number of visitors arrived at the house, all demanding individual rooms! Again the caretaker was able to accommodate them. He merely asked each tenant to move to a room number that was double his current room number. That is, the occupant of room 1 moved to room 2, the occupant of room 2 moved to room 4, room 3 to room 6, and room n to room $2n$. After this move was made, the new arrivals were placed in rooms 1, 3, 5, and so forth. Here we have an example of another interesting fact in the language of transfinite arithmetic:

$$\aleph_0 + \aleph_0 = \aleph_0$$

As another example of this last fact, note that the set of even counting numbers is of size $\aleph_0$, and the set of odd counting numbers is also of size $\aleph_0$. But the even counting numbers together with the odd counting numbers form the set of all counting numbers, which we have agreed is of size $\aleph_0$. Therefore, again, we see that $\aleph_0 + \aleph_0 = \aleph_0$.

Apparent paradoxes also arise in geometry. Consider the fact that a line segment contains an infinite number of points. From this one may demonstrate the fact that two line segments of unequal length nevertheless contain the same number of points. Thus consider segments AB and CD where lines CA and DB meet at a point P.

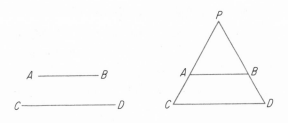

We can show that there is a one-to-one correspondence between the points of segments AB and CD. Given any point M on CD, draw line segment PM. This segment crosses AB at a point M' that corresponds to M. Also given any point N on segment AB, draw line segment PN and extend it until it meets CD at a point N' that corresponds to N. Thus there is a one-to-one correspondence between the points of segments AB and CD, and there are just as many points on segment AB as there are on segment CD.

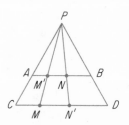

EXERCISES FOR SECTION 1-3

1. Estimate how long it would take you to count to one billion at the rate of one number per second. Then compute this to the nearest day.

2. You are offered a job that pays 1¢ the first day, 2¢ the second day, 4¢ the third day, and so forth. That is, your wages are doubled each day. First estimate, then compute, your salary for the thirtieth day on the job.

3. In Exercise 2 compute the total salary that you will earn in thirty days. Try to find this sum without adding each of the daily salaries. To help you discover a way of doing this, consider these sums first:

  (a) $1 + 2 + 4$ (b) $1 + 2 + 4 + 8$
  (c) $1 + 2 + 4 + 8 + 16$ (d) $1 + 2 + 4 + 8 + 16 + 32$

4. Show that the set of counting numbers $(1, 2, 3, 4, 5, \ldots)$ is equivalent to the set of whole numbers $(0, 1, 2, 3, 4, 5, \ldots)$.

5. (a) Estimate the number of seconds that elapse in a century. (b) Find this number to the nearest million.

6. How long would it take you to spend one million dollars if you spent one dollar every minute for eight hours every day?

7. Show that there are just as many multiples of five (5, 10, 15, 20, . . .) as there are counting numbers.

8. Estimate how many pennies it would take to make a stack one inch high. Approximately how high would a stack of one million pennies be?

*9. How many zeros are there in the number represented as a googol times a googol? Express this number using exponents. Is this number smaller or larger than a googolplex?

*10. Place a half-dollar, a quarter, and a nickel in one position, A, as in the figure. Then try to move these coins, one at a time, to position C. Coins may also be placed in position B. At no time may a larger coin be placed on a smaller coin. This can be accomplished in $2^3 - 1$; that is, 7 moves.

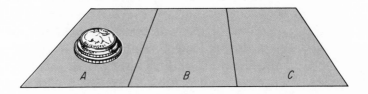

Next add a penny to the pile and try to make the change in $2^4 - 1$; that is, 15 moves.

This is an example of a famous problem called the **Tower of Hanoi**. The ancient Brahman priests were to move a pile of 64 such discs of decreasing size, after which the world would end. This would require $2^{64} - 1$ moves. Try to estimate how long this would take at the rate of one move per second.

1-4 IMPOSSIBLE AND UNSOLVED PROBLEMS

Before you are led to the false conclusion that mathematicians know everything, we will conclude this chapter with a discussion of things that mathematicians do not know.

There are some problems in mathematics that are impossible. That is, mathematicians have *proved* that certain problems cannot be done. An outstanding example of this is the problem of angle trisection. It has been proved that in general it is not possible to divide a given angle into three equal parts if only an unmarked straight edge and a compass are used. Nevertheless, each year there are numerous reports of "angle trisectors" who wish to claim fame by asserting that they have solved the problem. They are wasting their time; the problem has been solved—it cannot be done.

The angle trisection problem is one of three so-called **problems of antiquity**. Another is the problem of the duplication of a cube; that is, constructing a cube with a volume twice that of a given cube. Historians say that the ancient Delians were told that they could eliminate a pestilence that had befallen them if they would double the size of Apollo's cubical altar. This problem, known also as the Delian problem, was studied by the ancient Greeks and by mathematicians thereafter for many centuries.

The third famous problem is that of "squaring a circle"; that is, of constructing a square with an area equal to that of a given circle. All three of these problems were studied by mathematicians, and gave rise to many important discoveries in geometry. It was not until the nineteenth century that it was finally proved that none of the three constructions are possible if only an unmarked straight edge and a compass are permitted.

In another category are those problems that remain unsolved to this date despite the efforts of mathematicians for centuries. Many of these are of interest in that they are very easy to state so that the nonmathematician can understand them. Here are several for which no solution is yet available.

FERMAT'S LAST THEOREM

We know that there are many replacements for x, y, and z such that $x^2 + y^2 = z^2$. For example, $3^2 + 4^2 = 5^2$ and $5^2 + 12^2 = 13^2$. (Can you find several others?) It is conjectured that it is not possible to find replacements for x, y, and z such that $x^n + y^n = z^n$ where n is greater than 2 and where x, y, and z are counting numbers. For example, we cannot find replacements for x, y, and z so that $x^3 + y^3 = z^3$. A great mathematician named Pierre de Fermat (1601–1665) wrote in the margin of his book that he had a proof of the impossibility of this problem, but that he had no room to write it there. No mathematician since has been able to prove or disprove this conjecture, although it has been proved for values of n up to 4002.

GOLDBACH'S CONJECTURE

An integer greater than 1 that is divisible only by 1 and by itself is called a **prime number**. Some examples of prime numbers are

$$2, 3, 5, 7, 11, 13, 17, 19, 23.$$

A mathematician named Goldbach conjectured that every even number greater than 2 could be written as the sum of two primes; e.g., $12 = 5 + 7$, $20 = 7 + 13$, and $30 = 13 + 17$. No one has ever been able to find a number that cannot be so expressed, nor has anyone been able to prove that every even number can be written as the sum of two prime numbers.

There are other unproved statements concerning prime numbers. Pairs of primes like 3 and 5, 11 and 13, 41 and 43, and 101 and 103 are called **twin primes**. Are there an infinite number of pairs of primes that differ by two? No one knows!

No one has ever been able to invent a formula that would always produce a prime number. One effort produced the formula

$$n^2 - n + 41.$$

If you substitute the numbers $1, 2, 3, \ldots, 40$ in this formula for n, a prime number will be produced. However, for $n = 41$ we do not get a prime number. Pierre de Fermat thought he had a formula, the expression

$$2^{2^n} + 1.$$

Prime numbers are produced for $n = 1, 2, 3$, and 4. About a century later another mathematician discovered that for $n = 5$ this formula gives the number 4,294,967,297, which is not a prime number since

$$4,294,967,297 = 641 \times 6,700,417.$$

Euclid proved that there is no largest prime. However, mathematicians have always been interested in searching for large primes in the hope of gaining further insight into this branch of number theory. As of the time of the writing of this text the largest prime known to man is

$$2^{11,213} - 1,$$

a number with 3376 digits. To date no one has been able to discover a formula that will always generate prime numbers, nor has anyone been able to prove that such a formula is impossible. The problem is left for the mathematician of the future; you may be reading about such a discovery in your daily newspaper tomorrow.

THE FOUR-COLOR PROBLEM

About the middle of the nineteenth century a problem related to map making was proposed; it remains unsolved to this date. This problem, known as the four-color problem, involves the coloring of maps using at most four colors. When two countries have common boundaries, they must have different colors. When two countries have only single points in common they may use the same color. The figure gives two examples of these restrictions.

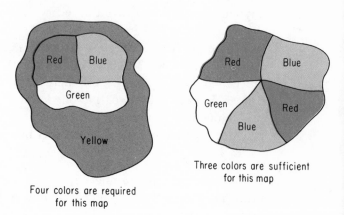

Four colors are required
for this map

Three colors are sufficient
for this map

No one has ever been able to produce a map that would require more than four colors, but no one has been able to prove that four colors are sufficient for all maps. However, it has been proved that if a map could be drawn that would require five colors, there would have to be at least 36 countries on it. It has also been proved that five colors are sufficient for all maps, but may not be necessary.

INFINITE DECIMALS

Every real number can be represented by a decimal. In particular, $\sqrt{2} = 1.4142. \ldots$ This is a nonrepeating, nonterminating decimal; we may carry out the decimal to as many places as desired. However, there does not seem to be any way to answer such questions as these regarding the decimal expansion for $\sqrt{2}$:

(a) Will there ever be five consecutive 5's?
(b) Are there infinitely many 1's?
(c) Will the sequence 1, 2, 3, 4, 5 ever appear?

Thus you see that there is room for you, the reader, to claim fame by solving some of these problems—or else by proposing other problems that mathematicians cannot solve. The problems proposed in the following set of exercises call for some discovery on your part. All of them are solvable, although for some the solution may be that they are impossible. You should try to find answers for the possible and to identify the impossible.

EXERCISES FOR SECTION 1-4

1. A diagonal of a polygon is a line segment connecting two nonadjacent vertices. For example, in the accompanying figure AC and BD are two diagonals.

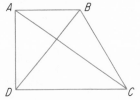

(**a**) How many diagonals can be drawn in a pentagon? (A pentagon is a five-sided polygon.)

(**b**) How many diagonals can be drawn in a hexagon, a six-sided polygon?

(**c**) In general, write a formula for D, the number of diagonals in an n-gon, a polygon of n sides.

2. We wish to color each of the pyramids in the accompanying figure so that no two of the sides (faces) that have a common edge are of the same color.

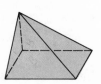

(**a**) What is the minimum number of colors required for each pyramid?

*(b) What is the relationship between the minimum number of colors required and the number of faces in a pyramid?

3. Note each of the following relationships:

$$25^2 = 2 \times 300 + 25 = 625$$
$$35^2 = 3 \times 400 + 25 = 1225$$
$$45^2 = 4 \times 500 + 25 = 2025$$

(a) State a shortcut for squaring a two-digit number whose units digit is 5.

*(b) Find an algebraic explanation for this shortcut.

4. Try to draw lines to show how three houses located at A, B, and C can be connected to three utilities at X, Y, and Z so that no two lines intersect.

   • A • B • C

   • X • Y • Z

5. Try to traverse each of the following figures, tracing each line segment exactly once without removing the point of the pencil from the paper.

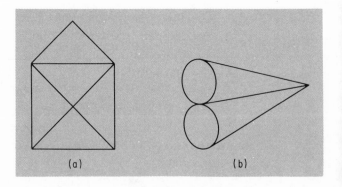

(a)   (b)

6. Write the decimal representations for $\frac{1}{7}$, $\frac{2}{7}$, $\frac{3}{7}$, $\frac{4}{7}$, $\frac{5}{7}$ and $\frac{6}{7}$. See if you can discover a relationship among the sequences of repeating digits.

7. An infinite series is one in which the sum goes on without end. Some of these series approach numbers as limits. Consider this series:

$$\frac{1}{2} + \frac{1}{4} + \frac{1}{8} + \frac{1}{16} + \frac{1}{32} + \cdots$$

Consider the sum of the first two terms, the first three terms, the first four terms, etc. Then conjecture an answer for the limit of the series as the terms go on without end.

8. Use the procedure suggested in Exercise 7 to determine the limits, if any, of these series:

(a) $1 + 2 + 4 + 8 + 16 + 32 + \cdots$

(b) $\frac{1}{3} + \frac{1}{9} + \frac{1}{27} + \frac{1}{81} + \cdots$

9. You wish to travel from A to B on the accompanying figure. In how many ways can this be done if you are permitted to move neither to the left nor up?

10. Repeat Exercise 9 for each of the following figures.

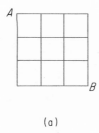

(a)

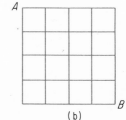

(b)

*****11.** Consider n given points such that no three are on a line. How many line segments are there with both endpoints at these given points if n is (a) 3; (b) 4; (c) 5; (d) n?

*****12.** You are given a checkerboard and a set of dominoes. The size of each domino is such that it is able to cover two squares on the board. Can you arrange the dominoes in such a way that all of the board is covered with the exception of two squares in opposite corners? (That is, you are to leave uncovered the two squares marked **XX** in the figure.)

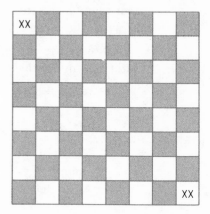

*13. A *perfect number* is one that is equal to the sum of its divisors, not including the number itself. The number 6 is a perfect number because $6 = 1 + 2 + 3$. No one has ever been able to find an odd perfect number, but no one has yet been able to prove that all perfect numbers are even. Can you find the next perfect number after 6?

chapter 2

SYSTEMS
OF NUMERATION

We habitually take for granted the use of our system of notation, as well as our computational procedures. However, these represent the creative work of man through the ages. We can gain a better appreciation of our system of numeration and methods of computation by examining other systems.

In this chapter we shall travel through the years and first examine the system of numeration used by the ancient Egyptians as found in their hieroglyphics. Then we shall move to contemporary times and study binary notation, the mathematical basis for the modern computer.

Throughout this exploration the reader should note the liberation in mankind's mathematical thinking that has taken place from early times to the present day, a liberation that matches his creative developments in other areas as well. Systems of numeration form an important part of each educated person's knowledge and provide the basis for many topics that are currently emphasized in elementary and secondary school mathematics curricula.

2-1 EGYPTIAN NUMERATION

First we distinguish between a *number* and a *numeral*. A number is an abstract concept; a **numeral** is the name of a number. We write numerals; we cannot write numbers. From a similar point of view, when you see the word "dog" on a piece of paper, you see the name of an animal rather than the animal itself.

We shall make this distinction between a number and a numeral in this book only where it proves helpful in understanding some concept. As an example, consider the number that represents the number of items in the following collection of symbols:

$$x \quad x \quad x \quad x \quad x$$
$$x \quad x \quad x \quad x \quad x$$

We would write this, in our system of notation, as 10. The ancient Egyptians used the symbol ∩. The ancient Babylonians used the symbol <. The Romans used X. All of these symbols—and there are others—are merely numerals; that is, they are different ways of representing (providing a name for) the same number.

Let us explore one system, the one used by the ancient Egyptians, in greater detail. They used a new symbol for each power of ten. Here are some of their symbols, a description of the physical objects they are supposed to represent, and the number they represent as expressed in our notation:

l	Vertical staff	1
∩	Heel-bone	10
�	Scroll	100
 ⌇	Lotus flower	1000
↗	Pointing finger	10,000

This Egyptian system is said to have a **base of ten**, but has no place value. The "base" ten is due to the use of powers of ten. We call our system of numeration a **decimal system** to emphasize our use of powers of ten. The absence of a place value means that the position of the symbols does not affect the number represented. For example, in our decimal system of numeration, 23 and 32 represent different numbers. In the Egyptian system ∩| and |∩ are different ways of writing eleven, that is, different names or numerals for the same number. (The former notation is the one normally found in their hieroglyphics.) Here are some other comparisons of decimal and ancient Egyptian number symbols.

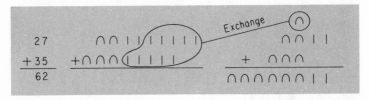

Computation in the ancient Egyptian system is possible, although tedious. For example, we use these steps to add 27 and 35.

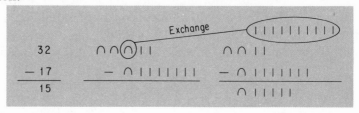

Observe that, in this Egyptian system, an indicated collection of ten ones was replaced by a symbol for ten before the final computation took place. In our decimal system we mentally perform a similar exchange of ten ones for a ten when we express $(7 + 5)$ as one ten and two ones. We exchange kinds of units in a similar manner in subtraction.

The ancient Egyptians multiplied by a process of doubling. This process is based on the fact that any number may be represented as a sum of powers of two. For example, $19 = 1 + 2 + 16$. To find the product 19×25 we first double 25 as follows:

$$\begin{array}{ccc}
① & \times \ 25 \ = & ㉕ \\
② & \times \ 25 \ = & ㊿ \\
4 & \times \ 25 \ = & 100 \\
8 & \times \ 25 \ = & 200 \\
⑯ & \times \ 25 \ = & ④⓪⓪
\end{array}$$

Then we find the product 19×25 by adding the multiples of 25 that correspond to 1, 2, and 16:

$$19 = 1 + 2 + 16$$
$$19 \times 25 = (1 + 2 + 16) \times 25$$
$$= 25 + 50 + 400 = 475$$

EXAMPLE 1: Use the Egyptian method of multiplication to find the product 23×41.

Solution:

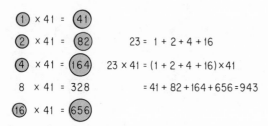

Later the Egyptians adopted a more refined and automatic procedure for multiplication known as **duplation and mediation** that involves doubling one factor and halving the other. For example, to find the product 19×25 we may successively halve 19, discarding remainders at each step, and successively double 25 as follows:

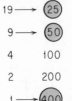

$$19 \longrightarrow 25$$
$$9 \longrightarrow 50$$
$$4 \qquad 100$$
$$2 \qquad 200$$
$$1 \longrightarrow 400$$

Note: since all remainders are discarded, one-half of 19 is recorded as 9 and one-half of 9 is recorded as 4.

This process is complete when a 1 appears in the column of numbers which are being halved. Opposite each number in this column of halves there is a corresponding number in the column of numbers being doubled. The product 19 × 25 is found as the sum of the numbers that are opposite the *odd* numbers in the column of halves:

$$19 \times 25 = 25 + 50 + 400 = 475$$

Note that this process automatically selects the addends to be used in determining the product; one need not search for the appropriate powers of two to be used.

EXAMPLE 2: Use the process of duplation and mediation to find the product 23 × 41.

Solution:

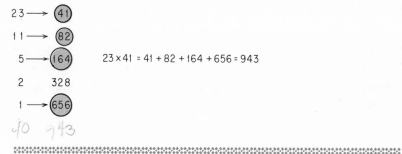

$$23 \times 41 = 41 + 82 + 164 + 656 = 943$$

EXERCISES FOR SECTION 2-1

Write in ancient Egyptian notation:

1. 25   2. 138
3. 1426   4. 40
5. 12,407   6. 5723

Write in decimal notation:

7. ∩∩ı ı   9. ⌐9 ı ı   11. ⌐999∩∩ı ı ı ı

8. 99∩ı   10. ⌐⌐99∩ı   12. ⌐99∩ı ı

Write in ancient Egyptian notation and perform the indicated operation in that system:

13.	42	**14.**	153
	+21		+62

15.	238	**16.**	431
	+135		−213

17.	1243	**18.**	507
	−137		−124

Use the Egyptian method of doubling to find these products:

19. 17 × 45   **20.** 15 × 35

21. 27 × 31   **22.** 31 × 19

Use the Egyptian method of duplation and mediation and find these products:

23. 19 × 33   **24.** 24 × 51

25. 21 × 52   **26.** 37 × 80

27. The Egyptians did not have a symbol for zero. Why do we need such a symbol in our system of numeration? Why did they find it unnecessary to invent such a symbol in order to have symbols for other numbers?

2-2 OTHER METHODS OF COMPUTATION

There exist numerous examples of the ways in which ancient man performed his computations. Some of these may prove of interest to the reader. The method of multiplication that appeared in one of the first published arithmetic texts in Italy, the *Treviso Arithmetic* (1478), is an interesting one. Let us use it to find the product of 457 and 382. (We shall refer to this process here as "galley" multiplication, although it was called "Gelosia" multiplication in the original text.)

First prepare a "galley" with three rows and three columns, and draw the diagonals as in the figure. Our choice for the number of

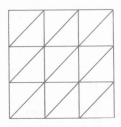

rows and columns was based on the fact that we are to multiply two three-digit numerals.

Place the digits 4, 5, and 7 in order from left to right at the top of the columns. Place the digits 3, 8, and 2 in order from top to bottom at the right of the rows. Then each product of a digit of 457 and a digit of 382 is called a **partial product** and is placed at the intersection of the column and row of the digits. The diagonal separates the

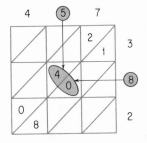

digits of the partial product (tens digit above units digit). For example, $3 \times 7 = 21$, and this partial product is placed in the upper right-hand corner of the "galley"; $5 \times 8 = 40$, and this partial product is placed in the center of the galley; $4 \times 2 = 8$, and this partial product is entered as 08 in the lower left-hand corner of the galley. See if you can justify each of the entries in the completed array shown below.

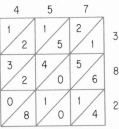

After all partial products have been entered in the galley, we add along diagonals, starting in the lower right-hand corner and carrying to the next diagonal sum where necessary. The next diagram indicates this pattern.

The completed problem appears in the form shown below. We read the final answer, as indicated by the arrow in the figure, as 174,574. Note that we read the digits in the opposite order to that in which they were obtained.

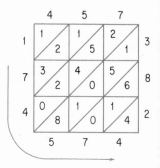

EXAMPLE: Use galley multiplication and multiply 372 by 47.

Solution:

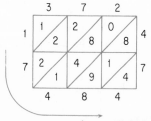

Answer: 17,484

This procedure works because we are really listing all partial products before we add. Compare the following two computations.

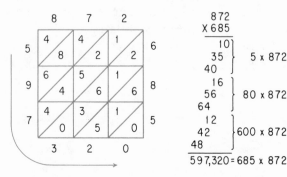

Note that the numerals along the diagonals correspond to those in the columns at the right.

The English mathematician, John Napier, made use of this system as he developed what proved to be one of the forerunners of the modern computing machines. His device is referred to as **Napier's rods,** or **Napier's bones,** named after the material on which he had numerals printed. Napier (1550–1617) is often spoken of as the inventor of logarithms.

To make a set of these rods we need to prepare a collection of strips of paper, or other material, with multiples of each of the digits listed. Study the set of rods shown below as Figure A.

(A)

Index	1	2	3	4	5	6	7	8	9
1	0/1	0/2	0/3	0/4	0/5	0/6	0/7	0/8	0/9
2	0/2	0/4	0/6	0/8	1/0	1/2	1/4	1/6	1/8
3	0/3	0/6	0/9	1/2	1/5	1/8	2/1	2/4	2/7
4	0/4	0/8	1/2	1/6	2/0	2/4	2/8	3/2	3/6
5	0/5	1/0	1/5	2/0	2/5	3/0	3/5	4/0	4/5
6	0/6	1/2	1/8	2/4	3/0	3/6	4/2	4/8	5/4
7	0/7	1/4	2/1	2/8	3/5	4/2	4/9	5/6	6/3
8	0/8	1/6	2/4	3/2	4/0	4/8	5/6	6/4	7/2
9	0/9	1/8	2/7	3/6	4/5	5/4	6/3	7/2	8/1

(B)

Index	4	8	3
1	0/4	0/8	0/3
2	0/8	1/6	0/6
3	1/2	2/4	0/9
4	1/6	3/2	1/2
5	2/0	4/0	1/5
6	2/4	4/8	1/8
7	2/8	5/6	2/1
8	3/2	6/4	2/4
9	3/6	7/2	2/7

Note, for example, that the rod headed by the numeral 9 lists the multiples of 9: 9, 18, 27, 36, 45, 54, 63, 72, and 81.

We can use these rods to multiply two numbers. To multiply 7×483, place the rods headed by numerals 4, 8, and 3 alongside the index as shown above as Figure B.

Consider the row of numerals alongside 7 on the index.

Add along the diagonals, as in "galley multiplication."

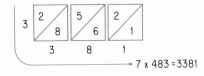

7 x 483 = 3381

The same arrangement of rods may be used to read immediately the product of 483 and any other one-digit number. With practice one can develop skill in using these rods for rapid computation. For example, 8 × 483 = 3864 as follows:

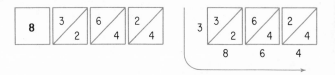

Combining the two previous results, we can find the product 87 × 483:

$$
\begin{array}{ll}
483 & 7 \times 483 = 3{,}381 \\
\underline{\times 87} & \underline{80 \times 483 = 38{,}640} \\
 & 87 \times 483 = 42{,}021
\end{array}
$$

Note that we are able to read only products with a one-digit multiplier directly from the rods.

EXERCISES FOR SECTION 2-2

Multiply, using the "galley" method:

1. 492
$\times 37$

2. 568
$\times 429$

3. 432
$\times 276$

4. 4876
$\times 27$

5. 7025
$\times 398$

6. 5081
$\times 2376$

Construct a set of Napier rods and use them to find each of the following products:

7. 256	8. 427
$\times 8$	$\times 9$
9. 387	10. 592
$\times 5$	$\times 7$
11. 7256	12. 427
$\times 8$	$\times 36$

2-3   DECIMAL NOTATION

We now turn our attention to the **decimal system of notation.** It is a decimal system in that it is based on powers or groups of tens. Furthermore, it has place value in that the value of any digit used depends upon the position which it occupies. Thus, the two numerals 4 in 484 have quite different values.

To illustrate this latter concept we will write this number, 484, in what is known as **expanded notation:**

$$484 = 4 \text{ hundreds} + 8 \text{ tens} + 4 \text{ ones}$$
$$= (4 \times 100) + (8 \times 10) + (4 \times 1)$$

Note that one of the numerals 4 represents 4 hundreds, whereas the other 4 represents 4 units; that is, 4 ones.

It is convenient to use exponents when one is writing a number in expanded notation. An **exponent** is a number that tells how many times another number, called the **base,** is used as a factor in a product. For example, in the expression 7^2, the numeral 2 is the exponent and 7 is the base. Note that $7^2 = 7 \times 7 = 49$; also $7^3 = 7 \times 7 \times 7 = 343$.

Using exponents to write 484 in expanded notation, we have

$$484 = (4 \times 100) + (8 \times 10) + (4 \times 1)$$
$$= (4 \times 10^2) + (8 \times 10) + (4 \times 1).$$

Zero plays an important role in place value notation. Indeed, it is the use of the symbol 0 that allows us to write numbers as large as we wish in decimal notation, using only the ten digits. In Egyptian numeration, $\cap$ represents 10, $\mathcal{9}$ represents 100, $\mathcal{r}$ represents 1000, etc. Each new power of 10 requires a new symbol, whereas in our decimal system the symbol 0 allows us to write 10, 100, 1000, etc., using only the digits 0 and 1.

EXAMPLE 1:   Write 2306 in expanded notation.

Solution:

$2306 = (2 \times 10^3) + (3 \times 10^2) + (0 \times 10) + (6 \times 1).$

We may use the exponent 1 to indicate that a number is to be used as a factor only once; thus $10^1 = 10$. We define $10^0 = 1$. Using these exponents, we have

$2306 = (2 \times 10^3) + (3 \times 10^2) + (0 \times 10^1) + (6 \times 10^0).$

Let us see why we define $10^0 = 1$. Consider the quotient $\dfrac{a^m}{a^m}$. By a law of exponents, we subtract to find the quotient as $a^{m-m} = a^0$. On the other hand, any number (except zero) divided by itself is 1. Thus $\dfrac{a^m}{a^m} = 1$. Therefore we say $a^0 = 1$ for any $a \neq 0$.

Negative exponents are used in writing decimals as follows:

$$10^{-1} = \frac{1}{10} = 0.1$$

$$10^{-2} = \frac{1}{100} = 0.01$$

$$10^{-3} = \frac{1}{1000} = 0.001$$

Notice that for any integer k we have $10^{-k} = \dfrac{1}{10^k}$. In general, $b^{-k} = \dfrac{1}{b^k}$. For example,

$$2^{-3} = \frac{1}{2^3} = \frac{1}{8};$$

$$5^{-2} = \frac{1}{5^2} = \frac{1}{25};$$

$$3^2 = \frac{1}{3^{-2}}.$$

Now we are able to write any number given in decimal notation in expanded notation as in the following example.

EXAMPLE 2:   Write 8027.45 in expanded notation.

Solution:

$$8027.45 = (8 \times 10^3) + (0 \times 10^2) + (2 \times 10^1)$$
$$+ (7 \times 10^0) + (4.\times 10^{-1}) + (5 \times 10^{-2}).$$

EXERCISES FOR SECTION 2-3

Write in decimal notation:

1. 5^3 **2.** 3^5

3. 10^{-3} **4.** 10^{-5}

5. 8^0 **6.** 8×10^2

7. 4×10^{-2} **8.** 5×10^{-1}

9. 2×10^3 **10.** 9×10^{-3}

*11. 0.2×10^{-3} ***12.** 0.01×10^4

Write in expanded notation:

13. 432   **14.** 407

15. 4.23   **16.** 79.8

17. 2345   **18.** 2.758

19. 423.83   **20.** 2302.05

21. 0.007   **22.** 2.0301

23. 0.0001   **24.** 9000.09

Write in decimal notation:

25. $(3 \times 10^3) + (2 \times 10^2) + (5 \times 10^1) + (3 \times 10^0)$

26. $(2 \times 10^{-1}) + (3 \times 10^{-2}) + (5 \times 10^{-3})$

27. $(5 \times 10^1) + (2 \times 10^0) + (1 \times 10^{-1})$
$$+ (7 \times 10^{-2}) + (3 \times 10^{-3})$$

28. $(7 \times 10^1) + (0 \times 10^0) + (0 \times 10^{-1})$
$$+ (8 \times 10^{-2}) + (2 \times 10^{-3})$$

29. $(2 \times 10^{-2}) + (5 \times 10^{-3}) + (1 \times 10^{-4})$

30. $(5 \times 10^3) + (7 \times 10^2) + (0 \times 10^1)$
$$+ (5 \times 10^0) + (5 \times 10^{-1})$$

2-4 OTHER SYSTEMS OF NOTATION

In our decimal system of notation objects are grouped and counted in tens and powers of ten. For example, the diagram below shows how one might group and count 134 items.

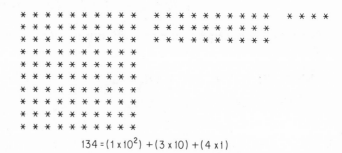

$$134 = (1 \times 10^2) + (3 \times 10) + (4 \times 1)$$

We could, however, just as easily group sets of items in other ways. In the next figure we see 23 asterisks grouped in three different ways.

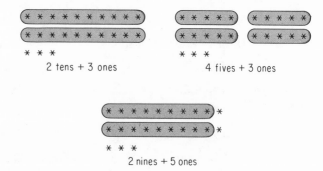

If we use a subscript to indicate our manner of grouping, we may write many different numerals (names) for the number of items in the same collection:

$$23_{\text{ten}} \qquad = \qquad 43_{\text{five}} \qquad = \qquad 25_{\text{nine}}$$

(2 *tens* + 3 ones)   (4 *fives* + 3 ones)   (2 *nines* + 5 ones)

43_{five} is read "four three, base five."

25_{nine} is read "two five, base nine."

Each of these numerals represents the number of asterisks in the same set of asterisks. Still another numeral for this number is 35_{six}:

$$35_{\text{six}} = 3 \; sixes + 5 \text{ ones} = 18 + 5 = 23$$

We call our decimal system of notation a **base ten** system; when no subscript is used, the numeral is understood to be expressed in base ten. When we group by fives we have a **base five** system of notation; that is, we name our system of notation by the manner in which the grouping is accomplished.

EXAMPLE 1: Draw a diagram for 18 objects and write the corresponding numeral (a) in base five and (b) in base eight notation.

Solution:

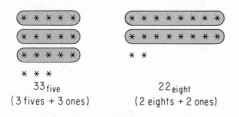

33_{five} 22_{eight}

(3 fives + 3 ones)   (2 eights + 2 ones)

EXAMPLE 2: Write, in base six notation, a numeral for 27.

Solution: We note that $27 = 4$ sixes $+ 3$ ones; thus $27 = 43_{\text{six}}$.

EXERCISES FOR SECTION 2-4

Write numerals for each of the following collections in the bases indicated by the manner of grouping.

Draw a diagram to show the meaning of each of the following:

5. 24_{five} **6.** 23_{six}

7. 25_{seven} **8.** 32_{nine}

9. 23_{four} **10.** 12_{three}

Change to base ten notation:

11. 43_{five} **12.** 24_{seven}

13. 32_{eight} **14.** 51_{six}

15. 34_{five} **16.** 32_{four}

17. Write, in base five notation, a numeral for 17.

18. Write, in base eight notation, a numeral for 43.

19. Write, in base six notation, a numeral for 20.

*20. Change 132_{five} to base ten notation.

2-5 BASE FIVE NUMERATION

In this section we will explore, in some detail, the manner of writing numerals in another number base. We will work with a base five system since it is convenient to think of numbers written in base five notation in terms of hands and fingers. Thus 23_{five} may be thought of in terms of two hands and three fingers; that is, as 2 fives and 3 ones.

For convenience we will write all numbers in base five notation using the numeral 5 as a subscript, such as 23_5. As usual, numbers written without a subscript will be assumed to be in base ten notation. Thus it is correct to write

$$23_5 = 13.$$

Recall that these are merely two different names for the same number. (Two fives + three ones represent the same number as one ten + three ones.)

We can draw a diagram to show the meaning of 23_5 by drawing two groups of five and three ones as shown below.

In a similar manner we picture 123_5 as one group of 25, two groups of 5, and three ones. Note that the group of 25 represents five groups of 5; that is, one group of 5^2.

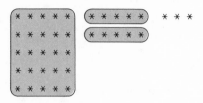

In the decimal system of notation we write numbers in terms of powers of ten using digits 0, 1, 2, 3, 4, 5, 6, 7, 8, and 9. For example,

$$234 = (2 \times 10^2) + (3 \times 10^1) + (4 \times 10^0).$$

In base five notation we write numbers in terms of powers of five using digits 0, 1, 2, 3, and 4. For example,

$$43_5 = (4 \times 5^1) + (3 \times 5^0);$$
$$324_5 = (3 \times 5^2) + (2 \times 5^1) + (4 \times 5^0);$$
$$2143_5 = (2 \times 5^3) + (1 \times 5^2) + (4 \times 5^1) + (3 \times 5^0).$$

Note that $5^0 = 1$.

The numbers 1 to 30 are written in the base five in the following table.

Base 10	Base 5	Base 10	Base 5	Base 10	Base 5
1	1	11	21_5	21	41_5
2	2	12	22_5	22	42_5
3	3	13	23_5	23	43_5
4	4	14	24_5	24	44_5
5	10_5	15	30_5	25	100_5
6	11_5	16	31_5	26	101_5
7	12_5	17	32_5	27	102_5
8	13_5	18	33_5	28	103_5
9	14_5	19	34_5	29	104_5
10	20_5	20	40_5	30	110_5

To translate a number that is not listed in the table from base 5 notation to base 10 notation, express the number in terms of powers of 5 and simplify.

EXAMPLE 1:   Write 3214_5 in base 10 notation.

Solution:

$$3214_5 = (3 \times 5^3) + (2 \times 5^2) + (1 \times 5^1) + (4 \times 5^0)$$
$$= (3 \times 125) + (2 \times 25) + (1 \times 5) + (4 \times 1)$$
$$= 434.$$

In base five notation we may use a quinary point. Then digits to the right of this point represent powers of $\frac{1}{5}$. For example,

$$0.3_{\text{five}} = 3 \times \frac{1}{5} = \frac{3}{5};$$

$$0.23_{\text{five}} = \left(2 \times \frac{1}{5}\right) + \left(3 \times \frac{1}{5^2}\right) = \frac{2}{5} + \frac{3}{25} = \frac{13}{25} = 0.52.$$

EXAMPLE 2:   Write 2.34_5 in base 10 notation.

Solution:

$$2.34_5 = (2 \times 5^0) + (3 \times 5^{-1}) + (4 \times 5^{-2})$$

$$= (2 \times 1) + \left(3 \times \frac{1}{5}\right) + \left(4 \times \frac{1}{25}\right)$$

$$= 2 + \frac{3}{5} + \frac{4}{25}$$

$$= 2\frac{19}{25}$$

$$= 2.76.$$

To translate from base 10 to base 5, any one of several procedures may be adopted. Consider the problem

$$339 = (\quad)_5.$$

When a number is expressed to the base 5, it is written in terms of powers of 5:

$$5^0 = 1, \qquad 5^1 = 5, \qquad 5^2 = 25, \qquad 5^3 = 125, \qquad 5^4 = 625, \qquad \ldots.$$

The highest power of 5 that is not greater than the given number is 5^3. This power of 5, namely $5^3 = 125$, can be subtracted from 339 twice. Then the remainder 89 is positive and less than 125.

$$
\begin{array}{r}
339 \\
-125 \\
\hline
214 \\
-125 \\
\hline
89
\end{array}
$$

Thus, we write 2×5^3 in the expansion of 339 to the base 5.

The next power of 5 is 5^2. This number can be subtracted from 89 three times to obtain a nonnegative remainder less than 25.

$$
\begin{array}{r}
89 \\
-25 \\
\hline
64 \\
-25 \\
\hline
39 \\
-25 \\
\hline
14
\end{array}
$$

Thus, we write 3×5^2 in the expansion.

Finally, we subtract 5 from 14 twice, write 2×5 in the expansion, and obtain 4 as a remainder.

$$
\begin{array}{r}
14 \\
-5 \\
\hline
9 \\
-5 \\
\hline
4
\end{array}
$$

$$
\begin{aligned}
339 &= 2(125) + 3(25) + 2(5) + 4 \\
&= (2 \times 5^3) + (3 \times 5^2) + (2 \times 5^1) + (4 \times 5^0) = 2324_5.
\end{aligned}
$$

A group of 339 elements can be considered as 2 groups of 125 elements, 3 groups of 25 elements, 2 groups of 5 elements, and 4 elements.

An alternative procedure for changing 339 to the base 5 depends upon successive division by 5:

$$
\begin{aligned}
339 &= 67 \times 5 + 4 \\
67 &= 13 \times 5 + 2 \\
13 &= 2 \times 5 + 3
\end{aligned}
$$

Next, substitute from the third equation into the second. Then substitute from the second equation to the first, and simplify as follows:

$$13 = 2 \times 5 + 3$$
$$67 = 13 \times 5 + 2 = (2 \times 5 + 3) \times 5 + 2$$
$$339 = 67 \times 5 + 4 = [(2 \times 5 + 3) \times 5 + 2] \times 5 + 4$$
$$= (2 \times 5^3) + (3 \times 5^2) + (2 \times 5^1) + (4 \times 5^0) = 2324_5$$

The arithmetical steps involved in these computations can be performed as shown in the following array (often called an *algorithm*).

$$
\begin{array}{r|l}
5 & 339 \\
\hline
5 & 67 - 4 \\
\hline
5 & 13 - 2 \\
\hline
5 & 2 - 3 \\
\hline
 & 0 - 2
\end{array}
$$

Read upward as 2324_5.

Note that the remainder is written after each division by 5. Then the remainders are read in reverse order to obtain the expression for the number to the base 5. This procedure works for integers only, not for fractional parts of a number.

EXAMPLE 3:   Write 423 in base 5 notation.

Solution:

$$
\begin{array}{r|l}
5 & 423 \\
\hline
5 & 84 - 3 \\
\hline
5 & 16 - 4 \\
\hline
5 & 3 - 1 \\
\hline
 & 0 - 3
\end{array}
$$

Answer: 3143_5.

Check:

$$3143_5 = (3 \times 5^3) + (1 \times 5^2) + (4 \times 5^1) + (3 \times 5^0)$$
$$= 375 + 25 + 20 + 3 = 423.$$

After computations in other bases have been considered, the method of successive division by the new base may be used in changing from one base to another. For example, we will be able to use this procedure to change from base 5 to base 10, successively dividing by 20_5. The computation must be done in base 5 notation. For the present we may change from base 5 to base 10 by expressing the number in terms of powers of 5. We may also use powers of the base whenever fractional parts are involved, as in Example 2.

EXERCISES FOR SECTION 2-5

Write each number in decimal notation:

1. 423_5		**2.** 230_5	
3. 444_5		**4.** 4230_5	
5. 321_5		**6.** 3403_5	
7. 1031_5		**8.** 342_5	
9. 131.4_5		**10.** 4.23_5	

Write each number in base 5 notation:

11. 382	**12.** 293
13. 782	**14.** 394
15. 625	**16.** 917
17. 137	**18.** 858
19. 507	**20.** 1000

Extend the concepts of this section and write each number in decimal notation:

*21. 437_8 287	***22.** 2013_4
*23. 1011_2	***24.** 321_{12}
*25. 132_{20}	***26.** 312_6
*27. 214_{15}	***28.** 135.2_8

2-6 OTHER NUMBER BASES

The base 5 system has been explored in detail merely for illustrative purposes; any other positive integer greater than 1 would have served just as well as a base. For each base N, the digits used are $0, 1, 2, 3, \ldots, N - 1$. For each base, powers of that base are used as place values for the digits. Consider, for example, the following numerals for the numbers 0 through 10 in several different bases.

Base 10	Base 3	Base 4	Base 5	Base 6	Base 7	Base 8
1	1	1	1	1	1	1
2	2	2	2	2	2	2
3	10_3	3	3	3	3	3
4	11_3	10_4	4	4	4	4
5	12_3	11_4	10_5	5	5	5
6	20_3	12_4	11_5	10_6	6	6
7	21_3	13_4	12_5	11_6	10_7	7
8	22_3	20_4	13_5	12_6	11_7	10_8
9	100_3	21_4	14_5	13_6	12_7	11_8
10	101_3	22_4	20_5	14_6	13_7	12_8

Note that for any positive integer N the numeral 10_N represents one group of N elements and no groups of one element. Thus, from the table:

$$10_3 = (1 \times 3) + (0 \times 1) = 3$$
$$10_4 = (1 \times 4) + (0 \times 1) = 4$$
$$10_5 = (1 \times 5) + (0 \times 1) = 5$$
$$10_6 = (1 \times 6) + (0 \times 1) = 6$$
$$10_7 = (1 \times 7) + (0 \times 1) = 7$$
$$10_8 = (1 \times 8) + (0 \times 1) = 8$$

To change from another base to base 10 notation, express the number in terms of powers of that base and simplify as in the following examples.

EXAMPLE 1:   Change 324_8 to base 10.

Solution:

$$324_8 = (3 \times 8^2) + (2 \times 8^1) + (4 \times 8^0) = 212.$$

EXAMPLE 2:   Change 1231_4 to base 10.

Solution:

$$1231_4 = (1 \times 4^3) + (2 \times 4^2) + (3 \times 4^1) + (1 \times 4^0) = 109.$$

Any number may be changed from base 10 to another base by dividing successively by the new base and using the remainders as in §2-5. This procedure is always performed in the notation of the old base. It has already been used for the base 5 and may be adapted for other bases as well.

EXAMPLE 3:   Change 354 to base 8.

Solution:

$$8\,\lfloor\,354$$
$$8\,\lceil\,44 - 2$$
$$8\,\lceil\,5 - 4 \qquad \textit{Answer: } 542_8.$$
$$\overline{\,0 - 5\,}$$

Check:

$$542_8 = (5 \times 8^2) + (4 \times 8^1) + (2 \times 8^0)$$
$$= 320 + 32 + 2$$
$$= 354.$$

Number bases greater than 10 are possible, but then new symbols must be introduced. Consider, for example, a base 12 system of numeration. The numeral 10_{12} represents $(1 \times 12) + (0 \times 1)$; that is, 12. Thus new symbols are necessary for 10 and 11. Let us use t for 10 and e for 11. Then we can count in base 12 as follows:

$$1, 2, 3, 4, 5, 6, 7, 8, 9, t, e, 10_{12}, 11_{12}, 12_{12}, \ldots$$

We can change a base 12 numeral to base 10 as in the following example.

EXAMPLE 4:   Change $2te5_{12}$ to base 10.

Solution:

$$2te5_{12} = (2 \times 12^3) + (10 \times 12^2) + (11 \times 12^1) + (5 \times 12^0)$$
$$= 3456 + 1440 + 132 + 5 = 5033$$

The reader should note that we make use of a base 12 system in many of our everyday uses of measurements. For example, linear measurement in terms of feet and inches is based on units of 12. Thus a person who is 5 feet 8 inches tall would be listed as having a height of 58_{12} in base 12 notation. Similarly, the use of dozens and gross is based on units of 12. An order for 3 gross, 5 dozen, 7 pencils could be written as 357_{12}:

$$357_{12} = (3 \times 12^2) + (5 \times 12) + (7 \times 12^0) = 499$$

EXERCISES FOR SECTION 2-6

Change to base 10:

1. 472_8	**2.** 3213_4
3. 4552_6	**4.** 347_{12}
5. 1212_3	**6.** 523_7
7. 472_{12}	**8.** $3t5_{12}$
9. $15et_{12}$	**10.** 1101_2

Write each of the following as a base 12 numeral:

11. $(3 \times 12^3) + (5 \times 12^2) + (9 \times 12^1) + (8 \times 12^0)$

12. $(5 \times 12^3) + (10 \times 12^2) + (6 \times 12^1) + (5 \times 12^0)$

13. $(8 \times 12^3) + (7 \times 12^2) + (11 \times 12^1) + (0 \times 12^0)$

14. $(7 \times 12^3) + (11 \times 12^2) + (10 \times 12^1) + (8 \times 12^0)$

Change to the stated base:

15. $324 = ($ $)_4$	**16.** $576 = ($ $)_8$
17. $427 = ($ $)_6$	**18.** $114 = ($ $)_3$
19. $798 = ($ $)_5$	**20.** $257 = ($ $)_7$
21. $536 = ($ $)_9$	**22.** $182 = ($ $)_{12}$
23. $247 = ($ $)_{12}$	**24.** $2033 = ($ $)_{12}$
*25.** $283 = ($ $)_{12}$	*26.** $27 = ($ $)_2$
*27.** $47 = ($ $)_2$	*28.** $175 = ($ $)_2$

2-7 COMPUTATION IN BASE FIVE NOTATION

We can form an addition table for the numbers in base 5 notation very easily. Consider, for example, the problem $4_5 + 3_5$. This may be written as $4_5 + 1_5 + 2_5$. Now, $(4_5 + 1_5)$ is one group of 5, or 10_5. We then add 2_5 to obtain 12_5. This is equivalent to

$$(1 \times 5^1) + (2 \times 5^0) = (1 \times 5^1) + (2 \times 1) = 5 + 2 = 7.$$

In a similar manner, $4_5 + 4_5 = 4_5 + 1_5 + 3_5$. Now $(4_5 + 1_5) = 10_5$. We then add 3_5 to obtain the sum 13_5. This result could also have been obtained by grouping: $4_5 + 4_5$ can be represented as (****) + (****), which can be regrouped as (*****) + (***); that is, 13_5.

Shown below is a table of the number facts needed for addition problems in base 5. (You should verify each entry.)

The facts in this table may be used in finding sums of numbers, as illustrated in the following example.

+	0	1	2	3	4
0	0	1	2	3	4
1	1	2	3	4	10_5
2	2	3	4	10_5	11_5
3	3	4	10_5	11_5	12_5
4	4	10_5	11_5	12_5	13_5

EXAMPLE 1:   Find the sum of 432_5 and 243_5. Then check in base 10 notation.

Solution:

$$\begin{array}{r} 432_5 \\ +243_5 \\ \hline 1230_5 \end{array}$$

Check:

$$432_5 = (4 \times 5^2) + (3 \times 5^1) + (2 \times 5^0) = 117$$
$$+243_5 = (2 \times 5^2) + (4 \times 5^1) + (3 \times 5^0) = 73$$
$$\overline{1230_5 = (1 \times 5^3) + (2 \times 5^2) + (3 \times 5^1) + (0 \times 5^0) = 190}$$

Here are the steps used in Example 1. In each case the familiar symbol 5 has been used in place of 10_{five} to help the reader recognize that powers of 5 are involved. This convention will be followed throughout this chapter.

First add the column of 1's.

$$
\begin{array}{r}
(4 \times 5^2) + (3 \times 5^1) + (2 \times 5^0) \\
\underline{(2 \times 5^2) + (4 \times 5^1) + (3 \times 5^0)} \\
10_5
\end{array}
$$

Next write the sum 10_5 of the 1's as 1×5^1 in the 5's column, and add the column of 5's.

$$
\begin{array}{r}
1 \times 5^1 \\
(4 \times 5^2) + (3 \times 5^1) + (2 \times 5^0) \\
\underline{(2 \times 5^2) + (4 \times 5^1) + (3 \times 5^0)} \\
(13_5 \times 5^1) + (0 \times 5^0)
\end{array}
$$

Then write $10_5 \times 5^1$ from the previous sum in the 5^2 column and add the column of 5^2 entries.

$$
\begin{array}{r}
1 \times 5^2 \\
(4 \times 5^2) + (3 \times 5^1) + (2 \times 5^0) \\
\underline{(2 \times 5^2) + (4 \times 5^1) + (3 \times 5^0)} \\
(12_5 \times 5^2) + (3 \times 5^1) + (0 \times 5^0) = 1230_5
\end{array}
$$

Note that we "carry" groups of five in base 5 computation, just as we "carry" groups of ten in decimal computation.

Subtraction is not difficult if it is thought of as the inverse of addition. The table of addition facts in base 5 may again be used.

EXAMPLE 2: Subtract in base 5 and check in base 10: $211_5 - 142_5$.

Solution: Think of 211_5 as

$$(2 \times 5^2) + (1 \times 5^1) + (1 \times 5^0);$$

then as

$$(1 \times 5^2) + (11_5 \times 5^1) + (1 \times 5^0);$$

then as

$$(1 \times 5^2) + (10_5 \times 5^1) + (11_5 \times 5^0).$$

Thus:

$$211_5 = (1 \times 5^2) + (10_5 \times 5^1) + (11_5 \times 5^0)$$
$$\underline{-142_5 = (1 \times 5^2) + \quad (4 \times 5^1) + \quad (2 \times 5^0)}$$
$$14_5 \qquad\qquad\qquad\quad (1 \times 5^1) + \quad (4 \times 5^0)$$

Check:

$$211_5 = 56$$
$$\underline{-142_5 = 47}$$
$$14_5 = \ 9$$

This problem can be solved by borrowing and thinking in base 5 in the following steps:

(a) $\quad 211_5$ (b) $\quad 20^11_5$ (c) $\quad 1^10^11_5$

$\underline{\quad -142_5} \qquad\quad \underline{\ -14\ 2_5} \qquad\quad \underline{-1\ 4\ 2_5}$

$\qquad\qquad\qquad\qquad\qquad 4_5 \qquad\qquad\qquad 1\ 4_5$

Each raised "1" can be interpreted to show that the number 211_5 has not been changed but rather expressed in a different form:

$$211_5 = (2 \times 5^2) + (1 \times 5^1) + (1 \times 5^0)$$
$$20^11_5 = (2 \times 5^2) + (0 \times 5^1) + (1 \times 5^1) + (1 \times 5^0) = 211_5$$
$$1^10^11_5 = (1 \times 5^2) + (1 \times 5^2) + (0 \times 5^1) + (1 \times 5^1) + (1 \times 5^0)$$
$$= 211_5$$

Problems in multiplication can be performed as repeated additions or as in base 10.

EXAMPLE 3: Find the product of 243_5 and 4_5.

Solution: We need the following facts:

$$4 \times 3 = 12_{10} = (2 \times 5^1) + (2 \times 5^0) = 22_5$$
$$4 \times 4 = 16_{10} = (3 \times 5^1) + (1 \times 5^0) = 31_5$$
$$4 \times 2 = \ 8_{10} = (1 \times 5^1) + (3 \times 5^0) = 13_5$$

The pattern for the computation when multiplying and "carrying" in base 5 notation is then precisely the same as that used in base 10 computation. For example, partial products are indented to represent the powers of 5 involved. In the long form, no attempt is made to "carry" mentally from one place to the next.

$$243_5 \qquad\qquad \textit{Condensed form:} \qquad 243_5$$
$$\underline{\times 4_5} \qquad\qquad\qquad\qquad\qquad\qquad \underline{\times 4_5}$$
$$22_5 \qquad\qquad\qquad\qquad\qquad\qquad 2132_5$$
$$31_5$$
$$\underline{13_5}$$
$$2132_5$$

Multiplication by more than a one-digit multiplier is possible in other bases. Again, the pattern for computation is similar to that used in base 10 computation. Consider, for example, the product $34_5 \times 243_5$:

$$243_5$$
$$\underline{34_5}$$
$$2132 \;\;=\;\; 4_5 \times 243_5$$
$$\underline{13340} \;\;=\;\; 30_5 \times 243_5$$
$$21022_5$$

As in base 10 computation, the product $30_5 \times 243_5$ can be written without the final numeral 0 since the place value is taken care of by indenting.

The pattern used for division in base 10 can also be used for division in base 5. Consider, for example, the problem $121_5 \div 4_5$. As a first step it is helpful to make a table of multiples of 4_5 in base 5:

$$1_5 \times 4_5 = \;\;4_5$$
$$2_5 \times 4_5 = 13_5$$
$$3_5 \times 4_5 = 22_5$$
$$4_5 \times 4_5 = 31_5$$

Since 12_5 is greater than 4_5 and less than 13_5, the first numeral in the quotient is 1.

$$\begin{array}{r} 1 \\ 4_5 \overline{\smash{)}121_5} \\ \underline{4} \\ 31 \end{array}$$

As in base 10 computation, we multiply $1_5 \times 4_5$ and subtract this from 12_5 in the dividend. The next digit is then brought down. Note that $12_5 = 7$ and thus $12_5 - 4 = 3$.

Next we must divide 31_5 by 4_5. Note that $4_5 \times 4_5 = 31_5$. Thus we can complete the division, and there is no remainder.

$$
\begin{array}{r}
14_5 \\
4_5\overline{)121_5} \\
4 \\
\hline
31 \\
31 \\
\end{array}
\qquad
\begin{array}{rr}
Check: & 14_5 \\
& \times 4_5 \\
\hline
& 121_5 \\
\end{array}
$$

EXAMPLE 4: Divide 232_5 by 3_5 and check by multiplication in base 5.

Solution:

$$
\begin{array}{l}
1_5 \times 3_5 = 3_5 \\
2_5 \times 3_5 = 11_5 \\
3_5 \times 3_5 = 14_5 \\
4_5 \times 3_5 = 22_5 \\
\end{array}
\qquad
\begin{array}{r}
42_5 \\
3_5\overline{)232_5} \\
22 \\
\hline
12 \\
11 \\
\hline
1 \\
\end{array}
\qquad
\begin{array}{rr}
Check: & 42_5 \\
& \times 3_5 \\
\hline
& 231_5 \\
& +1_5 \\
\hline
& 232_5 \\
\end{array}
$$

The quotient is 42_5 and the remainder is 1_5. Note that in the check we multiply the quotient by the divisor, and add the remainder to obtain the dividend.

EXERCISES FOR SECTION 2-7

Add in base 5 and check in base 10:

1. $\begin{array}{r} 32_5 \\ +24_5 \end{array}$ 2. $\begin{array}{r} 24_5 \\ +34_5 \end{array}$

3. $\begin{array}{r} 143_5 \\ +234_5 \end{array}$ 4. $\begin{array}{r} 432_5 \\ +443_5 \end{array}$

5. $\begin{array}{r} 2341_5 \\ +3421_5 \end{array}$ 6. $\begin{array}{r} 4324_5 \\ +1442_5 \end{array}$

Subtract in base 5 and check in base 10:

7. 143_5
    -31_5

8. 43_5
    -24_5

9. 312_5
    -123_5

10. 421_5
    -234_5

11. 1321_5
    -403_5

12. 3204_5
    -1342_5

13. 400_5
    -123_5

*14. 2003_5
     -1344_5

Multiply in base 5 and check in base 10:

15. 342_5
    $\times 4_5$

16. 243_5
    $\times 3_5$

17. 1423_5
    $\times 2_5$

18. 2304_5
    $\times 3_5$

19. 24_5
    $\times 32_5$

20. 32_5
    $\times 43_5$

21. 243_5
    $\times 34_5$

*22. 3243_5
     $\times 324_5$

Divide in base 5 and check in base 10:

23. $4_5\overline{)143_5}$

24. $3_5\overline{)121_5}$

25. $3_5\overline{)1234_5}$

26. $4_5\overline{)3042_5}$

27. $11_5\overline{)143_5}$

28. $32_5\overline{)3031_5}$

29. $23_5\overline{)2043_5}$

30. $41_5\overline{)43201_5}$

31. Complete a table showing the basic multiplication facts for base 5.

*32. Complete the following tables of addition and multiplication facts for base 4:

+	0	1	2	3
0				
1				
2				
3				

x	0	1	2	3
0				
1				
2				
3				

*33. Complete the following tables of addition and multiplication facts for base 8:

+	0	1	2	3	4	5	6	7
0								
1								
2								
3								
4								
5								
6								
7								

x	0	1	2	3	4	5	6	7
0								
1								
2								
3								
4								
5								
6								
7								

*34. Using t for 10 and e for 11, complete the following tables of addition and multiplication facts for base 12:

+	0	1	2	3	4	5	6	7	8	9	t	e
0												
1												
2												
3												
4												
5												
6												
7												
8												
9												
t												
e												

x	0	1	2	3	4	5	6	7	8	9	,	e
0												
1												
2												
3												
4												
5												
6												
7												
8												
9												
t												
e												

Complete each of the indicated operations:

*35. 2453_6
       $+3425_6$

*36. 13201_4
       $+12323_4$

*37. 374_8
       -146_8

*38. 5206_7
       -2354_7

*39. 256_8
      $\times 45_8$

*40. 1302_4
      $\times 213_4$

*41. $3_4\overline{)1231_4}$

*42. $25_6\overline{)3245_6}$

2-8 BINARY NOTATION

Numbers written to the base 2 are of special interest because of their application in modern electronic computers. This system of notation is called **binary notation,** and makes use of only two digits, 0 and 1.

Recent spacecraft that took pictures of the planet Mars transmitted the data back to earth in binary notation. On earth, with the aid of computers, this data was converted into pictures of the surface of the planet that appeared in many local newspapers.

Although there is some evidence that the basic concepts of binary notation were known to the ancient Chinese about 2000 B.C., it is only within recent years that it has been widely applied in computer mathematics, card sorting operations, and other electronic devices. Some of the place values in the binary system are as follows:

$$2^7 \quad 2^6 \quad 2^5 \quad 2^4 \quad 2^3 \quad 2^2 \quad 2^1 \quad 2^0$$
$$128 \quad 64 \quad 32 \quad 16 \quad 8 \quad 4 \quad 2 \quad 1$$

Thus, in binary notation, $11011101_2 = 215$ as shown in the following example.

EXAMPLE 1:   Write 11011101_2 in base 10 notation.

Solution:

$$11011101_2 = (1 \times 2^7) + (1 \times 2^6) + (0 \times 2^5) + (1 \times 2^4)$$
$$+ (1 \times 2^3) + (1 \times 2^2) + (0 \times 2^1) + (1 \times 2^0)$$
$$= 128 + 64 + 16 + 8 + 4 + 1$$
$$= 221.$$

Here are the first 16 counting numbers written in binary notation:

Base 10	Base 2	Base 10	Base 2
1	1	9	1001_2
2	10_2	10	1010_2
3	11_2	11	1011_2
4	100_2	12	1100_2
5	101_2	13	1101_2
6	110_2	14	1110_2
7	111_2	15	1111_2
8	1000_2	16	10000_2

Tables for addition and multiplication in binary notation are easy to complete.

+	0	1
0	0	1
1	1	10_2

x	0	1
0	0	0
1	0	1

EXAMPLE 2: Multiply: $101_2 \times 1101_2$.

Solution:

$$
\begin{array}{r}
1101_2 \\
101_2 \\
\hline
1101 \\
11010 \\
\hline
1000001_2
\end{array}
$$

Check:
$$
\begin{aligned}
1101_2 &= 13 \\
101_2 &= \underline{5} \\
&\;65 \\
1000001_2 &= (1 \times 2^6) + (1 \times 2^0) \\
&= 64 + 1 \\
&= 65.
\end{aligned}
$$

The seven-digit numeral 1000001 is the name for the letter A when that letter is sent over teletype to a computer. The American Standard Code for Information Interchange (ASCII) was adopted in 1967 and is used to convert all letters, numerals, and other symbols into binary notation.

Binary numerals can be shown by means of electric lights flashing on and off. If a light is on, the digit 1 is represented; whereas if it is off, the digit 0 is shown. Similarly the digits 0 and 1 can be used in a card sorting operation. The reader can gain an appreciation of the process used by construction of a small set of punched cards. First prepare a set of sixteen index cards with four holes punched in each and a corner notched as in the figure.

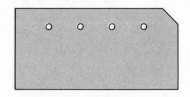

Next represent the numbers 0 through 15 on these cards in binary notation. Cut out the space above each hole to represent 1; leave the hole untouched to represent 0. Several cards are shown in the figure.

After all the cards have been completed in this manner, shuffle them thoroughly and align them, making certain that they remain "face up." (The notched corners will help indicate when the cards are right side up.) Then, going from right to left, perform the following operation: Stick a pencil or other similar object through the first hole and lift up. Some of the cards will come up, namely, those in which the holes have not been cut through to the edge of the card (that is, those cards representing numbers whose units digit in binary notation is 0).

Place the cards that lift up in front of the other cards and repeat the same operation for the remaining holes in order from right to left. When you have finished, the cards should be in numerical order, 0 through 15.

Note that only four operations are needed to arrange the sixteen cards. As the number of cards is doubled, only one additional operation will be needed each time to place them in order. That is, 32 cards may be placed in numerical order with five of the described card sorting operations; 64 cards may be arranged with six operations; 128 cards with seven operations; and so forth. Thus a large number of cards may be arranged in order with a relatively small number of operations. For example, over one billion cards may be placed in numerical order with only thirty sortings.

EXERCISES FOR SECTION 2-8

Write each number in binary notation:

1. 28	**2.** 45
3. 19	**4.** 128
5. 152	**6.** 325

Change each number to decimal notation:

7. 1111_2	**8.** 10101_2
9. 110111_2	**10.** 101010_2
11. 100110_2	**12.** 11011011_2

Perform the indicated operation in binary notation and check in base 10:

13. 1101_2	**14.** 10011_2
$+1011_2$	$+10101_2$

15. 11011_2
          -1011.0_2

16. 110101_2
          -10111_2

17. 1101_2
        $\times 11_2$

18. 10110_2
        $\times 101_2$

19. In the ASCII code the numbers for B, D, and G are 66, 68, and 71, respectively. Find the binary representation of (**a**) B; (**b**) D; (**c**) G.

20. In the ASCII code capital letters A, B, C, . . . in alphabetical order are assigned numbers 65, 66, 67, ... What is the word transmitted by the code 1010010, 1010101, 1001110?

*21. Write the number 214 in base 8 and then in base 2 notation. Can you discover a relationship between these two bases?

*22. Complete a set of 32 punched cards to represent the numbers 0 through 31. Here five holes are needed on each card and five "lifting" operations are necessary to place the set in numerical order.

2-9 JUST FOR FUN

Many recreational items are based on the binary system of notation. Consider, for example, the boxes shown below, within which the numbers 1 to 15 are placed according to the following scheme.

D	C	B	A
8	4	2	1
9	5	3	3
10	6	6	5
11	7	7	7
12	12	10	9
13	13	11	11
14	14	14	13
15	15	15	15

In box A place all numbers that have a 1 in the units place when written in binary notation. In box B place those with a 1 in the second position from the right in binary notation. In C and D are those numbers with a 1 in the third and fourth positions, respectively.

Next, ask someone to think of a number and tell you in which box
or boxes it appears. You then tell that person his number by finding
the sum of the first number in each box he mentions. Thus, if his
number is 11, he lists boxes *A*, *B*, and *D*. You then find the sum
$1 + 2 + 8$ as the number under discussion.

EXERCISES FOR SECTION 2-9

1. Explain why the method given in §2-9 for finding a number
after knowing the boxes in which it appears works as it does.

2. Extend the boxes in §2-9 to include all the numbers through
31. (A fifth column, *E*, will be necessary.) Then explain for the set
of five boxes how to find a number if one knows in which boxes it
appears.

3. You can use binary notation to identify any one of eight numbers by means of three questions that can be answered as "yes" or
"no." Thus consider the numbers from 0 through 7 written in binary
notation. The place values are identified by columns *A*, *B*, and *C*.

	C	*B*	*A*
0	0	0	0
1	0	0	1
2	0	1	0
3	0	1	1
4	1	0	0
5	1	0	1
6	1	1	0
7	1	1	1

The three questions to be asked are: "Does the number have a 1 in
position *A*?" "Does the number have a 1 in position *B*?" "Does the
number have a 1 in position *C*?" Suppose the answers are "Yes, No,
Yes." Then the number is identified as 101_2; that is, 5. Extend this
process to show how you can guess a number that someone is thinking
of from 0 through 15 by means of four "yes–no" questions.

4. One can count on one's fingers in base 2 by considering a
finger held up as 1 and a finger down as 0. Here are several representations for the first five counting numbers.

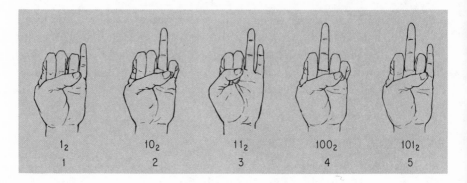

Show how to count through 31 in binary notation using the fingers on one hand.

*5. Find a reference to the game of Nim and study its relationship to the binary system of notation.

TEST FOR CHAPTER 2

1. Use the Egyptian method of duplation and mediation to find the product 17×31.

2. Multiply, using the "galley" method: 325×437.

3. Write in expanded notation: 234.57.

4. Write a numeral for 58 in: **(a)** base 8 notation; **(b)** base 5 notation.

5. Change to base 10:

    (a) 234_5 **(b)** 125_6

6. Change to base 10:

    (a) $3te_{12}$ **(b)** 1011_2

7. Change to the stated base:

    (a) $243 = ($ $)_5$ **(b)** $47 = ($ $)_4$

8. Compute in base 5:

    (a) 243_5 **(b)** 3021_5

         $+132_5$ -1314_5

9. Compute in base 5:

(a) 1342_5 (b) $4_5\overline{)3212_5}$
    $\underline{\times\ \ 3_5}$

10. Compute in binary notation:

(a) 1111_2 (b) 1011_2
    $\underline{+1101_2}$ $\underline{\times 11_2}$

chapter 3

MATHEMATICAL SYSTEMS

In the preceding chapter we discussed various systems of numeration as well as operations with elements in each of these systems. Much of mathematics is concerned with the study of basic principles. In this chapter we shall explore some of these basic principles while studying a collection of abstract, but interesting, systems.

A **mathematical system** involves a set of elements (such as the set of integers), one or more operations (such as addition, subtraction, multiplication, and division), one or more relations (such as the equality $2 \times 3 = 6$), and some axioms (rules) which the elements, operations, and relations satisfy. For example, we assume that every system involves the relation of equality and the axiom that $a = a$; that is, any quantity is equal to itself. Actually, you have been working with mathematical systems ever since you started school. We shall begin this chapter with the study of a specific mathematical system, and shall relate the properties of this system to those of familiar sets of numbers.

3-1 AN ABSTRACT SYSTEM

Let us define an abstract system composed of the set of elements:

$$\{*, \#, \Sigma, [\ \ ]\}$$

For ease of notation we shall call this set Y; that is,

$$Y = \{*, \#, \Sigma, [\ \ ]\}.$$

Next we define an operation which we call "multition" and denote this with the symbol $\sim$. The operation is defined by means of the following table:

~	*	#	Σ	[ ]
*	*	#	Σ	[ ]
#	#	Σ	[ ]	*
Σ	Σ	[ ]	*	#
[ ]	[ ]	*	#	Σ

The operation $\sim$ is a **binary operation**, since it associates a single element with any *two* elements of the given set.

To "multify" two elements of Y, we read the first of these elements in the vertical column at the left and the second in the horizontal row across the top. The answer is found where the column and the row intersect within the table. Verify from the table that each of the following statements is correct:

$$\# \sim \Sigma = [\ \ ]$$
$$[\ \ ] \sim \# = *$$
$$\Sigma \sim * = \Sigma$$

The task of major importance before us is to examine this system for its basic properties. The following are some of the more important ones.

1. Whenever any two elements of the set Y are combined by the process of multition, the result is a unique element of the original collection Y of elements. In other words, there is one and only one answer whenever two elements of Y are multified, and this answer is always one of the elements of Y. We say that *the set Y is closed under the operation of multition.*

In general a set S is said to be **closed** under a given binary operation if that operation associates a unique element of the set S with any two elements of the set.

Consider, in ordinary arithmetic, all the numbers that we use for counting:

$$C = \{1, 2, 3, 4, 5, \ldots\}$$

We call this collection the set C of **counting numbers** and use the three dots to indicate that the elements of the set cannot all be listed; that is, that C is an **infinite set.**

This set of counting numbers is closed under the operations of addition and multiplication. That is, the sum of any two counting numbers is again a counting number and the product of any two counting numbers is a counting number. Is the set of counting numbers closed under subtraction? That is, is the difference of *any* two counting numbers always a counting number?

2. Consider the order in which we combine any two elements of the set Y. Does $\# \sim \Sigma = \Sigma \sim \#$? Does $[\ \ ] \sim * = * \sim [\ \ ]$? In general, if a and b represent any two elements of the set Y, does $a \sim b = b \sim a$? We find the answer to be in the affirmative in each case and summarize this property by saying that *the elements of set Y satisfy the commutative property for multition.*

In general, a set of elements is said to satisfy the **commutative property** for a particular operation if the result obtained by combining any two elements of the set under that operation does not depend upon the order in which these elements are combined.

The set of counting numbers is commutative under addition and multiplication. That is, the sum of any two counting numbers is the same, regardless of the order in which the elements are added. Thus $5 + 7 = 7 + 5$, $8 + 3 = 3 + 8$, etc. Similarly, the set of counting numbers satisfies the commutative property for multiplication, since the product of any two counting numbers is the same regardless of the order in which the elements are multiplied. Thus $5 \times 7 = 7 \times 5$, $8 \times 3 = 3 \times 8$, etc.

EXAMPLE 1:   Show that subtraction of counting numbers is not commutative.

Solution: A single *counterexample* is sufficient to show that a property does not hold. Since $7 - 3 = 4$ and $3 - 7 = -4$, $7 - 3 \neq 3 - 7$ and subtraction is not commutative. (The symbol $\neq$ is read "is not equal to.")

3. Next we combine three elements of the set Y. Can you find the answer for $\Sigma \sim [\;\;] \sim \#$? Here we see that two possibilities exist. We could combine Σ and $[\;\;]$ first and then combine the result with $\#$, or we could combine $[\;\;]$ and $\#$ first and then combine Σ with the result obtained. Let us try both ways:

$$(\Sigma \sim [\;\;]) \sim \# = \# \sim \# = \Sigma$$
$$\Sigma \sim ([\;\;] \sim \#) = \Sigma \sim * = \Sigma$$

We obtain the same result in both cases and will do so for any choice of three members of the set Y. We call this the **associative property** for multition, and write, in symbols:

$$a \sim (b \sim c) = (a \sim b) \sim c$$

where a, b, and c may be replaced by any elements of the set Y.

The set of counting numbers is associative with respect to both addition and multiplication. That is, the sum or product of any three counting numbers is the same regardless of the order in which they are associated. For example,

$$3 + (5 + 7) = 3 + 12 = 15 \quad \text{and} \quad (3 + 5) + 7 = 8 + 7 = 15;$$
$$3 \times (5 \times 7) = 3 \times 35 = 105 \quad \text{and} \quad (3 \times 5) \times 7 = 15 \times 7 = 105.$$

Thus

$$3 + (5 + 7) = (3 + 5) + 7 \quad \text{and} \quad 3 \times (5 \times 7) = (3 \times 5) \times 7.$$

EXAMPLE 2:   Show that the set of counting numbers is not associative with respect to division.

Solution: Again, one counterexample is sufficient.

$24 \div (6 \div 2) = 24 \div 3 = 8,$

$\qquad\qquad\qquad$ whereas $(24 \div 6) \div 2 = 4 \div 2 = 2.$

Thus $24 \div (6 \div 2) \neq (24 \div 6) \div 2$, and division of counting numbers is not associative.

4. The set Y contains a unique element, *, which leaves every other element unchanged with respect to multition. For example,

$$* \sim * = *, \qquad \# \sim * = \#, \qquad \Sigma \sim * = \Sigma, \quad \text{and} \quad [\ \ ] \sim * = [\ \ ].$$

The element with this property is called the **identity element** for multition.

In ordinary arithmetic what is the identity element for addition? That is, what can we add to 7 to obtain 7? Does $9 + 0 = 9$? Do you see that 0 is the identity element for addition? However, 0 is not an element of the set of counting numbers. Therefore, we must say that the set of counting numbers does not contain an identity element with respect to addition. Does the set of counting numbers contain an identity element with respect to multiplication?

5. We examine one more property of the set Y. Replace each blank in the following by an element of the set Y to obtain a correct statement:

$$* \sim \underline{\quad} = *$$
$$\# \sim \underline{\quad} = *$$
$$\Sigma \sim \underline{\quad} = *$$
$$[\ \ ] \sim \underline{\quad} = *$$

The correct answers are, respectively, *, $[\ \ ]$, Σ, and $\#$. We find that for each element of the set Y there is another element of Y such that the first "multified" by the second produces the identity element *. Each of these second elements is called the **inverse with respect to multition** (or simply the **inverse**) of the first element of the statement in which it was used. Thus the inverse of * is *, the inverse of $\#$ is $[\ \ ]$, the inverse of Σ is Σ, and the inverse of $[\ \ ]$ is $\#$. Note that * and Σ serve as their own inverses.

The set of counting numbers does not contain the inverses for its elements with respect to either addition or multiplication. However, when we extend our system to include *all* integers, then every element has an inverse under addition. Thus the inverse of 5 is −5, in that 5 + (−5) = 0. Similarly, the inverse of −3 is 3, in that (−3) + 3 = 0.

In later extensions of our number system we consider all fractions of the form $\frac{a}{b}$, where a and b are integers and $b \neq 0$. This set then contains the inverse for each of its nonzero elements under multiplication. Thus the inverse of 5 is $\frac{1}{5}$, in that $5 \times \frac{1}{5} = 1$. Similarly, the inverse of $\frac{2}{3}$ is $\frac{3}{2}$, in that $\frac{2}{3} \times \frac{3}{2} = 1$.

In summary, the set Y

1. Is closed with respect to multition.
2. Is commutative with respect to multition.
3. Is associative with respect to multition.
4. Contains an identity element with respect to multition.
5. Contains an inverse for each of its elements with respect to multition.

We may summarize all five of these properties by saying that the elements of the set Y form a **commutative group** under multition.

EXERCISES FOR SECTION 3-1

Find the answer to each of the following from the table given in this section:

1. # ∼ *   #
2. * ∼ Σ   E
3. [ ] ∼ [ ]   E
4. Σ ∼ #   [ ]

Verify that each of the following is true and state the name of the property that each illustrates:

5. Σ ∼ # = # ∼ Σ   Communitative
6. [ ] ∼ (# ∼ Σ) = ([ ] ∼ #) ∼ Σ   Comm
7. # ∼ * = #   Identity
8. # ∼ [ ] = *   Inverse
9. (# ∼ Σ) ∼ * = # ∼ (Σ ∼ *)   Ass.
10. [ ] ∼ * = [ ]   Identity
11. [ ] ∼ # = *   Inverse
12. [ ] ∼ * = * ∼ [ ]   Commut

Answer Exercises 13 through 21 by using the following table, which defines an operation ⊙ for the elements of the set {△, □, Q}:

Identity

⊙	△	□	Q
△	Q	△	□
□	△	□	Q
Q	□	Q	△

13. Find △ ⊙ □.   △

14. Find Q ⊙ △.   □

15. Does Q ⊙ □ = □ ⊙ Q? *yes*

16. Does △ ⊙ Q = Q ⊙ △? *yes* *comm.*

17. Does (Q ⊙ □) ⊙ △ = Q ⊙ (□ ⊙ △)? *yes* *comm.*

18. Does □ ⊙ (Q ⊙ △) = (□ ⊙ Q) ⊙ △?   □   *Associative*

19. Does an affirmative answer to the two preceding exercises prove that the set satisfies the associative property with respect to ⊙? Explain your answer. *No - must show all possibilities*

20. Is there an identity element for ⊙? If so, what is it? *yes* □

21. Does each element have an inverse with respect to ⊙? If so, name the inverse of each element. *No* □ □ □

22. Summarize the properties of the set {△, □, Q} with respect to the operation ⊙. *yes*

Answer Exercises 23 through 26 by using the following table, which defines an operation ⌀ for the set {•, [, !, $}:

⌀	•	[	!	$
•	•	[	!	$
[	[	!	•	~
!	!	•	~	[
$	$	[	!	•

23. Is the set closed with respect to ⌀? Justify your answer. *No because*

24. Does the set satisfy the commutative property for ⌀? Explain. *No*

[ ] answer

25. Does the set contain an identity element for $\boxslash$? If so, what is it?   yes

26. Which elements of the set have inverses with respect to $\boxslash$? Name each of these inverses.

yes

SUPPLEMENTARY EXERCISES FOR SECTION 3-1

classed

In each of Exercises 1 through 6 try to discover the meaning of the operation # *from the examples given.* (*It has a different meaning in each.*)

1. $3 \# 4 = 7$; $2 \# 0 = 2$; $5 \# 1 = 6$; $2 \# 2 = 4.$ sum of 2#

2. $2 \# 4 = 3$; $5 \# 7 = 6$; $8 \# 10 = 9$; $0 \# 2 = 1.$ sum & larger

3. $5 \# 3 = 9$; $2 \# 4 = 7$; $0 \# 3 = 4$; $1 \# 5 = 7.$ sum +1

4. $2 \# 3 = 7$; $3 \# 4 = 13$; $1 \# 5 = 6$; $0 \# 3 = 1.$

*5. $3 \# 4 = 2$; $4 \# 3 = 5$; $5 \# 1 = 9$; $1 \# 1 = 1.$ 2 - twice the 1st

*6. $3 \# 5 = 2$; $4 \# 5 = 1$; $2 \# 8 = 0$; $1 \# 6 = 3.$ sum of the 1st - 10

7. Show that the set of counting numbers is not commutative with respect to division. 6 ÷ 11 ≤ 11 ÷ 6

8. Show that the set of counting numbers is not associative with respect to subtraction. (6 - 5) - 3 = 6 - (5 - 3)

9. What is the identity element with respect to multiplication for the set of counting numbers? Give several specific examples to justify your answer.   1 (1×1=1) 1×3=3

10. Show that the set of counting numbers does not form a group under addition. 0 Not in set {1,2,3,4 ···}

11. Let # mean "Select the number if the two given numbers are equal, and the smaller of the two given numbers if they are unequal." Then $5 \# 5 = 5$ and $5 \# 3 = 3$. For the set of counting numbers, does $a \# b = b \# a$? Does $a \# (b \# c) = (a \# b) \# c$? yes commutative yes Associative

12. Let \$ mean "Select the first of two given numbers." Then $5 \$ 2 = 5$. For the set of counting numbers, does $a \$ b = b \$ a$? Does $a \$ (b \$ c) = (a \$ b) \$ c$? No yes Associative

*13. Use the definitions given in Exercises 11 and 12 and show that $a \$ (b \# c) = (a \$ b) \# (a \$ c)$ for all counting numbers a, b, and c.   Extra credit

*14. Referring to the definitions given in Exercises 11 and 12, does $a \# (b \$ c) = (a \# b) \$ (a \# c)$?

b

3-2 THE DISTRIBUTIVE PROPERTY

See if you can discover the meaning of the operations $\#$ and $\otimes$ from the following examples:

$$5 \# 3 = 3 \qquad 8 \otimes 3 = 8$$
$$2 \# 8 = 2 \qquad 0 \otimes 3 = 0$$
$$3 \# 7 = 3 \qquad 6 \otimes 1 = 6$$
$$4 \# 4 = 4 \qquad 3 \otimes 3 = 3$$

You should have discovered the following meanings of $\#$ and $\otimes$:

$\#$: Select the smaller number of the two if the numbers are differ-
      ent; select that number if both are the same.
$\otimes$: Select the first number of the two.

Thus $5 \# 9 = 5$ because 5 is smaller than 9, whereas $5 \otimes 9 = 5$ because 5 is the first of the two numbers in the given expression. Note that where both numbers were the same we wrote $4 \# 4 = 4$.

We may also combine both operations and determine the meaning of expressions such as

$$a \# (b \otimes c) \quad \text{and} \quad (a \# b) \otimes (a \# c),$$

where a, b, and c represent any of the numbers of ordinary arithmetic. For example, let $a = 3$, $b = 5$, $c = 1$; then the first expression becomes

$$3 \# (5 \otimes 1) = 3 \# 5 = 3.$$

Using the same values in the second expression, we have

$$(3 \# 5) \otimes (3 \# 1) = 3 \otimes 1 = 3.$$

Thus we find

$$3 \# (5 \otimes 1) = (3 \# 5) \otimes (3 \# 1).$$

In general, we may write

$$a \# (b \otimes c) = (a \# b) \otimes (a \# c)$$

for all replacements of a, b, and c. We state, formally, that $\#$ is **distributive** with respect to $\otimes$. This property, known as the **distributive property**, may be somewhat easier to visualize for the numbers of arithmetic.

Consider, for example, the expression $3(5 + 8)$. According to the distributive property, we may evaluate this expression in two different ways and obtain the same answer either way. Thus

$$3(5 + 8) = 3(13) = 39,$$
$$(3)(5) + (3)(8) = 15 + 24 = 39,$$

so that

$$3(5 + 8) = (3)(5) + (3)(8).$$

This example illustrates the fact that because of the distributive property we may either add first and then multiply, or find the two products first and then add. In general, we say that for all replacements of a, b, and c

$$a(b + c) = ab + ac.$$

Formally we call this the **distributive property for multiplication with respect to addition,** or simply the *distributive property*. Note that addition is *not* distributive with respect to multiplication since, for example,

$$3 + (5 \times 8) \neq (3 + 5) \times (3 + 8);$$

that is, $3 + 40 \neq 8 \times 11$.

It is the distributive property that allows us, in algebra, to make such statements as:

$$2(a + b) = 2a + 2b$$
$$3(x - y) = 3x - 3y$$

It is the distributive property that elementary school youngsters use in multiplication. Consider the problem 7×43. The distributive property is used by thinking of 7×43 as $7 \times (40 + 3)$, as shown in the example.

$$43$$
$$\underline{\times 7}$$
$$\underline{21} = 7 \times 3$$
$$\underline{280} = 7 \times 40$$
$$301 = (7 \times 3) + (7 \times 40)$$

The distributive property can also be used in developing shortcuts in multiplication. Thus the product 8×99 can be found quickly as follows:

$$8 \times 99 = 8(100 - 1) = 800 - 8 = 792$$

It has been said that the distributive property is one of the unifying themes of mathematics. We have seen several applications here and will discuss this property again in Chapter 5.

EXERCISES FOR SECTION 3-2

For Exercises 1 through 6, let $ mean "select the larger of the two given numbers," and let $\otimes$ mean "select the first of two given numbers":

1. Find 3 $ 8, 8 $ 3, 3 $\otimes$ 7, 7 $\otimes$ 3.

2. Find 3 $ (5 $ 2), (3 $ 5) $ 2.

3. Find 7 $\otimes$ (2 $\otimes$ 3), (7 $\otimes$ 2) $\otimes$ 3.

4. Find 5 $ (1 $\otimes$ 3), (5 $ 1) $\otimes$ (5 $ 3).

5. Find 3 $\otimes$ (2 $ 7), (3 $\otimes$ 2) $ (3 $\otimes$ 7).

6. Show that $a \otimes (b \, \$ \, c) = (a \otimes b) \, \$ \, (a \otimes c) = a$ for all replacements of a, b, and c. Does $a \, \$ \, (b \otimes c) = (a \, \$ \, b) \otimes (a \, \$ \, c)$?

7. In ordinary arithmetic is addition distributive with respect to addition? That is, does $a + (b + c) = (a + b) + (a + c)$ for all possible replacements of a, b, and c? No ; A sso. prop. Yes if A = O

8. In ordinary arithmetic is multiplication distributive with respect to multiplication? That is, does $a \times (b \times c) = (a \times b) \times (a \times c)$ for all possible replacements of a, b, and c? No. Asso. Yes if A = 1 OR O

Use the distributive property to find each of these products by means of a shortcut: 7 × 70 = 490   2×80=··   8 × 50 = 400

9. 7 × 79   7 × 9 = 63   **10.** 8 × 58   8 × 8 = 64
                553   464

Find a replacement for n to make each sentence true:

11. $8(2 + 3) = 8 \cdot 2 + 8 \cdot n$ **12.** $5(3 + 4) = 5 \cdot 3 + n \cdot 4$

13. $7(4 + n) = 7 \cdot 4 + 7 \cdot 5$ **14.** $n(5 + 7) = 3 \cdot 5 + 3 \cdot 7$

15. $(6 + 7)5 = 6 \cdot 5 + n \cdot 5$ **16.** $(5 + n)3 = 5 \cdot 3 + 9 \cdot 3$

17. $3 \cdot 5 + 3 \cdot 7 = 3(5 + n)$ **18.** $4 \cdot 6 + 4 \cdot n = 4(6 + 3)$

19. $3 \cdot n + 7 \cdot n = (3 + 7)n$ **20.** $3(4 + n) = 3 \cdot 4 + 3 \cdot n$
                                          anything

3-3 CLOCK ARITHMETIC

Let us create another finite mathematical system to establish firmly the ideas presented thus far. If it is now 9 P.M. as you begin to read this section, what time will it be in 5 hours? (We hope it won't take you that long to complete your reading!) Do you see that the statement

$$9 + 5 = 2$$

is a correct statement if we are talking about positions on a 12-hour clock?

Let us consider the numerals 1 through 12 on a 12-hour clock as the elements of a set T and consider addition on this clock to be based upon counting in a clockwise direction. Thus to find the sum $9 + 5$ we start at 9 and count 5 units in a clockwise direction to obtain the result 2.

Verify that each of the following is correct:

$$8 + 7 = 3 \quad \text{(on a 12-hour clock)}$$
$$5 + 12 = 5 \quad \text{(on a 12-hour clock)}$$
$$3 + 11 = 2 \quad \text{(on a 12-hour clock)}$$

We may make a table of addition facts on a 12-hour clock as follows:

+	1	2	3	4	5	6	7	8	9	10	11	12
1	2	3	4	5	6	7	8	9	10	11	12	1
2	3	4	5	6	7	8	9	10	11	12	1	2
3	4	5	6	7	8	9	10	11	12	1	2	3
4	5	6	7	8	9	10	11	12	1	2	3	4
5	6	7	8	9	10	11	12	1	2	3	4	5
6	7	8	9	10	11	12	1	2	3	4	5	6
7	8	9	10	11	12	1	2	3	4	5	6	7
8	9	10	11	12	1	2	3	4	5	6	7	8
9	10	11	12	1	2	3	4	5	6	7	8	9
10	11	12	1	2	3	4	5	6	7	8	9	10
11	12	1	2	3	4	5	6	7	8	9	10	11
12	1	2	3	4	5	6	7	8	9	10	11	12

Note that regardless of where we start on the clock, we shall always be at the same place 12 hours later. Thus for any element t of set T we have

$$t + 12 = t \quad \text{(on the 12-hour clock)}.$$

Let us attempt to define several other operations for this arithmetic on the 12-hour clock. What does multiplication mean? Multiplication by an integer may be considered as repeated addition. For example, 3×5 on the 12-hour clock is equivalent to $5 + 5 + 5$. Since $5 + 5 = 10$ and $10 + 5 = 3$, we know that $3 \times 5 = 3$ on the 12-hour clock.

Verify that each of the following is correct:

$$4 \times 5 = 8 \qquad \text{(on the 12-hour clock)}$$
$$3 \times 9 = 3 \qquad \text{(on the 12-hour clock)}$$
$$3 \times 7 = 9 \qquad \text{(on the 12-hour clock)}$$

The following examples provide further illustrations of clock arithmetic.

EXAMPLE 1: Solve the equation $t + 6 = 2$ for t, where t may be replaced by any one of the numerals on a 12-hour clock.

Solution: On the 12-hour clock $8 + 6 = 2$; therefore $t = 8$. Note that we may also solve for t by starting at 6 on the clock and counting, in a clockwise direction, until we reach 2.

EXAMPLE 2: Using the numerals on a 12-hour clock, find a replacement for t such that $\frac{9}{7} = t$.

Solution: We can think of the statement $\frac{9}{7} = t$ as one of the four equivalent statements:

$$9 = 7 \times t \qquad 9 = t \times 7$$
$$\frac{9}{7} = t \qquad \frac{9}{t} = 7$$

Then use the sentence $9 = 7 \times t$ to solve the problem. How many groups of 7 are needed to produce 9 on the 12-hour clock? From a multiplication table, or by trial and error, we find that $7 \times 3 = 9$ (on the 12-hour clock); thus $t = 3$.

EXAMPLE 3: What is $3 - 7$ on the 12-hour clock?

Solution: Let t represent a numeral on the 12-hour clock. The statement "$3 - 7 = t$" is equivalent to "$t + 7 = 3$." From the table of addition facts we find that $8 + 7 = 3$ (on the 12-hour clock); thus $t = 8$.

From a slightly different point of view we may solve Example 3 by counting in a clockwise direction from 12 to 3, and then counting 7 units in a counterclockwise direction. We complete this process at 8. Thus $3 - 7 = 8$ (on the 12-hour clock).

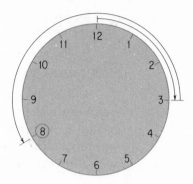

The reader may wish to compare clock arithmetic as developed in this section with the base 12 number system as in §2-6. Note that clock arithmetic is actually a system of remainders. Every multiple of 12 greater than 12 is discarded, and answers are given as a number from 1 through 12. Consider the product $5 \times 8 = 40$. In clock arithmetic and in the base 12 number system

$$5 \times 8 = 40 = (3 \times 12) + 4.$$

In clock arithmetic (3×12) represents 3 rotations and is disregarded:

$$5 \times 8 = 4 \qquad \text{(on the 12-hour clock)}$$

However, in the base 12 system our aim is to write a numeral for 5×8 in terms of 12:

$$5 \times 8 = 34_{12}$$

EXAMPLE 4:   Compare 7×9 in (a) clock arithmetic and in (b) base 12 notation.

Solution: (a) $7 \times 9 = 63$; $63 = (5 \times 12) + 3 = 3$ (on the 12-hour clock). (b) $7 \times 9 = 63$; $63 = (5 \times 12) + 3 = 53_{12}$.

EXERCISES FOR SECTION 3-3

1. Is the set of numbers used in clock arithmetic closed (**a**) with respect to addition? (**b**) with respect to multiplication? yes

yes,

2. Make and complete a table of multiplication facts on the 12-hour clock.

3. Do the set of numbers on the clock contain identity elements with respect to addition and multiplication? If so, what are they?

yes,   0·12

4. List the numbers of clock arithmetic in a column. Beside each number list the inverse with respect to addition and the inverse with respect to multiplication, if one exists. (Thus the inverse of 3, with respect to addition, is 9, whereas 3 does not have an inverse with respect to multiplication.)

Inverse element operation = Id.

Solve each problem as on a 12-hour clock:

5. $8 + 7$

6. $8 + 11 = 7$

7. $9 - 12$

8. $5 - 9 = 3$ $5 - 9 = t$ $t + 9 = 5$

9. 3×9

10. $5 \times 5 = 1$

11. $1 \div 5$

12. $2 \div 7 = 2$ $2 = 7t$ $x = 2$

Find all possible replacements for t for which each sentence is a true sentence for the numerals on a 12-hour clock:

13. $t + 9 = 5$

14. $t - 3 = 11$

15. $8 + t = 2$ 6

16. $3 - t = 10$

17. $3 \times t = 3$ 1,5,9

18. $7 \times t = 11$

19. $\dfrac{t}{5} = 8$

20. $\dfrac{t}{7} = 9$

*21. $\dfrac{2}{t} = 3$ $2 = 3t$ $t = $ No solution

*22. $2 + t = 2 - t$

*23. $t + 12 = t$ $t - 12$

*24. $3 - t = 5 + t$

Solve each problem (a) as on a 12-hour clock, and (b) as in base 12 notation:

25. $9 + 9$

26. $8 + 6$

27. 5×9

28. 3×8

29. 6×6

30. 8×7

3-4 MODULAR ARITHMETIC

Let us next consider a mathematical system based on a clock for five hours, numbered 0, 1, 2, 3, and 4 as in the accompanying figure.

Addition on this clock may be performed by counting as on an ordinary clock. However, it seems easier to think of addition as rotations in a clockwise direction. Thus $3 + 4$ indicates that we are to start at 0 and move 3 units, then 4 more. The result is 2.

We interpret 0 to mean no rotation as well as to designate a position on the clock. Then we have such facts as:

$$3 + 0 = 3 \quad \text{(on a five-hour clock)}$$
$$4 + 1 = 0 \quad \text{(on a five-hour clock)}$$

Verify that the following table of addition facts on a five-hour clock is correct:

+	0	1	2	3	4
0	0	1	2	3	4
1	1	2	3	4	0
2	2	3	4	0	1
3	3	4	0	1	2
4	4	0	1	2	3

Multiplication on the five-hour clock is defined as repeated addition, as in §3-3. For example, 3×4 on the five-hour clock is equivalent to $4 + 4 + 4$. Since $4 + 4 = 3$, and $3 + 4 = 2$, we see that $3 \times 4 = 2$ on the five-hour clock.

We define subtraction and division using equivalent statements as follows:

Subtraction: Since the statements "$a - b = x$" and "$a = b + x$" are equivalent, we define $a - b = x$ *if and only if* $b + x = a$.

Division: Since the statements "$a \div b = x$" and "$a = b \times x$" are equivalent, we define $a \div b = x$ *if and only if* $b \times x = a$.

Regardless of where we start on this five-hour clock, we shall always be at the same place five hours later. Usually the symbols of a mathematical system based on clock arithmetic begin with 0, and the system is called a **modular arithmetic.** In the illustration of this section we say that we have an arithmetic modulo 5, and we use the symbols 0, 1, 2, 3, 4. Formally, specific facts in this mathematical system are written as follows:

$3 + 4 \equiv 2 \pmod 5$, read "$3 + 4$ is congruent to 2, modulo 5"
$4 \times 2 \equiv 3 \pmod 5$, read "$4 \times 2$ is congruent to 3, modulo 5"

In general, two numbers are **congruent modulo 5** if and only if they differ by a multiple of 5. Thus 3, 8, 13, and 18 are all congruent to each other modulo 5. We may write, for example,

$$18 \equiv 13 \pmod 5;$$
$$8 \equiv 3 \pmod 5.$$

Notice that every integer in ordinary arithmetic is congruent modulo 5 to exactly one element of the set F, where $F = \{0, 1, 2, 3, 4\}$. Indeed, the set F is the set of all possible remainders when any number is divided by 5. The elements of F are the elements of arithmetic modulo 5.

EXAMPLE 1: Solve for x where x may be replaced by any element in arithmetic modulo 5: $2 - 3 = x$.

Solution: Note that the statement "$2 - 3 = x$" is equivalent to "$3 + x = 2$." Since $3 + 4 = 2$, $x = 4$.

EXAMPLE 2: Solve for x in arithmetic modulo 5: $\frac{2}{3} = x$.

Solution: Note that the statement "$\frac{2}{3} = x$" is equivalent to "$3 \times x = 2$." Since $3 \times 4 = 2$, $x = 4$.

Let us explore the properties of the mathematical system based upon the set $F = \{0, 1, 2, 3, 4\}$ and the operation addition as defined in this section. The following properties are of special interest.

1. *The set F of elements in arithmetic modulo 5 is closed with respect to addition.* That is, for any pair of elements, there is a unique element which represents their sum and which is also a member of the original set. We note, for example, that there is one and only one entry in each place of the table given in this section, and that each entry is an element of the set F.

2. *The set F of elements in arithmetic modulo 5 satisfies the commutative property for addition.* That is,

$$a + b = b + a,$$

where a and b are any elements of the set F. Specifically, we see that $3 + 4 = 4 + 3, 2 + 3 = 3 + 2$, etc.

3. *The set F of elements in arithmetic modulo 5 satisfies the associative property for addition.* That is,

$$(a + b) + c = a + (b + c),$$

for all elements a, b, and c of the set F.

As a specific example we evaluate $3 + 4 + 2$ in two ways:

$$(3 + 4) + 2 \equiv 2 + 2 \text{ or } 4, \text{ modulo } 5$$
$$3 + (4 + 2) \equiv 3 + 1 \text{ or } 4, \text{ modulo } 5$$

4. *The set F of elements in arithmetic modulo 5 includes an identity element for addition.* That is, the set contains an element 0, such that the sum of any given element and 0 is the given element. That is,

$$0 + 0 = 0, \quad 1 + 0 = 1, \quad 2 + 0 = 2,$$
$$3 + 0 = 3, \quad 4 + 0 = 4.$$

5. *Each element in arithmetic modulo 5 has an inverse with respect to addition.* That is, for each element a of set F there exists an element a' of F such that $a + a' = 0$, the identity element. The element a' is said to be the inverse of a. Specifically, we have the following:

The inverse of 0 is 0;	$0 + 0 \equiv 0 \pmod 5$.
The inverse of 1 is 4;	$1 + 4 \equiv 0 \pmod 5$.
The inverse of 2 is 3;	$2 + 3 \equiv 0 \pmod 5$.
The inverse of 3 is 2;	$3 + 2 \equiv 0 \pmod 5$.
The inverse of 4 is 1;	$4 + 1 \equiv 0 \pmod 5$.

As in §3-1, we may summarize these five properties by saying that the set F of elements in arithmetic modulo 5 forms a commutative group under addition.

EXERCISES FOR SECTION 3-4

Each of the following is based upon the set of elements in arithmetic modulo 5:

1. Make and complete a table of multiplication facts.

2. Verify that the commutative property for multiplication holds for at least two specific instances.

3. Verify that the associative property for multiplication holds for at least two specific instances.

4. What is the identity element with respect to multiplication?

5. Find the inverse of each element with respect to multiplication.

6. Verify for at least two specific instances that arithmetic modulo 5 satisfies the distributive property for multiplication with respect to addition.

Solve each of the following for x:

7. $2 + x \equiv 1 \pmod 5$ **8.** $x + 4 \equiv 2 \pmod 5$

9. $x + 3 \equiv 2 \pmod 5$ **10.** $4 + x \equiv 1 \pmod 5$

11. $1 - 3 \equiv x \pmod 5$ **12.** $1 - 4 \equiv x \pmod 5$

13. $2 - 4 \equiv x \pmod 5$ **14.** $3 - x \equiv 4 \pmod 5$

15. $2 \times x \equiv 3 \pmod 5$ **16.** $4 \times x \equiv 2 \pmod 5$

17. $4 \times x \equiv 1 \pmod 5$ **18.** $3 \times x \equiv 1 \pmod 5$

19. $\frac{1}{2} \equiv x \pmod 5$ **20.** $\frac{4}{3} \equiv x \pmod 5$

21. $\frac{3}{x} \equiv 2 \pmod 5$ **22.** $\frac{2}{x} \equiv 3 \pmod 5$

23. $x + 3 \equiv x \pmod 5$ **24.** $x + 1 \equiv 3 - x \pmod 5$

SUPPLEMENTARY EXERCISES FOR SECTION 3-4

1. Consider arithmetic on a clock with four elements, (0, 1, 2, 3), as in the figure. Complete tables for the addition and multiplication facts for arithmetic modulo 4. Explore these systems and list as many properties as you can for each.

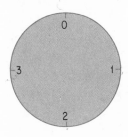

2. Use the results of Exercise 1 and tell whether the set of elements in arithmetic modulo 4 forms a commutative group with respect to (**a**) addition and (**b**) multiplication. If not, tell which properties are not satisfied under the given operation.

Find all possible replacements for x for which each sentence is a true statement:

3. $x + 5 \equiv 0 \pmod 7$ 2   **4.** $x - 3 \equiv 2 \pmod 4$

5. $3x \equiv 1 \pmod 7$ 5   **6.** $x \times x \equiv 1 \pmod 8$

7. $\dfrac{x}{4} \equiv 3 \pmod 9$ **8.** $\dfrac{2}{x} \equiv 3 \pmod 7$

9. $1 - x \equiv 4 \pmod 6$ **10.** $4 + x \equiv 1 \pmod 7$

11. $x + 5 \equiv 1 \pmod 8$ **12.** $2 - x \equiv 3 \pmod 6$

13. $2x \equiv 3 \pmod 6$ No solution   **14.** $\dfrac{x}{3} \equiv 4 \pmod 8$

15. $x - 5 \equiv 2 \pmod 7$ **16.** $7 + x \equiv 1 \pmod{12}$

17. We describe the property illustrated by the equation $3 \times 4 = 0$ in arithmetic modulo 12, where the product is zero but neither number is zero, by saying that 3 and 4 are zero divisors. Are there other zero divisors in arithmetic modulo 12? If so, list them.

18. Consider a modulo 7 system where the days of the week correspond to numbers as follows: Monday $-$ 0; Tuesday $-$ 1; Wednesday $-$ 2; Thursday $-$ 3; Friday $-$ 4; Saturday $-$ 5; Sunday $-$ 6; Memorial Day, May 30, is the 150th day of the year and falls on a Thursday. In that same year, on what day of the week does July 4, the 185th day of the year, fall? On what day does Christmas, the 359th day of the year, fall?

19. Take an index card and label it in each corner as shown. Also write these same letters in the corresponding corners on the reverse side of the card. Call this initial position *I*. Rotate the card 180° to obtain position *R*. Rotate the card about its horizontal axis, from the initial position, to obtain position *H*. Finally, rotate the card about its vertical axis, from the initial position, to obtain position *V*.

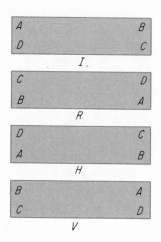

Use the symbol $\sim$ to mean "followed by." Thus $H \sim R$ means a rotation about the horizontal axis followed by a rotation of 180°. You should find $H \sim R = V$. Verify also that $V \sim H = R$.

Make and complete a table for this system whose horizontal and vertical headings are *I*, *R*, *H*, and *V*. List as many properties for this system as you can find.

20. Consider a soldier facing in a given direction. He is then given various commands, such as "right face," "left face," "about face," and "as you were." The last command tells him to retain whatever position he may be in at the time.

A few specific examples of his movements should clarify matters. If he is facing to the north and is given the command "about face," then in his new position he is facing to the south. If we let *R* represent the command "right face," *A* represent the command "about face," and *L* represent the command "left face," then *R* followed by *A* is equivalent to the single command *L*.

Use the symbol o to represent the operation "followed by" and verify that each of the following is correct:

$$L \circ L = A$$
$$L \circ A = R$$
$$A \circ R = L$$

Now suppose that our soldier makes a left turn and then we wish him to remain in that position. We make use of the command "as you were," represented by E. Thus $L \circ E = L$; also $E \circ L = L$.

(a) Make a table summarizing all possible movements, using the headings E, R, L, and A.

(b) Find $R \circ R$, $A \circ A$, $L \circ L$.

(c) Does $R \circ L = L \circ R$?

(d) Does $R \circ (L \circ A) = (R \circ L) \circ A$?

(e) Do the set of given commands appear to be commutative and associative with respect to the operation $\circ$?

(f) Find the identity element with respect to $\circ$.

(g) List the inverse of each of the elements of the set.

(h) Is the set of command closed with respect to $\circ$?

TEST FOR CHAPTER 3

Refer to the table below to answer Exercises 1 through 4:

$\otimes$	#	*	Σ	Δ
#	Σ	Δ	#	*
*	Δ	#	*	Σ
Σ	#	*	Σ	Δ
Δ	*	Σ	Δ	#

1. Which element is the identity element?

2. What is the inverse of Δ?

3. What is $(\# \otimes \Delta) \otimes *$?

4. For all replacements for a and b for the set $Y = \{\#, *, \Sigma, \Delta\}$, $a \otimes b$ is an element of Y. What property does this illustrate?

Solve as on a 12-hour clock:

5. (a) $9 + 7$ (b) 5×11

6. (a) $2 - 7$ (b) $2 \div 5$

Find all possible replacements for x for which each sentence is a true statement:

7. (a) $3 + x \equiv 1 \pmod 5$ (b) $2 - x \equiv 4 \pmod 5$

8. (a) $x + 2 \equiv 0 \pmod 7$ (b) $3 - x \equiv 5 \pmod 8$

9. (a) $3x \equiv 2 \pmod 6$ (b) $\dfrac{x}{3} \equiv 2 \pmod 5$

10. Use the distributive property to evaluate $3(2 + 4)$ in arithmetic modulo 5 in two different ways.

chapter 4

SETS AND STATEMENTS

The concept of a set pervades all of mathematics and is used in many of our daily activities. Think of the many times that you refer to a pen and pencil set, a set of dishes, a set of encyclopedias, or in some other way identify a collection of items as a set. Statements are important to each of us as the primary basis for written and oral communication.

In mathematics we use

Sets of numbers in arithmetic.
Sets of solutions of equations in algebra.
Sets of points in geometry.

Many people consider the use of sets of elements to be a unifying theme throughout all branches of mathematics. The extent to which the concept of a set permeates all of mathematics is illustrated by the fact that set concepts are introduced in the early grades of elementary schools and also provide the basis for graduate mathematics courses at universities.

93

4-1 SET NOTATION

There are many words in our language that indicate sets: *school* of
fish, *swarm* of bees, *gaggle* of geese, *herd* of cattle, *squadron* of planes, etc.

A **set** is a collection of things which are called **elements** or
members of the set. Thus we may speak of

1. The set of letters of the English alphabet.
2. The set of states of the United States of America.
3. The set of English names of the days of the week.
4. The set of counting numbers 1 through 5.

Each of the preceding sets is said to be **well-defined.** That is,
from the description you can tell whether or not any given element
belongs to the set. For example, we know that r, s, and t are members
of the first set listed above, whereas θ and $\aleph_0$ clearly are not members.
Can you tell, from the description given, which of the following
numbers belong to the last of the sets previously described?

$$3, \quad 2\tfrac{1}{2}, \quad 8, \quad 1, \quad 12$$

You should note that 3 and 1 are members of the set described,
whereas $2\tfrac{1}{2}$, 8, and 12 are not. The set of counting numbers 1 through
5 is a well-defined set when the set of counting numbers is defined as
the set 1, 2, 3, 4, 5, 6, 7, 8, 9, 10, and so forth.

Not all sets are well-defined. See if you can explain why each set in
the next list is not a well-defined one.

1. The set of good tennis players.
2. The set of interesting numbers.
3. The set of beautiful movie stars.
4. The set of well-written books.

In this text we shall be concerned primarily with well-defined sets.
Furthermore, we shall agree to name a set by an arbitrarily chosen
capital letter and to list the elements of the set within a pair of braces
as in the following examples.

EXAMPLE 1:   Write in set notation: the set W of English names
of the days of the week.

Solution:

$W = \{$Sunday, Monday, Tuesday,
Wednesday, Thursday, Friday, Saturday$\}$.

EXAMPLE 2: List the elements in the set *I* of counting numbers
1 through 5.

Solution:
$$I = \{1, 2, 3, 4, 5\}.$$

The **membership symbol** $\in$ is often used as in
$$2 \in \{1, 2, 3, 4, 5\} \quad \text{and} \quad 7 \notin \{1, 2, 3, 4, 5\}$$
to indicate that elements are or are not members of sets. We read $\in$
as "is a member of" and $\notin$ as "is not a member of" a given set.
Where it becomes tedious to list individually all of the members of
a set, we frequently use three dots to indicate missing elements.

EXAMPLE 3: List the elements in the set *A* of letters of the
English alphabet.

Solution:
$$A = \{a, b, c, \ldots, z\}.$$

Notice that when three dots are used to show that some elements
are missing, it is necessary to state the elements in some order so that
a pattern can be observed and used to identify the missing elements.

We also use three dots at the end of a sequence of elements to
indicate that the set continues indefinitely in the pattern indicated;
that is, that there is an infinite number of elements in the set.

EXAMPLE 4: List the elements in the set *G* of counting numbers
greater than 100.

Solution:
$$G = \{101, 102, 103, \ldots\}.$$

It is interesting, at times, to seek verbal descriptions for given sets of elements which have already been listed. The next example illustrates this point.

EXAMPLE 5:   Write a verbal description for the set

$$Y = \{1, 3, 5, 7, 9\}.$$

Solution: There are several correct responses that might be given. Two of these are: "The set of odd numbers 1 through 9"; "The set of odd numbers between 0 and 11." Note that the word "between" implies that the first and last numbers (that is, 0 and 11) are not included as members of the given set.

The basic property of a set of elements is the identification of its members. A set is well-defined if its members can be identified. The sets $A = \{1, 2, 3\}$ and $B = \{3, 1, 2\}$ are the same since they have the same members. When two sets consist of precisely the same elements they are said to be **equal sets;** that is, **identical sets.** We write $\{1, 2, 3\} = \{3, 1, 2\}$, since order of listing does not affect membership, $\{1, 1, 2\} = \{1, 2\}$, since listing an element more than once does not affect membership, and in general $A = B$ to show that sets A and B have the same members. We write $A \neq B$ to show that sets A and B do not have the same members.

EXERCISES FOR SECTION 4-1

Replace the asterisk (*) by $\in$ or $\notin$ to obtain a true statement:

1. $7 * \{1, 3, 5, 7, 9\}$ $\in$ **2.** $7 * \{2, 4, 6, 8, 0\}$

3. $\triangle * \{., |, \square\}$ $\notin$ **4.** $\triangle * \{/, \wedge, \triangle\}$

Tell whether or not each of the following sets is well-defined:

 5. The set of U.S. astronauts who have orbited the earth.

 6. The set of cities that are state capitals in the United States of America.

$\digamma$ **7.** The set of large states in the United States.

   8. The set of states in the United States with good climates.

State whether or not the sets of letters are equal as sets.

$\top$ **9.** $\{r, a, t\}$; $\{t, a, r\}$.

   10. $\{t, r, a, p\}$; $\{a, p, a, r, t\}$.

$\top$ **11.** $\{w, o, l, f\}$; $\{f, o, l, l, o, w\}$.

   12. $\{p, r, o, f, e, s, s, o, r\}$; $\{f, r, a, p, p, e, s\}$.

List the elements in each of the following sets, using the notation developed in this section:

   13. The set of English names of the months in the year.

   14. The set of letters in the English alphabet that precede j.

   15. The set of counting numbers between 1 and 10.

   16. The set of odd counting numbers less than 25.

Write a verbal description for each of the following sets:

   17. $N = \{1, 2, 3, 4, 5, 6\}$

   18. $R = \{1, 2, 3, \ldots, 99\}$

   19. $S = \{51, 52, 53, \ldots\}$

   20. $M = \{5, 10, 15, 20, \ldots\}$

   21. $K = \{10, 20, 30, \ldots, 150\}$

   22. $T = \{1, 4, 9, 16, 25, 36\}$

   23. $P = \{0, 2, 6, 12, 20, \ldots, 90\}$

   24. $A = \{8, 5, 4, 9, 1, 7, 6, 3, 2\}$

4-2 SUBSETS

The set containing the totality of elements for any particular discussion is called the **universal set** U, and may vary for each discussion. For example, let us agree, for the present, to talk about the set of counting numbers 1 through 9. Then our universal set is

$$U = \{1, 2, 3, 4, 5, 6, 7, 8, 9\}.$$

A set A is a **subset** of U if the set A has the property that each element of A is also an element of U. We write $A \subseteq U$ (read "A is included in U"). There are many subsets of U; a few of them are listed below:

$$A_1 = \{1, 2, 3\}$$
$$A_2 = \{1, 5, 7, 8, 9\}$$
$$A_3 = \{2\}$$
$$A_4 = \{1, 2, 3, 4, 5, 6, 7, 8, 9\}$$

Note in particular that the set A_4 contains each of the elements of U and is classified as a subset of U. Any set is said to be a subset of itself.

A set A is said to be a **proper subset** of U if A is a subset of U and there is at least one element of U that is not an element of A. We write $A \subset U$ (read "A is properly included in U"). Intuitively we speak of a proper subset as part of, but not all of, a given set. Each of the subsets A_1, A_2, A_3, and A_4 are subsets of U; the sets A_1, A_2, and A_3 are proper subsets of U; the set A_4 is not a proper subset of U. We may write this in symbols as follows:

$$A_1 \subset U; \quad A_2 \subset U; \quad A_3 \subset U; \quad A_4 \subseteq U.$$

EXAMPLE 1: List three proper subsets of the set R where

$$R = \{1, 2, 3, 4\}.$$

Solution: Here are three proper subsets:

$$A = \{1, 2\}; \quad B = \{1, 3, 4\}; \quad C = \{1\}.$$

Do you see that there are others? Note that the choice of letters to name each of the subsets is completely arbitrary.

The **empty** set or **null** set is the set that contains no elements and is denoted by the symbol $\varnothing$ or by the symbol $\{\ \ \}$. Note that the first symbol given for the empty set is not included within a pair of braces. Some examples of empty sets are:

The set of counting numbers between 2 and 3.
The set of states of the United States with borders on both the Atlantic Ocean and the Pacific Ocean.

A set A has been defined to be a subset of a set B if each element of A is also an element of B. If we wish to prove that a set A is not a subset of a set B, we must find an element of A that is not an element of B. For example, if $G = \{1, 3, 5\}$ and $H = \{1, 2, 3, 4, 5\}$, then $G \subseteq H$ but $H \nsubseteq G$, since $2 \in H$ and $2 \notin G$; also $4 \in H$ and $4 \notin G$. Notice that since the empty set has no elements, there are no elements of the empty set that can fail to be elements of a set B. Thus the empty set is a subset of every set B; $\varnothing \subseteq B$ for every set B.

EXAMPLE 2:   List all the possible subsets of the set $\{1, 2\}$.

Solution:

$$\varnothing; \{1\}; \{2\}; \{1, 2\}.$$

Notice in the solution of Example 2 that the subsets of $\{1, 2\}$ are the sets obtained by selecting or not selecting each of the elements of the given set. If we select both elements, we obtain $\{1, 2\}$; if we select exactly one of the elements, we obtain $\{1\}$ or $\{2\}$; if we do not select either element, we obtain the empty set. Since there are two elements and two choices (take it or leave it) for each element, there are 2×2 subsets, as we obtained.

The subsets obtained in Example 2 may be paired as

$$\{1, 2\} \text{ with } \varnothing, \quad \text{and} \quad \{1\} \text{ with } \{2\}.$$

Notice that the two sets of each pair have no common elements and contain all elements of the given set $\{1, 2\}$. Relative to the given set, if we had the set $\{1\}$, we could find the corresponding set $\{2\}$; if we had the set $\{2\}$, we could find the corresponding set $\{1\}$; if we had the set $\{1, 2\}$, we could find the set $\varnothing$; and if we had the set $\varnothing$ we could find the set $\{1, 2\}$. This process may be described as finding the complement of a set relative to the given set $\{1, 2\}$.

For any given universal set U, each set A has a complement A' (also written $\overline{A}$) that consists of the elements of U that are not elements of A and is called the **complement of A relative to U**. For example, if $U = \{1, 3, 5, 7, 9\}$ and $A = \{1, 3, 7\}$, then $A' = \{5, 9\}$. If $A = U$, then $A' = \varnothing$; if $A = \varnothing$, then $A' = U$. In other words, the complement of the universal set is the empty set; the complement of the empty set is the universal set.

❋❋

EXAMPLE 3:   List the subsets of $\{1, 2, 3\}$ and pair each set with its complementary set.

Solution:

$$\{1, 2, 3\} \qquad \varnothing$$
$$\{1\} \qquad \{2, 3\}$$
$$\{2\} \qquad \{1, 3\}$$
$$\{3\} \qquad \{1, 2\}$$

It seems reasonable to expect that all possible subsets should be obtained by considering the elements three at a time, two at a time, one at a time, and zero at a time. As a check that we have found all possible subsets, notice that the original set had three elements; we have two choices (take it or leave it) for each ele-ment; $2 \times 2 \times 2 = 8$, and we found 8 subsets.

❋❋

EXERCISES FOR SECTION 4-2

1. Describe three empty sets.

2. Let $U = \{c, a, r, t\}$ and list the elements of A' when A is defined as

    (a) $\{c, a, r\}$ $\{t\}$ (b) $\{r, a, t\}$

    (c) $\{a, t\}$ $\{cR\}$ (d) $\varnothing$

3. Let $U = \{p, r, o, f, e, s, s, o, r\}$ and list the elements of A' when A is defined as

    (a) $\varnothing$ $= \{profes\}$ (b) $\{r, o, p, e\}$

    (c) $\{r, o, s, e\}$ $\{pf\}$ (d) $\{p, r, o, s, e\}$

4. Let U be the set of counting numbers $\{1, 2, 3, \ldots\}$. Let A be the set of even counting numbers and describe the set A'.

5. If $U = \{1, 2, 3, 4, 5, 6, 7, 8, 9\}$, $A = \{1, 3, 5, 7, 9\}$, and $B = \{3, 6, 9\}$, find

    (a) A' $\quad 2\,4\,6\,8$ (b) B' $\quad 1\,2\,4\,5\,7\,8$

6. List all possible subsets of each set:

    (a) $\{a\}$ (b) $\{a, b\}$

    (c) $\{a, b, c\}$ (d) $\{a, b, c, d\}$

    (e) $\{a, b, c, d, e\}$ (f) $\varnothing$

7. Use the results obtained in Exercise 6, copy, and complete this array:

Number of elements	0	1	2	3	4	5	6
Number of subsets	1						

8. Make an array as in Exercise 7 for the number of proper subsets of the sets in Exercise 6.

9. Use your answer for Exercise 7 and conjecture a formula for the number N of subsets that can be formed from a set consisting of n elements.

10. Use your answer for Exercise 8 and conjecture a formula for the number N of proper subsets that can be formed from a set consisting of n elements.

4-3 EQUIVALENT SETS

If you have a set of books, you can count them and use a number to tell how many books there are in the set. If you have a set of book-marks, you can count them and use a number to tell how many bookmarks there are in the set. If your purpose was to be sure that you had exactly one bookmark for each of your books, you could have done this without counting either the books or the bookmarks. Instead you could have placed one bookmark in each book. If this

one-to-one matching of books and bookmarks could be continued until all books and bookmarks were used, you would know that you had the same number of books in the set of books as you had bookmarks in the set of bookmarks. We would then say that there is a one-to-one correspondence between the books and the bookmarks.

Two sets, $X = \{x_1, x_2, \ldots\}$ and $Y = \{y_1, y_2, \ldots\}$ are said to be in **one-to-one correspondence** if we can find a pairing of the x's and y's such that each x corresponds to one and only one y and each y corresponds to one and only one x. Consider the sets $R = \{a, b, c\}$ and $S = \{\$, +, \%\}$. We can match the element $a \in R$ with any one of the elements in S (three choices); we can then match $b \in R$ with any one of the other two elements of S (two choices), and then match $c \in R$ with the remaining element of S (one possibility). Thus a one-to-one correspondence of the sets R and S can be shown in $3 \times 2 \times 1$ (that is, 6) ways:

$$\{a, \quad b, \quad c\} \qquad \{a, \quad b, \quad c\}$$
$$\{\$, \quad +, \quad \%\} \qquad \{\$, \quad \%, \quad +\}$$

$$\{a, \quad b, \quad c\} \qquad \{a, \quad b, \quad c\}$$
$$\{+, \quad \%, \quad \$\} \qquad \{+, \quad \$, \quad \%\}$$

$$\{a, \quad b, \quad c\} \qquad \{a, \quad b, \quad c\}$$
$$\{\%, \quad \$, \quad +\} \qquad \{\%, \quad +, \quad \$\}$$

Two sets A and B that can be placed in a one-to-one correspondence are said to be **equivalent sets** (written $A \leftrightarrow B$). Any two equivalent sets have the same number of elements; that is, the same **cardinality.**

You may use the concept of a one-to-one correspondence to show whether or not any two sets of elements have the same number of members. You also use this concept of a one-to-one correspondence when you count the elements of a set. To count, you use the set of counting numbers

$$\{1, 2, 3, 4, 5, 6, \ldots\}.$$

As in §4-1, the dots indicate that the pattern continues indefinitely. If you were to count the books in the set shown in the previous figure, you would use the set of numbers $\{1, 2, 3, 4, 5\}$. You would form a one-to-one correspondence of the books with the numbers. If you were to count the bookmarks, you would use the same set of numbers.

Two sets that may be placed in one-to-one correspondence with the same set of numbers may be placed in one-to-one correspondence with each other and thus have the same number of elements.

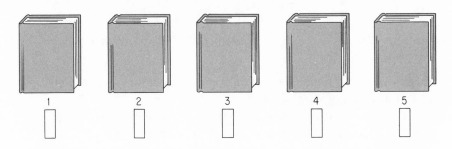

Any set A of elements that may be placed in one-to-one correspondence with the set of elements $\{1, 2, 3, 4, 5\}$ is said to have 5 elements; we write $n(A) = 5$ to show that the number of elements in the set A is 5. Any set B of elements that may be placed in one-to-one correspondence with the set of elements $\{1, 2, 3, 4, \ldots, k - 1, k\}$ is said to have k elements; $n(B) = k$. Notice this use of the set of counting numbers and one-to-one correspondences to determine how many elements there are in a set; that is, to determine the **cardinal number** of a set. When the counting numbers are taken in order, the last number used in the one-to-one correspondence is the cardinal number of the set. We define the cardinality of the empty set to be zero; that is, $n(\varnothing) = 0$.

We have used one-to-one correspondence to determine the cardinal number of a set of numbers. Specifically, we asserted that the last counting number used would be the cardinal number of the set. However, is there always a "last" counting number used? Consider each of the following sets:

$$A = \{1, 2, 3, 4, 5, \ldots, n, \ldots\}$$
$$B = \{2, 4, 6, 8, 10, \ldots, 2n, \ldots\}$$
$$C = \{1, 3, 5, 7, 9, \ldots, 2n - 1, \ldots\}$$
$$D = \{2, 2^2, 2^3, 2^4, 2^5, \ldots, 2^n, \ldots\}$$
$$E = \{1, \frac{1}{2}, \frac{1}{3}, \frac{1}{4}, \frac{1}{5}, \ldots, \frac{1}{n}, \ldots\}$$
$$F = \{10, 10^2, 10^3, 10^4, \ldots, 10^n, \ldots\}$$

In each case the set fails to have a last element; consequently, the set does not have a counting number as its cardinal number.

EXAMPLE: Consider the sets A and B:

$$A = \{1, 2, 3, 4, 5, \ldots, n, \ldots\}$$
$$B = \{2, 4, 6, 8, 10, \ldots, 2n, \ldots\}$$

Explain: (a) $B \subseteq A$; (b) $B \neq A$; (c) $B \subset A$; (d) B is equivalent to A.

Solution: (a) Each element of B is also an element of A; that is, B is a subset of A, $B \subseteq A$.

(b) There is at least one element of A (for example, 1) that is not an element of B; thus B and A are different sets, $B \neq A$.

(c) The set B is a subset of A [see part (a)] that does not contain all elements of A [see part (b)]; that is, B is a proper subset of A, $B \subset A$.

(d) The one-to-one correspondence of n to $2n$ between the elements of A and the elements of B establishes the equivalence of A and B as shown in this array.

$$A: \{1, \quad 2, \quad 3, \quad 4, \ldots, \quad n, \ldots\}$$
$$\quad\; \updownarrow \quad\; \updownarrow \quad\; \updownarrow \quad\; \updownarrow \qquad\quad \updownarrow$$
$$B: \{2, \quad 4, \quad 6, \quad 8, \ldots, \quad 2n, \ldots\}$$

Notice that we have shown that the set A is equivalent to one of its proper subsets.

A set that is equivalent to one of its proper subsets is an **infinite set.** Any infinite set fails to have a last element and fails to have a counting number as its cardinal number. The empty set and any set that has a counting number as its cardinal number are called **finite sets.**

The cardinal number of an infinite set is called a **transfinite cardinal number.** However, as in the case of the books and bookmarks, we do not need to find the cardinal numbers of two sets in order to show that they have the same number of elements. We need only demonstrate that a one-to-one correspondence exists between the sets. The sets A and B have the same number of elements, $n(A) = n(B)$, because there is a one-to-one correspondence of n to $2n$

between the elements of the sets. In other words, there are just as many even counting numbers as there are counting numbers.

Each of the sets A, B, C, D, E, and F may be placed in one-to-one correspondence with the set A. Each of these sets is an infinite set and each has the same transfinite cardinal number as the set of counting numbers.

The properties of infinite sets confused mathematicians for centuries. Indeed, it is only within the last century that infinite sets have been reasonably well understood. The symbol $\aleph_0$ (read "aleph-null") has been introduced in §1-3 as the transfinite cardinal number of the set of counting numbers. We shall consider a few properties of transfinite cardinal numbers and some of their apparent paradoxes in §5-1.

EXERCISES FOR SECTION 4-3

Show all possible one-to-one correspondences of the two sets:

   1. $\{1, 2\}$ and $\{p, q\}$.

   2. $\{1, 2, 3\}$ and $\{x, y, z\}$.

   3. $\{1, 2, 3, 4\}$ and $\{r, e, s, t\}$.

Describe a set with cardinal number:

   4. 5   **5.** 6

   6. 7   **7.** 0

Find the cardinal number of each of the sets in Exercises 8 through 13:

   8. $\{\triangle, >, =, \square\}$ **9.** $\{3, 5, 7\}$ 3

   10. $\{x\}$ **11.** $\{11, 12, \ldots, 18\}$ 8

   12. $\{6\}$ **13.** $\varnothing$ 0

14. Give a set that may be placed in one-to-one correspondence with the set of counting numbers.

15. Give a set that may be placed in one-to-one correspondence with the set of even counting numbers.

16. Consider the set $A = \{a, b, c, d, e\}$ and find a set that is (**a**) equivalent and identical (equal) to A; (**b**) equivalent but not equal to A.

17. Explain whether or not (**a**) any two equal sets are necessarily equivalent; (**b**) any two equivalent sets are necessarily equal.

Show a one-to-one correspondence between:

18. The set of counting numbers 4 through 8 and the set of vowels in the English language.

19. The set of vowels in the English language and the set of even counting numbers less than or equal to 10.

20. The set of counting numbers greater than 100 and the set of all counting numbers.

*21. The set of positive odd integers and the set of positive integral multiples of 5.

$O = \{1, 3, 5, 7 \cdots^{2n-1}\}$ $O \to 7$ Add 1 mult by $\frac{5}{2}$

$7 = \{5, 10, 15, 20 \cdots^{5n}\}$ $7 \to O$

Divide by $\frac{5}{2}$ sub. one

or

multiply $\frac{2}{5}$.

4-4 RELATIONSHIPS BETWEEN SETS

Let us consider two sets A and B, defined as follows:

$$A = \{1, 2, 3, 4, 5, 6, 7\}$$
$$B = \{2, 5, 7, 8, 9\}$$

From these two sets let us form another set C, whose members are those elements that appear in each of the two given sets:

$$C = \{2, 5, 7\}$$

The set C consists of the elements that the sets A and B have in common and is called the **intersection** of the sets A and B. Formally we say that the intersection of two sets A and B (written $A \cap B$) is the set of elements that are members of both of the given sets.

EXAMPLE 1: If $A = \{a, r, e\}$ and $B = \{c, a, t\}$, find $A \cap B$.

Solution: $A \cap B = \{a\}$; that is, a is the only letter that appears in each of the two given sets.

EXAMPLE 2: If $X = \{1, 2, 3, 4, 5\}$ and $Y = \{4, 5, 6, 7\}$, find $X \cap Y$.

Solution:

$$X \cap Y = \{4, 5\}.$$

EXAMPLE 3:   If $X = \{1, 2, 3\}$ and $Y = \{4, 5, 6\}$, find $X \cap Y$.

Solution: Sets X and Y have no elements in common and are said to be **disjoint;** their intersection is the null set. Thus we may write $X \cap Y = \varnothing$.

From the two given sets A and B of this section let us next form another set D, whose members are those elements that are elements of at least one of the two given sets:

$$D = \{1, 2, 3, 4, 5, 6, 7, 8, 9\}$$

The set D is called the **union** of sets A and B. Formally we say that the union of two sets A and B (written $A \cup B$) is the set of elements that are members of at least one of the given sets.

EXAMPLE 4:   Let A represent the set of names of boys on a particular committee, $A = \{$Bill, Bruce, Max$\}$. Let B represent the set of names of boys on another committee, $B = \{$Bruce, John, Max$\}$. Find $A \cup B$.

Solution: $A \cup B = \{$Bill, Bruce, John, Max$\}$. Here the union of the two sets is the set of names of the boys who are on at least one of the two committees. Note that the names Bruce and Max appear only once in the set $A \cup B$ even though these names are listed for both committees.

EXAMPLE 5:   If $A = \{1, 2, 3, 4, 5\}$ and $B = \{3, 5, 7, 9\}$, find $A \cup B$.

Solution:
$$A \cup B = \{1, 2, 3, 4, 5, 7, 9\}.$$

EXAMPLE 6:   If $U = \{1, 2, 3, \ldots, 10\}$, $A = \{1, 2, 3, 4, 5\}$, and $B = \{3, 4, 5, 6, 7\}$, list the elements in $A' \cap B'$.

Solution: $A' = \{6, 7, 8, 9, 10\}$, $B' = \{1, 2, 8, 9, 10\}$, and $A' \cap B' = \{8, 9, 10\}$.

EXERCISES FOR SECTION 4-4

For each of the following sets list the elements in (**a**) $A \cup B$; (**b**) $A \cap B$:

1. $A = \{1, 2, 3\}$; $B = \{1, 3, 5, 7\}$. a: 1,2,3,5 7   b 1 3

2. $A = \{3, 4, 5\}$; $B = \{4, 5, 6, 7\}$. a- 4 5   A) 3,4,5,6 7

3. $A = \{1, 3, 5, 7\}$; $B = \{7, 9\}$. b- 7   A) 1,35,79

4. $A = \{2, 4, 6, 8\}$; $B = \{4, 6, 7, 8\}$. b 4,6,8   A) 2,4,678

5. $A = \{1, 5, 10\}$; $B = \{3, 7, 8\}$. b, ∅   A) 1 3 578 10

6. $A = \{1, 3, 5, \ldots\}$; $B = \{2, 4, 6, \ldots\}$. b ∅   A) 1 2 3 4 5 6

7. $A = \varnothing$; $B = \{1, 2, 3, \ldots\}$. b)∅   A) 1 2 3

8. $A = \{1, 2, 3, \ldots\}$; $B = \{1, 3, 5, \ldots\}$. b, 1,3   A) 1 2 3 5

For each of the given universal sets list the elements in (**a**) A'; (**b**) B'; (**c**) $A' \cup B'$; (**d**) $A' \cap B'$:

9. $U = \{1, 2, 3, 4, 5\}$; $A = \{1, 2\}$; $B = \{1, 3, 5\}$.

10. $U = \{1, 2, 3, \ldots, 10\}$; $A = \{1, 3, 5, 7, 9\}$; $B = \{2, 4, 6, 8, 10\}$.

11. $U = \{1, 2, 3, \ldots\}$; $A = \{1, 3, 5, \ldots\}$; $B = \{2, 4, 6, \ldots\}$.

12. $U = \{1, 2, 3, 4, 5, 6, 7\}$; $A = \varnothing$; $B = \{1, 2, 3, 4, 5, 6, 7\}$.

13. $U = \{1, 2, 3\}$; $A = \{1\}$; $B = \{3\}$.

14. $U = \{1, 2, 3, \ldots, 10\}$; $A = \{1, 3, 5, 7, 9\}$; $B = \{1, 2, 3, 4, 5\}$.

For Exercises 15 through 20, let $U = \{1, 2, 3, 4, 5, 6, 7, 8, 9, 10\}$, $A = \{1, 3, 4, 5, 7, 9\}$, *and* $B = \{2, 4, 5, 9, 10\}$, *and list the elements in:*

15. $A' \cap B'$ 6,8   16. $(A \cup B)'$

17. $A' \cup B$ ~~2 7 10~~ 2 4 5 6 8 9 10   18. $(A' \cap B)'$

19. $A \cap B$ 4,5,9   20. $(A \cup B')'$

    21. If $A \subseteq B$, describe (**a**) $A \cap B$; (**b**) $A \cup B$; (**c**) $A \cap B'$; (**d**) $A' \cup B$. Let U be the set of all numbers.

    22. If $A \subseteq B$ and $B \subseteq A$, describe (**a**) $A \cup B$; (**b**) $A \cap B$; (**c**) $A \cap B'$; (**d**) $A' \cup B$. Let U be the set of all numbers.

Ex. 21) U = counting numbers.
A = {4,8,12,16...} A⊂B
B = {2,4,6...}

a) A∩B = A

b) A∪B = {2,4,6...} B

c) A∩B' = {4,8,12...}{1,3,5,7...} = ∅

d) A'∪B = {1,2,3,5,6,7,9,10,11, ...} ∪ B {2,4,...}

4-5 SETS OF POINTS

Relationships among sets are often represented by sets of points. For example, we may represent the universal set U as a set of points on a line, a set A by the shaded subset of U, and the set A' by the remaining points of U.

The sets of points that are most frequently used to represent sets of elements are rectangular regions and circular regions as identified in the next figure.

Rectangular region   Circular region

Rectangular regions and circular regions may be formally introduced but are used here simply as the sets of points that first grade children would color in coloring the points of a rectangle (or circle) and its interior points. Since there is no confusion about which points are meant, we shall not concern ourselves with formal definitions.

We shall use rectangular regions to represent universal sets and frequently shade the regions under consideration. As in the case of A', we use a dashed line for the part of the boundary of a region that does not belong to the region.

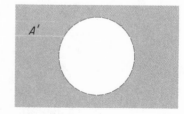

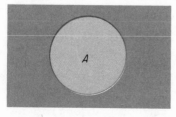

The shading is often omitted when the meaning is clear without the shading. With or without the shading, the figures are called **Euler diagrams.** We may use Euler diagrams to show the intersection of two sets.

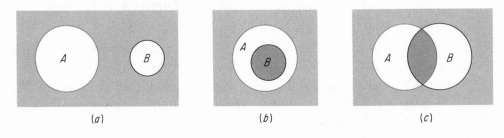

Note above that in Figure (a) $A \cap B$ is the empty set; in Figure (b) $A \cap B = B$. We may also use Euler diagrams to show the union of two sets. Note below that in Figure (b) $A \cup B = A$.

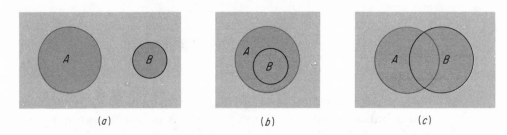

The figures for intersection and union may also be used to illustrate the following properties of any two sets A and B:

$$(A \cap B) \subseteq A \qquad (A \cap B) \subseteq B$$
$$A \subseteq (A \cup B) \qquad B \subseteq (A \cup B)$$

We consider only well-defined sets (§4-1), and thus each element of the universal set U is a member of exactly one of the sets A and A'. When two sets A and B are considered, an element of U must belong to exactly one of these four sets:

$$A \cap B, \qquad \text{i.e., both } A \text{ and } B;$$
$$A \cap B', \qquad \text{i.e., } A \text{ and not } B;$$
$$A' \cap B, \qquad \text{i.e., } B \text{ and not } A;$$
$$A' \cap B', \qquad \text{i.e., neither } A \text{ nor } B.$$

A Euler diagram in which each of these four regions is represented is often called a **Venn diagram.**

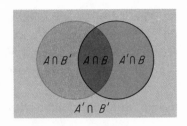

Venn diagrams may be used to show that two sets refer to the same set of points; that is, are equal.

EXAMPLE 1: Show by means of a Venn diagram that $(A \cup B)' = A' \cap B'$.

Solution: We make separate Venn diagrams for $(A \cup B)'$ and $A' \cap B'$. The diagram for $(A \cup B)'$ is made by shading the region for A horizontally, shading the region for B vertically, identifying the region for $A \cup B$ as consisting of the points in regions that are shaded in any way (horizontally, vertically, or both horizontally and vertically), and identifying the region for $(A \cup B)'$ as consisting of the points in the region without horizontal or vertical shading.

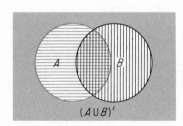

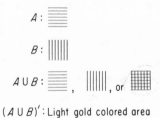

$(A \cup B)'$: Light gold colored area

The diagram for $A' \cap B'$ is made by shading the region for A' horizontally, shading the region for B' vertically, and identifying the region for $A' \cap B'$ as consisting of all points in regions that are shaded both horizontally and vertically.

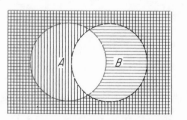

The solution is completed by observing that the region for $(A \cup B)'$ in the first Venn diagram is identical with the region for $A' \cap B'$ in the second Venn diagram; the two sets have the same elements and therefore are equal.

We may also use Venn diagrams for three sets. In this case there are eight regions that must be included, and the figure is usually drawn as follows:

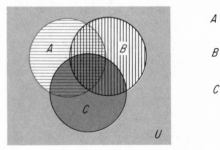

Venn diagrams for three sets are considered in these two examples and in Exercises 19 through 28.

EXAMPLE 2:   Show that $A \cap (B \cup C) = (A \cap B) \cup (A \cap C)$.

Solution: Set A is shaded with vertical lines; $B \cup C$ is shaded with horizontal lines. The intersection of these sets, $A \cap (B \cup C)$, is the subset of U which has both vertical and horizontal shading.

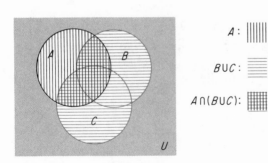

The set $A \cap B$ is shaded with horizontal lines; $A \cap C$ is shaded with vertical lines. The union of these sets is the subset of U, which is shaded with lines in either or in both directions.

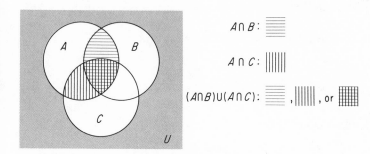

Note that the final results in the two diagrams are the same, thus showing the equivalence of the set $A \cap (B \cup C)$ and the set $(A \cap B) \cup (A \cap C)$.

EXAMPLE 3:   In a group of 35 students, 15 are studying algebra, 22 are studying geometry, 14 are studying trigonometry, 11 are studying both algebra and geometry, 8 are studying geometry and trigonometry, 5 are studying algebra and trigonometry, and 3 are studying all three subjects. How many of these students are not taking any of these subjects? How many are taking only geometry?

Solution: This problem can easily be solved by means of a Venn diagram with three circles to represent the set of students in each of the listed subject-matter areas. It is helpful to start with the information that there are 3 students taking all three subjects. We write the number 3 in the region that is the intersection of all three circles. Then we work backwards; since 5 are taking algebra and trigonometry, there must be 2 in the region representing algebra and trigonometry but *not* geometry. Continuing in this manner, we enter the given data in the figure

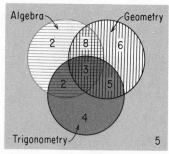

Since the total of the numbers in the various areas is 30, there must be 5 students not in any of the classes listed in the various regions. Also, reading directly from the figure, we find that there are 6 students taking geometry only.

EXERCISES FOR SECTION 4-5

Consider the given diagram and find:

1. (a) $n(A \cap B)$ 2   (b) $n(A)$ 9
   (c) $n(B \cap A')$ 4   (d) $n(B \cup A)$ 13

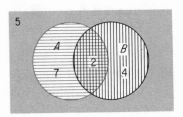

2. (a) $n(P \cup Q)$ 13   (b) $n(P' \cap Q')$
   (c) $n(P' \cup Q)$ (d) $n(P \cup Q')$

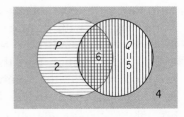

Use an Euler diagram to represent:

3. $A \subset B$

4. A and B are disjoint sets.

5. $A \cup B$ when $A \cap B = \emptyset$.

6. $A \subseteq B$ and $B \subseteq A$.

7. $(A \cup B)'$ when A and B are disjoint sets.

8. $(A \cup B \cup C)'$ when A, B, and C are disjoint sets.

Use a Venn diagram to represent:

   9. $A' \cup B$ **10.** $A' \cap B$

   11. $A \cap B'$ **12.** $A \cup B'$

Use Venn diagrams to show that:

   13. $A \cup B = B \cup A$ **14.** $A \cap B = B \cap A$

   15. $(A \cap B) \subseteq A$ **16.** $A \subseteq (A \cup B)$

   17. $(A \cap B)' = A' \cup B'$ **18.** $A \cup B' = (A' \cap B)'$

Consider the given diagram and find:

   19. **(a)** $n(A \cap B \cap C)$ **(b)** $n(A \cap B \cap C')$
          (c) $n(A \cap B' \cap C')$ **(d)** $n(A)$
          (e) $n(A \cup B)$ **(f)** $n(B \cup C)$

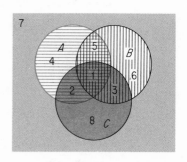

   20. **(a)** $n(R' \cap S \cap T)$ **(b)** $n(R')$
          (c) $n(R' \cup S)$ **(d)** $n(S' \cup T')$
          (e) $n(R' \cup S' \cup T')$ **(f)** $n(R \cup S' \cup T)$

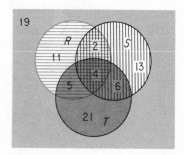

21. (a) $n(A \cup B)$ (b) $n(B \cap C)$
(c) $n(A \cap B')$ (d) $n(A \cup B \cup C)$
(e) $n(A \cup B' \cup C')$ (f) $n(A \cap B' \cap C')$

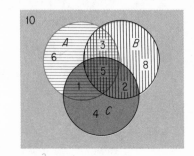

22. (a) $n(X \cup Y)$ (b) $n(X \cup Z)$
(c) $n(X')$ (d) $n(X \cup Y')$
(e) $n(X' \cap Y \cap Z)$ (f) $n(X \cap Y' \cap Z')$

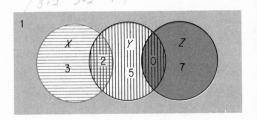

Use Venn diagrams to solve each problem:

23. In a survey of 50 students, the following data were collected: There were 19 taking biology, 20 taking chemistry, 19 taking physics, 7 taking physics and chemistry, 8 taking biology and chemistry, 9 taking biology and physics, 5 taking all three subjects. How many of the group are not taking any of the three subjects? How many are taking only chemistry? How many are taking physics and chemistry, but not biology?

24. A survey was taken of 30 students enrolled in three different clubs, A, B, and C. Show that the following data that were collected are inconsistent: 18 in A, 10 in B, 9 in C, 3 in B and C, 6 in A and B, 9 in A and C, 2 in A, B, and C.

Use a Venn diagram to represent:

25. (a) $A \cap B \cap C$ (b) $A \cap B \cap C'$
(c) $A \cap B' \cap C$ (d) $A \cap B' \cap C'$

26. **(a)** $A' \cap B \cap C$ **(b)** $A' \cap B \cap C'$
  (c) $A' \cap B' \cap C$ **(d)** $A' \cap B' \cap C'$

Use Venn diagrams to show that:

27. $A \cup (B \cup C) = (A \cup B) \cup C$

28. $A \cap (B \cap C) = (A \cap B) \cap C$

4-6 SETS OF STATEMENTS

The distinguishing feature of any statement is that it is either *true* or *false*. Each of the following is an example of a **simple statement:**

Today is Friday in Chicago.
This is a sunny day.

Notice that a command such as "Stand up and be counted" is neither true nor false and is not considered to be a statement as we are using the word here. This restriction upon statements corresponds to our restriction to well-defined sets in §4-1 and our use of sets A and A' in §4-5. Indeed, we often use Euler diagrams to represent situations in which a statement p is true.

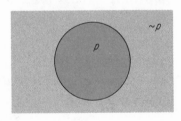

A **compound statement** is formed by combining two or more simple statements. An example is the following:

Today is Friday in Chicago and this is a sunny day.

In this illustration the two simple statements are combined by the connective "and." Other connectives could also have been used. Consider the same simple statements using the connective "or":

Today is Friday in Chicago or this is a sunny day.

We shall consider such compound statements and determine the conditions under which they are true or false, assuming that the simple statements are true. In doing this we use letters or variables to represent statements and symbols to represent connectives. For example, we may use p and q to represent these simple statements:

p: Today is Friday in Chicago.

q: This is a sunny day.

The following connectives are commonly used:

$\wedge$: and

$\vee$: or

$\sim$: not

We may use p and q as previously defined and write these statements in symbolic form together with their translations in words:

$p \wedge q$:   Today is Friday in Chicago and this is a sunny day.

$p \vee q$:   Today is Friday in Chicago or this is a sunny day.

$\sim p$:   Today is not Friday in Chicago.

EXAMPLE 1:   Translate $p \wedge (\sim q)$, where p and q are as given in this section.

Solution: Today is Friday in Chicago and this is not a sunny day.

EXAMPLE 2:   Write, in symbolic form: Today is not Friday in Chicago or this is not a sunny day.

Solution:

$$(\sim p) \vee (\sim q).$$

EXERCISES FOR SECTION 4-6

1. Use p: Jim is tall; q: Bill is short. Think of "short" as "not tall," and write each of these statements in symbolic form:

(a) Jim is short and Bill is tall.

(b) Neither Jim nor Bill is tall.

(c) Jim is not tall and Bill is short.

(d) It is not true that Jim and Bill are both tall.

(e) Either Jim or Bill is tall.

2. Assume that Bill and Jim are both tall. Which of the statements in Exercise 1 are true?

3. Use p: Joan is happy; q: Mary is sad. Think of "sad" as "not happy" and write each of these statements in symbolic form:

(a) Joan and Mary are both happy.

(b) Either Joan is happy or Mary is happy.

(c) Neither Joan nor Mary is happy.

(d) It is not true that Joan and Mary are both sad.

(e) It is not true that neither Joan nor Mary is happy.

4. Assume that Joan and Mary are both happy. Which of the statements in Exercise 3 are true?

5. Use p: I like this book; q: I like mathematics. Give each of these statements in words:

(a) $p \wedge q$ like Book dmath (b) $\sim q$

(c) $\sim p$ I Dont like Boo (d) $(\sim p) \wedge (\sim q)$

6. Continue as in Exercise 5 with the statements:

(a) $(\sim p) \wedge q$ (b) $p \vee q$

(c) $\sim (p \wedge q)$ (d) $\sim [(\sim p) \wedge q]$

7. Assume that you like this book and that you like matnematics. Which of the statements in Exercises 5 and 6 are true for you?

8. Assume that you like this book but that you do not like mathematics. Which of the statements in Exercises 5 and 6 are true for you?

*9. Assume that two given statements p and q are both true and indicate whether or not you would expect each of the following statements to be true:

(a) $p \wedge q$ True   (b) $p \vee q$ True

(c) $p \vee (\sim q)$ True.   (d) $(\sim p) \vee q$ True

*10. Repeat Exercise 9 under the assumption that p is true and q may be true or false.

a. $p \wedge q$?   c. $p \vee q$ T

b. $p \wedge (\sim q)$ T   D $(\sim p) \cup p$ F

4-7 TRUTH VALUES OF STATEMENTS

We first consider the **negation** $(\sim p)$ of a statement p. The symbol was introduced in the last section. As we would expect from the meaning of the word "negation," if p is true, then $\sim p$ is false; if p is false, then $\sim p$ is true. The truth values of the statement $\sim p$ are given in the following **truth table** where T stands for "true" and F stands for "false":

p	$\sim p$
T	F
F	T

Next consider the simple statements:

p: It is snowing.

q: This is the month of December.

The truth of any compound statement, such as $p \wedge q$, is determined by the truth of each of the simple statements. Since each of the statements p and q may be either true or false, there are four distinct possibilities:

p true, q true

p true, q false

p false, q true

p false, q false

For each of these possibilities we wish to determine the truth value of the statement $p \wedge q$. When we say that $p \wedge q$ is true, we mean that both p and q are true. We may define the truth values of $p \wedge q$ by means of the following truth table:

p	q	$p \wedge q$
T	T	T
T	F	F
F	T	F
F	F	F

The statement $p \wedge q$ is called the **conjunction** of p and q. The truth values of $p \wedge q$ are independent of the *meanings* assigned to the variables. For example, if you are told that each of two simple statements is true, it follows immediately that the conjunction of these statements is also true; in any other circumstance, it follows immediately that the conjunction of the statements is false.

Venn diagrams may be used to represent the truth values of two statements with the set A of situations under which p is true labeled p and the set B under which q is true labeled q. As in §4-5 there are

four possible regions. These regions correspond to the four possibilities for truth and falsity for two general statements (also to the
four rows of the truth table) and may be labeled by conjunctions of
statements. Notice the similarity of the meanings of $\wedge$ for statements
and $\cap$ for sets.

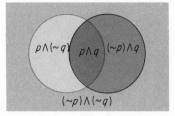

We next consider the compound statement $p \vee q$, called the **disjunction** of p and q. We translate " $\vee$ " as "or" even though we shall
use the word "or" more precisely than in the ordinary English
language. As we shall use it here, "p or q" means that at least one of
the statements p, q is true; that is, either p is true, or q is true, or both
p and q are true. In other words, the meaning of $\vee$ for statements
corresponds to the meaning of $\cup$ for sets.

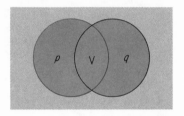

The truth values of $p \vee q$ are defined by the following truth table:

p	q	$p \vee q$
T	T	T
T	F	T
F	T	T
F	F	F

From the table we deduce the fact that the compound statement
$p \vee q$ is true unless both p and q are false.

We can use truth tables to summarize the truth values of various compound statements. To illustrate this procedure we shall construct a truth table for the statement $p \wedge (\sim q)$.

First set up a table with the appropriate headings as follows:

p	q	p	$\wedge$	$(\sim q)$
T	T			
T	F			
F	T			
F	F			

Now complete the column headed "p" by using the truth values that appear under p in the first column. In the column headed "$\sim q$" write the negation of the values given under q in the second column. (Why?) Our table now appears as follows:

p	q	p	$\wedge$	$(\sim q)$
T	T	T		F
T	F	T		T
F	T	F		F
F	F	F		T

Finally we find the conjunctions of the values given in the third and fifth columns. The completed table appears as follows, with the order in which the columns were considered indicated by (a), (b), and (c) and the final results in bold print:

p	q	p	$\wedge$	$(\sim q)$
T	T	T	**F**	F
T	F	T	**T**	T
F	T	F	**F**	F
F	F	F	**F**	T

(a) (c) (b)

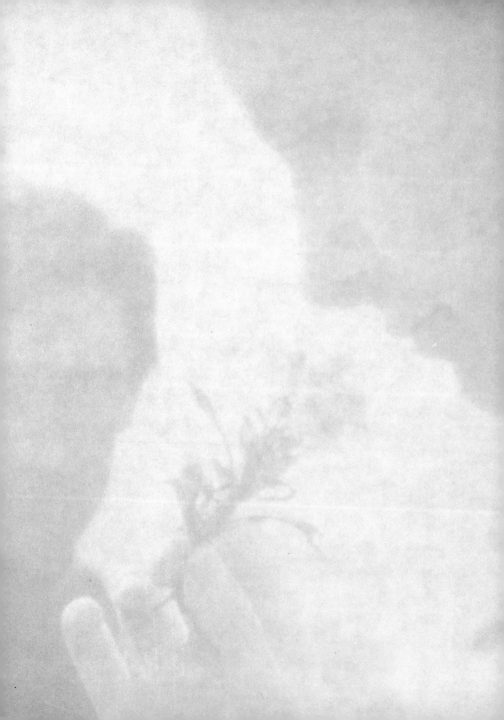

We can summarize this table by saying that the statement $p \wedge (\sim q)$ is true only in the case when p is true and q is false. Thus the statement "Today is Wednesday and it is not snowing" is a true statement on a hot Wednesday in July. (We must assume, of course, that it will not snow on a hot day in July.)

EXERCISES FOR SECTION 4-7

Construct truth tables for:

1. $(\sim p) \wedge q$ **2.** $(\sim p) \vee q$

3. $(\sim p) \vee (\sim q)$ **4.** $(\sim p) \wedge (\sim q)$

5. $\sim(p \wedge q)$ **6.** $p \vee (\sim q)$

In Exercises 7 through 10 copy and complete each truth table:

7.

p	q	$\sim$	$[$ p	$\vee$	$(\sim q)]$
T	T	F	T	T	F
T	F	F	T	T	T
F	T	T	F	F	F
F	F	F	F	T	T
		(d)	(a)	(c)	(b)

8.

p	q	$\sim$	$[(\sim p)$	$\vee$	$q]$
T	T	F	F	T	T
T	F	T	F	F	F
F	T	F	T	T	T
F	F	F	T	T	F
		(d)	(a)	(c)	(b)

9.

p	q	$\sim$	$[(\sim p)$	$\wedge$	$(\sim q)]$
T	T	T	F	F	F
T	F	T	F	F	T
F	T	T	T	F	F
F	F	F	T	T	T
		(d)	(a)	(c)	(b)

10.

p	q	$\sim$	$[(\sim p)$	$\vee$	$(\sim q)]$
T	T				
T	F				
F	T				
F	F				
		(d)	(a)	(c)	(b)

11. Define $p \veebar q$ to mean "p or q but not both" and construct a truth table for this connective.

12. Construct a truth table for $p \mid q$, which we define to be true when p and q are not both true and to be false otherwise.

13. In Exercise 12 express $p \mid q$ in terms of other connectives that we have previously defined.

14. Use p: I like this book; q: I like mathematics. Tell the conditions under which each of the statements in Exercises 1 through 6 is true.

4-8 CONDITIONAL STATEMENTS

Many of the statements that we make in everyday conversation are based upon a condition. For example, consider the following:

> If the sun shines, then I will cut the grass.
> If I have no homework, then I will go bowling.
> If I bribe the instructor, then I will pass the course.

Each of these statements is expressed in the **if-then** form:

> If p, then q.

Any if-then statement can be expressed in symbols as

$$p \rightarrow q,$$

which is read either as "if p, then q" or as "p implies q." The symbol "$\rightarrow$" is called the **implication symbol;** it is a connective used to form a compound statement called a **conditional statement.**

Our first task is to consider the various possibilities for p and q in order to define $p \rightarrow q$ for each of these cases. One way to do this would be to present a completed truth table and to accept this as our definition of $p \rightarrow q$. Let us, however, attempt to justify the entries in such a table. Consider again the conditional statement:

> If the sun shines, then I will cut the grass.

Now if the sun shines and I do cut the grass, then the statement is obviously true. On the other hand, the statement is false if the sun shines and I do not cut the grass. Assume now that the sun is not shining; then, whether I cut the grass or not, the original statement is true in that I only declared my intentions under the condition that the sun shines. We can summarize these assertions by means of a truth table:

p	q	$p \rightarrow q$
T	T	T
T	F	F
F	T	T
F	F	T

Consider the statement

If it rains, then I will give you a ride home.

Have I lied to you:

1. If it rains and I give you a ride home?
2. If it rains and I do not give you a ride home?
3. If it does not rain and I give you a ride home?
4. If it does not rain and I do not give you a ride home?

According to the accepted meanings of the words used, you have a right to feel that I lied to you only if it rains and I do not give you a ride home.

Many people feel uneasy about some of the truth values of $p \rightarrow q$. Actually truth values must be assigned to the conditional statement for each of the four possible combinations of truth values of p and q. Thus the only debatable question is:

Under what conditions is a statement of the form $p \rightarrow q$ considered to be a true statement?

In other words, we are concerned with the use of words in the English language. If we are to communicate with each other, we must accept definitions of the meanings of the words that we use. The accepted meaning of $p \rightarrow q$ is given in the truth table. Other meanings for the symbols could have been used, but since this meaning has been accepted we should use some other symbol if we wish to ascribe another meaning to a compound statement in terms of p and q.

EXAMPLE 1:   Give the truth value of each statement:
(a) If $5 + 7 = 12$, then $6 + 7 = 13$.
(b) If $5 \times 7 = 35$, then $6 \times 7 = 36$.
(c) If $5 + 7 = 35$, then $6 + 7 = 13$.
(d) If $5 + 7 = 35$, then $6 \times 7 = 36$.

Solution: Think of each statement in the form $p \rightarrow q$.
(a) For p true and q true, the statement $p \rightarrow q$ is *true*.
(b) For p true and q false, the statement $p \rightarrow q$ is *false*.
(c) For p false and q true, the statement $p \rightarrow q$ is *true*.
(d) For p false and q false, the statement $p \rightarrow q$ is *true*.

EXAMPLE 2:   Give the replacement set for the real variable x such that the following statement is true:

If $3 \times 4 = 34$, then $x - 3 = 5$.

Solution: Think of the statement in the form $p \to q$ for

$$p: \quad 3 \times 4 = 34$$
$$q: \quad x - 3 = 5$$

Since p is false, the given statement is true for all real values of x.

According to the truth table for $p \to q$, any statement of the form "if p, then q" is false only when p is true and q is false. On the other hand, if p is false; then the statement $p \to q$ is accepted as true regardless of the truth value of q. Thus each of the following statements is true by this definition:

If $2 + 3 = 7$, then George Washington is now the President of the United States.

If $2 + 3 = 7$, then the moon is made of green cheese.

If $2 + 3 = 7$, then July follows June.

If you have difficulty accepting any of these statements as true, then you should review the definition of the truth values of if-then statements. Remember also that there need be no relationship between p and q in an if-then statement, although we tend to use such statements in this way in everyday life.

EXERCISES FOR SECTION 4-8

In Exercises 1 through 4 consider the statements:

$$p: \quad \text{You will study hard.}$$
$$q: \quad \text{You will get an A.}$$

Then translate each of the following symbolic statements into an English sentence:

1. $p \to q$

2. $q \to p$

3. $(\sim p) \to (\sim q)$

4. $(\sim q) \to (\sim p)$

5. Repeat Exercises 1 through 4 for the statements:

p: The triangle is equilateral.
q: The triangle is isosceles.

6. Give the truth value of each statement:
   (a) If $2 \times 3 = 5$, then $2 + 3 = 6$. *T*
   (b) If $2 \times 3 = 5$, then $2 + 3 = 5$. *T*
   (c) If $2 + 3 = 5$, then $2 \times 3 = 5$. *F*

7. Give the truth value of each statement:
   (a) If $5 \times 6 = 56$, then $5 + 6 = 11$.
   (b) If $5 \times 6 = 42$, then $5 + 6 = 10$.
   (c) If $5 \times 6 = 42$, then $5 + 5 = 11$.

8. Assume that $a \times b = c$, $b \times c = d$, and $c \neq d$. Then give the truth value of each statement:
   (a) If $a \times b = c$, then $b \times c = d$.
   (b) If $a \times b = d$, then $b \times c = c$.
   (c) If $a \times b = d$, then $b \times c = d$.
   (d) If $a \times b = c$, then $b \times c = c$.

9. Show by means of truth tables that $(\sim p) \vee q$ has the same truth values as $p \rightarrow q$.

10. Show that $\sim[p \wedge (\sim q)]$ has the same truth values as $p \rightarrow q$.

Construct truth tables for:

11. $(p \rightarrow q) \wedge (q \rightarrow p)$
12. $q \rightarrow [(\sim p) \vee q]$

Copy and complete each truth table:

13.

p	q	$(\sim p)$	$\wedge$	$q]$	$\rightarrow$	$(p \vee q)$
T	T	F	F	T	T	T
T	F	F	F	F	T	F
F	T	T	T	T	T	T
F	F	T	F	F	T	F
		(a)	(c)	(b)	(e)	(d)

14.

p	q	$(\sim p)$	$\vee$	$q]$	$\rightarrow$	$(p \vee q)$
T	T	F	T	T	T	T
T	F	F	F	F	T	F
F	T	T	T	T	T	T
F	F	T	T	F	F	F
		(a)	(c)	(b)	(e)	(d)

Give the replacement set for the real variable x such that each statement is true:

   15. If $2 + 3 = 5$, then $x + 1 = 8$.

   16. If $2 + 3 = 6$, then $x + 1 = 8$.

   ***17.** If $x + 1 = 8$, then $2 + 3 = 5$.

   ***18.** If $x + 1 = 8$, then $2 + 3 = 6$.

   ***19.** If $3 - x = 1$, then $2 \times 5 = 13$.

   ***20.** If $3 - x = 1$, then $2 \times 5 = 10$

TEST FOR CHAPTER 4

   1. State whether or not the sets $\{b, a, t\}$ and $\{l, a, b\}$ are (**a**) equal; (**b**) equivalent.

   2. Let $U = \{m, e, m, o, r, a, b, l, e\}$ and list the elements of A' when A is defined as (**a**) $\{m, o, r, e\}$; (**b**) $\{l, a, b, o, r\}$.

   3. Show all possible one-to-one correspondences of the two sets $\{t, o, p\}$ and $\{r, a, t\}$.

   4. Let $U = \{0, 1, 2, 3, 4, 5, 6, 7, 8, 9\}$, $A = \{2, 4, 6\}$, and $B = \{0, 3, 6, 9\}$. Then find:

   (**a**) $A' \cap B$ (**b**) $(A \cup B)'$

   5. Use a Venn diagram to represent:

   (**a**) $A \cap B'$ (**b**) $A' \cap B \cap C$

   6. Consider the given diagram and find:

   (**a**) $n(A \cap B \cap C')$ (**b**) $n(A \cup B \cup C')$

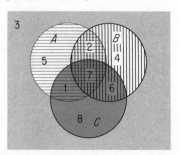

   7. Use p: John studies hard; q: Jim is lazy. Think of "is lazy" as "does not study hard" and write each of these statements in symbolic form:

(a) Neither John nor Jim is lazy.

(b) It is not true that John and Jim are both lazy.

8. Assume that John is lazy and Jim is not lazy. Which of the statements in Exercise 7 are true?

9. Copy and complete the truth table:

p	q	$\sim$	$[(\sim p)$	$\vee$	$q]$
T	T				
T	F				
F	T				
F	F				
		(d)	(a)	(c)	(b)

10. Give the truth value of each statement:

(a) If $6 + 2 = 10$, then $7 \times 2 = 11$.

(b) If $7 \times 2 = 10$, then $6 \times 2 = 12$.

chapter 5

SETS OF NUMBERS

Sets of elements were considered in Chapter 4. A number is associated with a set of elements whenever the elements of a set are counted. The set $\{1, 2, 3, \ldots\}$ of numbers used in counting is called the set of counting numbers. In this chapter we assume that the counting numbers are familiar to the reader. Then we shall consider properties of the counting numbers and extensions of the set of counting numbers to obtain other sets of numbers.

A difference of two counting numbers may or may not represent a counting number; $5 - 3 = 2$, but $3 - 5$ does not represent a counting number. Accordingly, we extend the set of numbers under consideration to include all integers (positive, negative, and zero) so that subtraction will always be possible.

A quotient of two counting numbers may or may not represent a counting number; $6 \div 2 = 3$, but $2 \div 6$ does not represent a counting number. Accordingly, we extend the set of numbers under consideration to include all rational numbers so that division, except by zero, will always be possible.

Finally, we include all real numbers so that all points on a line in our ordinary geometry will have coordinates. Further extensions of the set of numbers are possible but are not needed for the purposes considered here. In each case we shall examine some of the properties of the particular set of numbers under consideration.

5-1 USES OF NUMBERS

The set of numbers that we use in counting,

$$\{1, 2, 3, 4, 5, \ldots\},$$

is called the set of *counting numbers* and has been considered in several earlier sections. The counting numbers provide the basis for the development of other sets of numbers and also for consideration of various uses of numbers.

Counting numbers may be used as in §4-3 as *cardinal numbers* of finite sets of elements. Counting numbers may also be used to assign an order to the elements of a finite set. For example, you expect page 15 of this book to follow page 14. Numbers used to assign an order to the elements of a set are often called **ordinal numbers.**

Numbers are also used in other ways. For example, neither cardinality nor order is significant for the number of your driver's license, your telephone number, or your social security number. Such numbers are used solely for **identification.**

Mathematicians think of numbers as abstractions in the same sense that a color such as red is an abstraction. Thus mathematicians are concerned about properties of numbers such as the commutative property for addition, the associative property for multiplication, the distributive property, etc. This consideration of numbers as abstractions actually enhances the uses or applications of numbers, since applicable properties often add to our insight in using numbers. For example, the commutative property for multiplication helps us recognize that in counting 60 elements we may either count the number of dozens or the number of sets of five (possibly obtained by a matching with the fingers of one hand). That is,

$$5 \times 12 = 12 \times 5.$$

Throughout this chapter we shall be dealing with infinite sets of numbers and their properties. In preceding sections (§1-3, §4-3) we introduced the symbol $\aleph_0$ as the transfinite cardinal number of the set of counting numbers. We now list a few of the unusual arithmetic properties of this number and shall base the discussion upon the following sets:

$$A = \{1, 2, 3, 4, \ldots, n, \ldots\}$$
$$B = \{2, 4, 6, 8, \ldots, 2n, \ldots\}$$
$$C = \{1, 3, 5, 7, \ldots, 2n - 1, \ldots\}$$

1. $\aleph_0 + 1 = \aleph_0$. The set A has the transfinite cardinal number $\aleph_0$; the set A with one element 0 added has cardinal number $\aleph_0 + 1$. The equivalence of these two sets may be shown as follows:

$$\{0, \quad 1, \quad 2, \quad 3, \quad 4, \ldots, \quad n, \ldots\}$$
$$\updownarrow \quad \updownarrow \quad \updownarrow \quad \updownarrow \quad \updownarrow \qquad\qquad \updownarrow$$
$$\{1, \quad 2, \quad 3, \quad 4, \quad 5, \ldots, \quad n+1, \ldots\}$$

2. $\aleph_0 - 5 = \aleph_0$. The set A has the transfinite cardinal number $\aleph_0$; the set A with the numbers 1, 2, 3, 4, 5 removed has the cardinal number $\aleph_0 - 5$. The equivalence of the two sets may be shown as follows:

$$\{6, \quad 7, \quad 8, \quad 9, \quad 10, \ldots, \quad n+5, \ldots\}$$
$$\updownarrow \quad \updownarrow \quad \updownarrow \quad \updownarrow \quad \updownarrow \qquad\qquad \updownarrow$$
$$\{1, \quad 2, \quad 3, \quad 4, \quad 5, \ldots, \quad n, \ldots\}$$

3. $\aleph_0 + \aleph_0 = \aleph_0$. The sets B and C each have the transfinite cardinal number $\aleph_0$; the union of these sets has the cardinal number $\aleph_0 + \aleph_0$ since $B \cap C = \varnothing$. However, $B \cup C = A$, and the set A has cardinal number $\aleph_0$.

EXAMPLE: Show a one-to-one correspondence between the elements of the set of counting numbers and the set of even counting numbers.

Solution:

$$A: \{1, \quad 2, \quad 3, \quad 4, \quad 5, \quad \ldots, \quad n, \ldots\}$$
$$\updownarrow \quad \updownarrow \quad \updownarrow \quad \updownarrow \quad \updownarrow \qquad \updownarrow$$
$$B: \{2, \quad 4, \quad 6, \quad 8, \quad 10, \quad \ldots, \quad 2n, \ldots\}$$

The example demonstrates the *apparent* paradox that there are just as many even counting numbers as there are counting numbers altogether. Nevertheless, this is not a paradox but one of the amazing facts of transfinite arithmetic. Indeed, a formal definition of an infinite set is that it is one that can be placed in a one-to-one correspondence with a proper subset of itself. That is, a set that is equivalent to one of its proper subsets is an infinite set.

There are still many unanswered questions about transfinite numbers. For example, it can be shown that

$$\aleph_0^{\aleph_0}$$

leads to another transfinite cardinal number that is larger than $\aleph_0$ and is often called $\aleph_1$. The problem of determining whether or not there is a cardinal number between $\aleph_0$ and $\aleph_1$ has occupied mathematicians up to recent times and has still not been completely resolved. Indeed, you may be reading about further discoveries on this topic at any time, inasmuch as a number of mathematicians are currently at work on this famous problem.

EXERCISES FOR SECTION 5-1

In each of the following tell whether the number is used as a cardinal number, an ordinal number, or merely for identification:

1. This is the *first* problem on the list.

2. There are 20 volumes in the set of encyclopedias.

3. Mathematics is discussed in the 12th volume.

4. My license plate number is EZT 133.

5. Dorothy is in the eighth row.

6. There are 35 students in the class.

7. I am listening to 104 on the FM dial.

8. It takes 9 men to field a baseball team.

9. This is the third time he is taking the course.

10. The card catalog lists the book as 510.7.

Show a one-to-one correspondence between:

11. The set of counting numbers and the set of odd counting numbers.

12. The set of counting numbers and the set of counting numbers greater than 25.

13. The set of even counting numbers and the set of odd counting numbers.

14. The set of even counting numbers and the set of even counting numbers greater than 100.

15. The set of odd counting numbers greater than 100 and the set of even counting numbers greater than 100.

16. The set of odd counting numbers greater than 50 and the set of odd counting numbers greater than 150.

Classify each set as finite or infinite:

17. $A = \{1, 2, 3, \ldots\}$

18. $B = \{2, 4, 6, \ldots, 1000\}$

19. $C = \{2, 4, 6, \ldots, 1{,}000{,}000\}$

20. $D = \{1, 3, 5, \ldots, 2n - 1, \ldots\}$

21. The number of inhabitants in the world.

22. The number of words in this book.

23. The number of counting numbers greater than 1000.

24. The number of counting numbers less than a googol.

Use a one-to-one correspondence with the set of counting numbers to show each of the following facts:

25. $\aleph_0 + 2 = \aleph_0$ **26.** $\aleph_0 + 5 = \aleph_0$

27. $\aleph_0 - 1 = \aleph_0$ **28.** $\aleph_0 - 10 = \aleph_0$

5-2 PRIME NUMBERS

Before extending the set of counting numbers to other sets we shall explore an interesting and useful classification of the counting numbers according to several of its subsets. First, however, certain definitions are needed.

The counting number 6 is divisible by 2, since there is a counting number 3 such that $6 = 2 \times 3$; the counting number 7 is not divisible by 2, since there exists no counting number b such that $7 = 2 \times b$.

In general, a counting number n is **divisible by** a counting number t if and only if there is a counting number k such that $n = t \times k$. If n is divisible by t, then n is a **multiple of** t and t is a **factor of** n. For example, 6 is a multiple of 2 and 2 is a factor of 6.

The counting numbers are often considered in terms of the numbers by which they are divisible. The set

$$A = \{2, 4, 6, 8, 10, 12, \ldots\}$$

consists of the numbers that are divisible by 2—that is, the numbers expressible in the form $2k$, where k stands for a counting number. The set

$$B = \{3, 6, 9, 12, 15, 18, \ldots\}$$

consists of the numbers divisible by 3; the set

$$C = \{4, 8, 12, 16, 20, 24, \ldots\}$$

consists of the numbers divisible by 4; the set

$$D = \{5, 10, 15, 20, 25, 30, \ldots\}$$

consists of the numbers divisible by 5; the set

$$E = \{6, 12, 18, 24, 30, 36, \ldots\}$$

consists of the numbers divisible by 6; and so forth.

Notice that $C \subset A$; in other words, any number that is divisible by 4 is also divisible by 2. Notice also that $A \cap B = E$; in other words, the set of numbers that are divisible by both 2 and 3 is the set of numbers that are divisible by 6.

The number 1 divides every counting number since $k = 1 \times k$ for every counting number k. Accordingly, the number 1 is called a **unit.** Since the set A does not include all counting numbers, divisibility by 2 is a special property of the elements of the set A.

The number 2 is a member of the set A and is not a member of any other set; that is, 2 is not divisible by any counting number except itself and 1. Any counting number greater than 1 that is divisible only by itself and 1 is called a **prime number.** Thus 2 is prime, 3 is prime, 4 is not prime since 4 is divisible by 2 (that is, 4 is a member of the set A as well as the set C), 5 is prime, and 6 is not prime since 6 is divisible by both 2 and 3. The counting numbers that are greater than 1 and are not prime are called **composite numbers.** Note that every counting number greater than 1 is either prime or composite. The number 1 is not classified as belonging to either of these two sets.

We could extend the list of sets A, B, C, D, E, F to identify other prime numbers; that is, elements that belong to one and only one of these sets. However, the method used to select these sets may be applied to the entire set of counting numbers. We shall illustrate this for the set $\{1, 2, 3, \ldots, 100\}$ and thereby illustrate a method for finding prime numbers that was discovered by a Greek mathematician named Eratosthenes over two thousand years ago. The method is known as the **Sieve of Eratosthenes.** First we prepare a table of the counting numbers through 100. Then selected members of this set are excluded as follows.

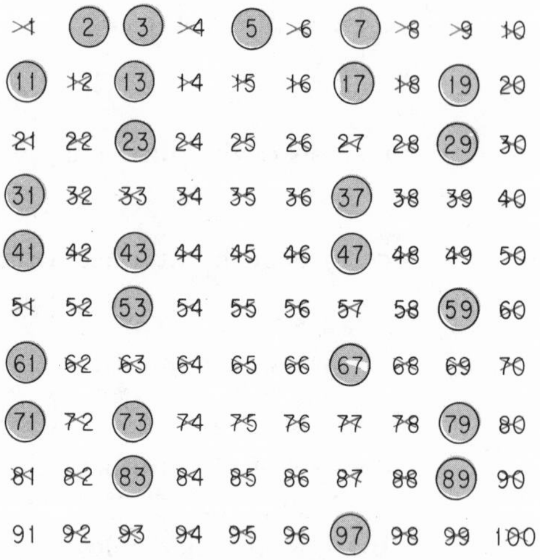
1 2 3 4 5 6 7 8 9 10
11 12 13 14 15 16 17 18 19 20
21 22 23 24 25 26 27 28 29 30
31 32 33 34 35 36 37 38 39 40
41 42 43 44 45 46 47 48 49 50
51 52 53 54 55 56 57 58 59 60
61 62 63 64 65 66 67 68 69 70
71 72 73 74 75 76 77 78 79 80
81 82 83 84 85 86 87 88 89 90
91 92 93 94 95 96 97 98 99 100

Cross out 1, since we know that it is not classified as a prime number. Draw a circle around 2, the smallest prime number. Then cross out every following multiple of 2, since each one is divisible by 2 and thus is not prime. That is, cross out the numbers in the set $\{4, 6, 8, \ldots, 100\}$.

Draw a circle around 3, the next prime number in our list. Then cross out each succeeding multiple of 3. Some of these numbers, such as 6 and 12, will already have been crossed out because they are multiples of 2. That is, they are members of both sets A and B.

The number 5 is prime and is circled, and we exclude each fifth number after 5. The next prime number is 7, and we exclude each seventh number after 7. Note that 49 is the first multiple of 7 that has not already been excluded as being a member of another set of multiples. The next prime number is 11. Since all multiples of 11 in this set have already been excluded, the remaining numbers that have not been excluded are prime numbers and may be circled.

Notice that 49 is the first number that is divisible by 7 and is not also divisible by a prime number less than 7. In other words, each composite number less than 7^2 has at least one of its factors less than 7. Similarly, we might have observed that each composite number less than 5^2 has at least one factor less than 5. In general, *for any prime number p each composite number less than p^2 has a prime number less than p as a factor.*

We use this property to tell us when we have excluded all composite numbers from a set. In the set of numbers $\{1, 2, \ldots, 100\}$ we have considered the primes 2, 3, 5, and 7. The next prime is 11. Thus by our method we have already excluded all composite numbers up to but not including 11^2; that is, 121. In particular, we have identified the set of prime numbers less than or equal to 100.

EXAMPLE 1:   List the set of prime numbers less than 70.

Solution: From the chart we identify this set as

$\{2, 3, 5, 7, 11, 13, 17, 19, 23, 29, 31, 37, 41, 43, 47, 53, 59, 61, 67\}$.

We have seen that every counting number greater than 1 is either a prime number or a composite number. Now we shall find that every counting number greater than 1 can be expressed in terms of its prime factors in essentially only one way.

Consider the various ways of factoring 24:

$$24 = 1 \times 24$$
$$24 = 2 \times 12$$
$$24 = 3 \times 8$$
$$24 = 4 \times 6$$
$$24 = 2 \times 2 \times 6$$
$$24 = 2 \times 3 \times 4$$
$$24 = 2 \times 2 \times 2 \times 3 = 2^3 \times 3$$

The last factorization in terms of the prime numbers 2 and 3 could be written as $2 \times 3 \times 2^2$ and in other ways. However, these ways are equivalent, since the order of the factors does not affect the product.

Thus 24 can be expressed in terms of its prime factors in one and only one way.

One of the easiest ways to find the prime factors of a number is to consider the prime numbers

$$2, 3, 5, 7, 11, 13, 17, 19, 23, 29, 31, \ldots$$

in order and use each one as a factor as many times as possible. Then for 24 we would have

$$\begin{aligned} 24 &= 2 \times 12 \\ &= 2 \times 2 \times 6 \\ &= 2 \times 2 \times 2 \times 3. \end{aligned}$$

Some people prefer to write these steps using division:

$$\begin{array}{r|l} 2 & 24 \\ 2 & \overline{12} \\ 2 & \overline{6} \\ & \overline{3} \end{array}$$

Since 3 is a prime number, no further steps are needed and $24 = 2^3 \times 3$.

EXAMPLE 2: Express 3850 in terms of its prime factors.

Solution:

$$\begin{array}{r|l} 2 & 3850 \\ 5 & \overline{1925} \\ 5 & \overline{385} \\ 7 & \overline{77} \\ & \overline{11} \end{array} \qquad 3850 = 2 \times 5^2 \times 7 \times 11.$$

In general, if a counting number n is greater than 1, then n has a prime number p_1 as a factor. Suppose

$$n = p_1 n_1.$$

Then if n is a prime number, $n = p_1$ and $n_1 = 1$. If n is not a prime number, then n_1 is a counting number greater than 1. In this case n_1 is either a prime number or a composite number. Suppose

$$n_1 = p_2 n_2 \quad \text{and thus} \quad n = p_1 p_2 n_2,$$

where p_2 is a prime number. As before, if $n_2 \neq 1$, then

$$n_2 = p_3 n_3 \quad \text{and thus} \quad n = p_1 p_2 p_3 n_3,$$

where p_3 is a prime number, and so forth. We may continue this process until some $n_k = 1$, since there are only a finite number of counting numbers less than n and

$$n > n_1 > n_2 > n_3 > \cdots > n_k = 1.$$

Then we have an expression for n as a product of prime numbers:

$$n = p_1 p_2 p_3 \cdots p_k$$

We call this the **prime factorization** of n; that is, the factorization of n into its prime factors. Except for the order of the factors, the prime factorization of any counting number greater than 1 is unique; that is, *any counting number greater than 1 may be expressed as a product of prime numbers in one and only one way.* As in the examples, we usually write the prime factorization as a product of powers of prime numbers.

EXAMPLE 3:   Find the prime factorization of 5280.

Solution:

$$
\begin{array}{r|r}
2 & 5280 \\ \cline{2-2}
2 & 2640 \\ \cline{2-2}
2 & 1320 \\ \cline{2-2}
2 & 660 \\ \cline{2-2}
2 & 330 \\ \cline{2-2}
3 & 165 \\ \cline{2-2}
5 & 55 \\ \cline{2-2}
  & 11
\end{array}
\qquad 5280 = 2^5 \times 3 \times 5 \times 11.
$$

EXERCISES FOR SECTION 5-2

Let A = the set of numbers divisible by 2, B = the set of numbers divisible by 3, D = the set of numbers divisible by 5, F = the set of numbers divisible by 12, and H = the set of numbers divisible by 15. Restate each of the statements in Exercises 1 through 6 in terms of divisibility.

   1. $H \subset B$ **2.** $H \subset D$

3. $B \cap D = H$ **4.** $F \subset A$

5. $F \subset B$ **6.** $F \subset (A \cap B)$

7. List the composite numbers between 20 and 40.

8. Adapt the Sieve of Eratosthenes to find the prime numbers less than or equal to 200.

9. Is every odd number a prime number? Is every prime number an odd number?

10. Exhibit a pair of prime numbers that differ by 1 and show that there is only one such pair possible.

11. Here is a famous theorem that has not yet been proved: Every even number greater than 2 is expressible as the sum of two prime numbers. (This theorem is often called **Goldbach's conjecture.**) Express each even number from 4 to 40 inclusive as a sum of two prime numbers.

12. Here is another famous theorem. Two prime numbers such as 17 and 19 that differ by 2 are called *twin primes*. It is believed but has not yet been proved that there are infinitely many twin primes. Find a pair of twin primes that are between (**a**) 25 and 35; (**b**) 55 and 65; (**c**) 95 and 105.

13. A set of three prime numbers that differ by 2 is called a *prime triplet*. Exhibit a prime triplet and explain why it is the only possible triplet of primes.

14. It has been conjectured but not proved that every odd number greater than 5 is expressible as the sum of three prime numbers. Verify this for the numbers 7, 9, 11, 13, and 15.

*15. What is the largest prime that you need to consider to be sure that you have excluded all composite numbers less than or equal to (**a**) 200; (**b**) 500; (**c**) 1000?

Express each number as the product of two counting numbers in as many different ways as possible:

16. 12   **17.** 15

18. 18   **19.** 20

20. 13   **21.** 29

Find the prime factorization of each number:

22. 76   **23.** 68

24. 215   **25.** 123

26. 738   **27.** 1425

28. 341   **29.** 818

5-3 APPLICATIONS OF PRIME FACTORIZATIONS

We can make effective use of the concept of prime factorization in many arithmetic situations. Let us first consider the various factors of counting numbers. Recall that a counting number t is said to be a factor of another counting number n if and only if there is a counting number k such that $n = t \times k$. Now consider the set of factors of 12 and the set of factors of 18:

$$12:\quad \{1, 2, 3, 4, 6, 12\}$$
$$18:\quad \{1, 2, 3, 6, 9, 18\}$$

The set of **common factors** of 12 and 18 consists of those numbers that are factors of both 12 and 18; that is,

$$\{1, 2, 3, 6\}.$$

The largest member of this set, 6, is called the *greatest common factor* (G.C.F.) of the two numbers. In general, the **greatest common factor** of two or more counting numbers is the largest counting number that is a factor of each of the given numbers.

We may use the prime factorization of two counting numbers to find their greatest common factor. We express each number by its prime factorization; consider the prime numbers that are factors of both of the given numbers; and take the product of those prime numbers with each raised to the highest power that is a factor of both of the given numbers. For $12 = 2^2 \times 3$ and $18 = 2 \times 3^2$ we have G.C.F. $= 2 \times 3$; that is, 6.

EXAMPLE 1:   Find the greatest common factor of 60 and 5280.

Solution:

$$\begin{array}{r|l} 2 & 60 \\ \hline 2 & 30 \\ \hline 3 & 15 \\ \hline & 5 \end{array} \qquad 60 = 2^2 \times 3 \times 5$$

As in Example 3 of §5-2 we have $5280 = 2^5 \times 3 \times 5 \times 11$. Then the highest power of 2 that is a common factor of 60 and 5280 is 2^2; 3 is a common factor; 5 is a common factor; 11 is not a common factor. The greatest common factor of 60 and 5280 is $2^2 \times 3 \times 5$; that is, 60.

EXAMPLE 2: Find the greatest common factor of 3850 and 5280.

Solution:
$$3850 = 2 \times 5^2 \times 7 \times 11$$
$$5280 = 2^5 \times 3 \times 5 \times 11$$

The greatest common factor of 3850 and 5280 is $2 \times 5 \times 11$; that is, 110.

EXAMPLE 3: Find the G.C.F. of 12, 36, and 60.

Solution: First write the prime factorization of each number:
$$12 = 2^2 \times 3$$
$$36 = 2^2 \times 3^2$$
$$60 = 2^2 \times 3 \times 5$$

The G.C.F. is $2^2 \times 3$; that is, 12.

We may use the greatest common factor when we reduce (simplify) a fraction. For example,

$$\frac{60}{4880} = \frac{(2^2 \times 5) \times 3}{(2^2 \times 5) \times (2^2 \times 61)} = \frac{3}{2^2 \times 61} = \frac{3}{244}.$$

Since 3 is the only prime factor of the numerator and 3 is not a factor of the denominator, the fraction $\frac{3}{244}$ is in **lowest terms.** The numerator and the denominator do not have any common prime factors and are said to be **relatively prime.**

EXAMPLE 4: Reduce the fraction $\frac{60}{168}$ to lowest terms.

Solution:

$$60 = 2^2 \times 3 \times 5$$
$$168 = 2^3 \times 3 \times 7$$

The greatest common factor is $2^2 \times 3$.

$$\frac{60}{168} = \frac{(2^2 \times 3) \times 5}{(2^2 \times 3) \times 2 \times 7} = \frac{5}{14}$$

Let us now turn our attention to the concept of a multiple of a number. Recall that if a counting number t is a factor of a counting number n, then n is said to be a multiple of t. Consider the set of multiples of 12 and the set of multiples of 18:

12:   $\{12, 24, 36, 48, 60, 72, 84, 96, 108, 120, \ldots\}$
18:   $\{18, 36, 54, 72, 90, 108, 126, \ldots\}$

The set of **common multiples** of 12 and 18 consists of those numbers that are multiples of both 12 and 18; that is,

$$\{36, 72, 108, \ldots\}.$$

The smallest member of this set, 36, is called the *least common multiple* (L.C.M.) of the two numbers. In general, the **least common multiple** of two or more counting numbers is the smallest number that is a multiple of each of the given numbers.

We may use the prime factorization of two numbers to find their lowest common multiple. We express each number by its prime factorization; consider the prime factors that are factors of either of the given numbers; and take the product of these prime numbers with each raised to the highest power that occurs in either of the prime factorizations. For $12 = 2^2 \times 3$ and $18 = 2 \times 3^2$, we have L.C.M. = $2^2 \times 3^2$; that is, 36.

EXAMPLE 5:   Find the lowest common multiple of 3850 and 5280.

Solution: As in Examples 1 and 2,

$$3850 = 2 \times 5^2 \times 7 \times 11;$$
$$5280 = 2^5 \times 3 \times 5 \times 11.$$

The lowest common multiple of 3850 and 5280 is

$$2^5 \times 3 \times 5^2 \times 7 \times 11;$$

that is, 184,800.

EXAMPLE 6:   Find the L.C.M. of 12, 18, and 20.

Solution: First write the prime factorization of each number:

$$12 = 2^2 \times 3$$
$$18 = 2 \times 3^2$$
$$20 = 2^2 \times 5$$

The L.C.M. is $2^2 \times 3^2 \times 5$; that is, 180.

We use the lowest common multiple of the denominators of two fractions when we add or subtract fractions. For example, the lowest common multiple of 12 and 18 is 36:

$$\frac{7}{12} + \frac{5}{18} = \frac{21}{36} + \frac{10}{36} = \frac{31}{36}$$

The answer is in reduced form, since 31 and 36 are relatively prime.

EXAMPLE 7:   Simplify: $\frac{37}{5280} - \frac{19}{3850}$.

Solution: We use the lowest common multiple as found in Example 5:

$$\frac{37}{5280} - \frac{19}{3850} = \frac{37}{2^5 \times 3 \times 5 \times 11} - \frac{19}{2 \times 5^2 \times 7 \times 11}$$

$$= \frac{37 \times 5 \times 7}{2^5 \times 3 \times 5^2 \times 7 \times 11} - \frac{19 \times 2^4 \times 3}{2^5 \times 3 \times 5^2 \times 7 \times 11}$$

$$= \frac{1295 - 912}{2^5 \times 3 \times 5^2 \times 7 \times 11} = \frac{383}{184,800}$$

The instruction "simplify" is used as in Example 7 to mean "perform the indicated operations and express the answer in simplest form." In the case of fractions "express in simplest form" means "reduce to lowest terms."

EXERCISES FOR SECTION 5-3

List the factors of:

   1. 20   **2.** 24

   3. 9   **4.** 16

   5. 28   **6.** 48

   7. 60   **8.** 72

Write the prime factorizations and find the G.C.F. of:

   9. 68 and 76.   **10.** 123 and 215.

   11. 76 and 1425.   **12.** 123 and 1425.

   13. 215 and 1425.   **14.** 68 and 738.

   15. 12, 15, and 20.   **16.** 18, 24, and 40.

   17. 12, 18, and 30.   **18.** 15, 45, and 60.

List the first five elements in the set of multiples of:

   19. 7   **20.** 8

   21. 15   **22.** 20

Write the prime factorizations and find the L.C.M. of:

   23. 68 and 76.   **24.** 123 and 215.

   25. 76 and 1425.   **26.** 123 and 1425.

   27. 215 and 1425.   **28.** 68 and 738.

   29. 12, 15, and 20.   **30.** 18, 24, and 40.

   31. 12, 18, and 30.   **32.** 15, 45, and 60.

Simplify:

   33. $\frac{123}{215}$ **34.** $\frac{76}{1425}$

35. $\frac{11}{12} - \frac{9}{18}$

36. $\frac{5}{68} + \frac{11}{76}$

37. $\frac{7}{123} - \frac{2}{215}$

38. $\frac{41}{215} + \frac{19}{1425}$

*39. What is the *least* common factor of any two counting numbers?

*40. What is the *greatest* common multiple of any two counting numbers?

5-4 THE SET OF INTEGERS

Using just the set of **whole numbers**

$$\{0, 1, 2, 3, 4, \ldots\},$$

we are unable to simplify expressions such as $3 - 5$ and $7 - 10$. Nor are we able to find replacements for n so as to make these sentences true:

$$n + 5 = 2$$
$$7 + n = 3$$

To make the solution of such equations always possible and to make subtraction always possible, we extend the number system by considering points on the number line to the left of the origin 0. For each point that is the coordinate of a counting number n, we locate a point to the left of the origin that is the same distance from 0 as the point with coordinate n. We call the coordinate of this new point **negative** n, written $-n$, and refer to the number that $-n$ represents as the **opposite** of n. Thus the opposite of 2 is -2; the opposite of 5 is -5; and we also say the opposite of 0 is 0. It is also agreed that the opposite of -2 is 2; the opposite of -5 is 5; etc. Furthermore, the sum of any number and its opposite is 0. That is,

$$2 + (-2) = 0;$$
$$5 + (-5) = 0;$$
$$n + (-n) = 0.$$

The set consisting of the counting numbers n, their negatives, and the number 0 is called the set of **integers**:

$$\{\ldots, -5, -4, -3, -2, -1, 0, 1, 2, 3, 4, 5, \ldots\}$$

The numbers of the set

$$\{1, 2, 3, 4, 5, \ldots\}$$

are called **positive integers** and the numbers of the set

$$\{-1, -2, -3, -4, -5, \ldots\}$$

are called **negative integers.** Notice that zero is an integer but is neither positive nor negative. The integers may be represented on a number line as follows:

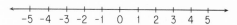

It is assumed that the reader has had past experience with the four fundamental operations with integers, and some practice on these skills is offered in the exercises as a means of review. It may be enlightening, however, to examine several of these operations in some detail. Thus we now find that subtraction is always possible; that is, the set of integers is closed with respect to subtraction. We can give a physical meaning to subtraction by referring to the number line. For example, the difference $3 - 7$ may be thought of as a movement of 3 units from the origin in a positive direction followed by a movement of 7 units in the negative direction. The terminal point has the coordinate -4 and represents the difference $3 - 7$.

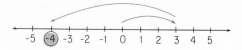

We may also find the differences of integers by defining the subtraction of two integers a and b as follows:

$$a - b = a + (-b)$$

Then, by definition, $3 - 7 = 3 + (-7) = -4$. This allows us to replace any subtraction problem by an equivalent addition problem. To subtract a number, add its opposite; that is, in the language of the old rule, "to subtract a number, change its sign and add."

EXAMPLE 1:   Illustrate on a number line: $-2 -3$.

Solution: By the definition of subtraction this can be thought of as $-2 + (-3)$; that is, -5. On the number line we think of this as a movement of 2 units from the origin in the negative direction, followed by a movement of 3 units in the negative direction.

All too often the rules for multiplication of integers have been learned by rote without any attempt to see or to understand their development. Thus most people know that the product of two negative numbers is a positive number. They know that the product of a positive number and a negative number is a negative number. However, they are unable to give any justification for these rules. Informally we might say that if you lose $5 a day for 2 days, then you have lost $10, so $2 \times (-5) = -10$. Let us examine a mathematical justification for this product based upon the use of the distributive property.

Notice that under the usual properties of addition and multiplication

$$5 + (-5) = 0;$$
$$2 \times [5 + (-5)] = 2 \times 0 = 0;$$
$$(2 \times 5) + [2 \times (-5)] = 0 \quad \text{(by the distributive property).}$$

Since the sum of 2×5 and $2 \times (-5)$ is zero, each must be the opposite of the other. Then $2 \times (-5) = -10$, since $2 \times 5 = 10$. Also since $2 \times (-5) = (-5) \times 2$, we have $(-5) \times 2 = -10$. In general, for any positive integers b and c:

$$b + (-b) = 0$$
$$c \times [b + (-b)] = c \times 0 = 0$$
$$(c \times b) + [c \times (-b)] = 0$$

Thus $c \times b$ and $c \times (-b)$ are each the opposite of the other; $c \times b = cb$ and $c \times (-b) = -cb$. Since $cb = bc$ and $c \times (-b) = (-b) \times c$, we have $(-b) \times c = -bc$. Thus the product of a positive integer and a negative integer is a negative integer.

Similarly, notice that under the usual properties of addition and multiplication

$$5 + (-5) = 0;$$
$$(-2) \times [5 + (-5)] = (-2) \times 0 = 0;$$
$$[(-2) \times 5] + [(-2) \times (-5)] = 0 \qquad \text{(by the distributive}$$
$$\text{property).}$$

Since the sum of $(-2) \times 5$ and $(-2) \times (-5)$ is zero, each must be the opposite of the other. Then, since $(-2) \times 5 = -10$, we have $(-2) \times (-5) = 10$. In general, for any positive integers b and c:

$$b + (-b) = 0$$
$$(-c) \times [b + (-b)] = (-c) \times 0 = 0$$
$$[(-c) \times b] + [(-c) \times (-b)] = 0$$

Thus $(-c) \times b$ and $(-c) \times (-b)$ are each the opposite of the other. Then, since $(-c) \times b = -cb$, we have $(-c) \times (-b) = cb$. Thus the product of two negative integers is a positive integer.

The set of integers is not closed with respect to division, as noted in the following example. The desire to make division always possible will lead to further extensions of the number system in the next section.

EXAMPLE 2: Show that the set of integers is not closed with respect to division.

Solution: We can show this by a single counterexample: $8 \div 3$ cannot be named by an integer. That is, there is no integer n such that $3 \times n = 8$.

Considering the mathematical system formed by the set of integers and the operation of addition, we can say that the integers form a *commutative group* under addition (see §3-1), since the set

1. Is *closed* with respect to addition (the sum of any two integers is an integer).

2. Is *commutative* with respect to addition ($p + q = q + p$ for any two integers p and q).

3. Is *associative* with respect to addition [for any three integers p, q, and r we have $p + (q + r) = (p + q) + r$].

4. Contains an *identity element*, 0, with respect to addition.

5. Contains an *inverse* (called the opposite) for each of its elements with respect to addition.

EXAMPLE 3: Show that the set of integers does *not* form a group with respect to multiplication.

Solution: The set of integers is closed, commutative, and associative with respect to multiplication, and contains an identity element 1 with respect to multiplication. However, the set of integers does not contain inverses for each of its elements with respect to multiplication. For example, there is no integer n such that $3 \times n = 1$.

There are a number of interesting proofs that we are now ready to explore which illustrate the type of reasoning that mathematicians use. First we need several definitions; then we shall consider several proofs and offer others in the exercises.

An integer is **even** if it is a multiple of 2; that is, if it may be expressed as $2k$, where k stands for an integer. Then the set of even integers is

$$\{\ldots, -6, -4, -2, 0, 2, 4, 6, \ldots\}.$$

An integer that is not even is said to be **odd**. Each odd integer may be expressed in the form $2k + 1$, where k stands for an integer. Then the set of odd integers is

$$\{\ldots, -7, -5, -3, -1, 1, 3, 5, 7, \ldots\}.$$

EXAMPLE 4: Prove that the sum of any two even integers is an even integer.

Proof: Any two even integers m and n may be expressed as $2k$ and $2r$, where k and r stand for integers. Then

$$m + n = 2k + 2r = 2(k + r),$$

where $k + r$ stands for an integer, since the sum of any two integers is an integer. Therefore, $m + n$ is an even integer.

EXAMPLE 5:   Prove that the square of any even integer is an even integer.

Proof: Any even integer may be expressed as $2k$, where k stands for an integer. Then the square of the integer may be expressed as $(2k)^2$, where

$$(2k)^2 = (2k)(2k) = 2(2k^2).$$

Since k, k^2, and $2k^2$ all stand for integers, $(2k)^2$ stands for an even integer.

EXERCISES FOR SECTION 5-4

Perform the indicated operations:

1. $-8 + 5$
2. $-6 + (-7)$
3. $5 - 8$
4. $-2 - (-5)$
5. $3 \times (-7)$
6. $(-7) \times (-8)$
7. $-12 \div 3$
8. $-15 \div (-3)$
9. $-3 + [-5 + (-7)]$
10. $[-3 + (-5)] + (-7)$
11. $-2 \times [4 \times (-3)]$
12. $(-2 \times 4) \times (-3)$
13. $12 \div [6 \div (-2)]$
14. $(12 \div 6) \div (-2)$

15. Use the results of Exercises 13 and 14 to form a conjecture about the associativity of integers with respect to division. Then find another example to help confirm your conjecture.

16. Use a counterexample to show that the set of integers is not commutative with respect to subtraction.

17. What is the intersection of the set of positive integers and the set of negative integers?

18. Is the union of the set of positive integers and the set of negative integers equal to the set of integers? Explain your answer.

19. Illustrate each difference on a number line: (a) $2 - 5$; (b) $-2 - 3$.

20. Show a one-to-one correspondence between the set of positive integers and the set of negative integers.

Classify each statement as true or false:

21. Every counting number is an integer.

22. Every integer is a counting number.

23. Every integer is the opposite of some integer.

24. The set of negative integers is the same as the set of opposites of the whole numbers.

25. The set of the opposites of the integers is the same as the set of integers.

Prove each statement in Exercises 26 through 29:

26. The sum of any two odd integers is an even integer.

27. The product of any two even integers is an even integer.

28. The square of any odd integer is an odd integer.

*29. If the square of an integer is odd, the integer is odd; if the square of an integer is even, the integer is even.

*30. Show that there is a one-to-one correspondence between the set of integers and the set of counting numbers.

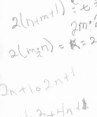

5-5 THE SET OF RATIONAL NUMBERS

Using just the set of integers, we are unable to simplify such expressions as

$$7 \div 5,$$
$$3 \div 4.$$

We are also unable to find replacements for n so as to make these sentences true:

$$3 \times n = 5$$
$$7 \div 2 = n$$

To make the solution of such equations always possible, and to make division, except by zero, always possible, we need to make another extension of the number system. We do so by first locating points on the number line that correspond to "halves"; that is, $\frac{1}{2}$, $1\frac{1}{2}$, $2\frac{1}{2}$, etc., as well as their opposites $-\frac{1}{2}$, $-1\frac{1}{2}$, $-2\frac{1}{2}$, etc.

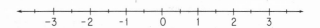

Next we locate points that correspond to the multiples of $\frac{1}{3}$, $\frac{1}{4}$, $\frac{1}{5}$, etc., both positive and negative. This new collection of numbers is called the set of rational numbers. A **rational number** is one that can be expressed in the form $\frac{a}{b}$; that is, a/b, where a is an integer and b is a counting number.

EXAMPLE 1: Show that every integer is a rational number.

Solution: Every integer n can be written in the form $\frac{n}{1}$, the quotient of an integer and a counting number, and is thus a rational number. For example, 7 can be written as $\frac{7}{1}$.

We must define the conditions under which two of the new symbols stand for the same number. Notice that $\frac{6}{12} = \frac{1}{2} = \frac{5}{10}$; also $\frac{6}{3} = \frac{18}{9} = \frac{2}{1}$. In general,

$$\frac{a}{b} = \frac{c}{d} \quad \text{if and only if} \quad ad = bc.$$

The equality $ad = bc$ involves only products of integers and thus only integers.

This definition gives rise to a very useful rule:

$$\frac{a}{b} = \frac{ak}{bk} \qquad \text{for any integer } k \neq 0$$

since $a(bk) = b(ak)$, even though we have not explicitly developed this property of integers. This rule enables us to find as many ways of writing a rational number as we like. For example,

$$\frac{2}{3} = \frac{4}{6} = \frac{6}{9} = \frac{8}{12} = \frac{10}{15} = \cdots.$$

The rule also allows us to "reduce" quotients by finding factors k as in these examples:

$$\frac{12}{30} = \frac{2 \times 6}{5 \times 6} = \frac{2}{5}$$

$$\frac{72}{18} = \frac{4 \times 18}{1 \times 18} = \frac{4}{1}$$

$$\frac{16}{80} = \frac{1 \times 16}{5 \times 16} = \frac{1}{5}$$

Each fraction $\dfrac{a}{b}$ has two parts: the **numerator** a and the **denominator** b. In one sense the denominator names the fractional part under consideration and the numerator tells the number of those units. For example, $\frac{3}{4}$ may be thought of as three fourths (i.e., as $3 \times \frac{1}{4}$) of a complete unit.

The rule $\dfrac{a}{b} = \dfrac{ak}{bk}$ means that the numerator a and the denominator b of any quotient $\dfrac{a}{b}$ may both be multiplied by the same integer k for any $k \neq 0$ without changing the **value** of the quotient; i.e., without changing the rational number that the quotient represents. When considered in the form $\dfrac{ak}{bk} = \dfrac{a}{b}$, the rule implies that the numerator and denominator may both be divided by any integer k that divides them both without changing the value of the quotient. We use this rule to pick the most useful representation of any set of quotients representing the same rational number. We select $\frac{1}{2}$ as the representative of the set

$$\left\{ \frac{1}{2}, \frac{2}{4}, \frac{3}{6}, \frac{4}{8}, \frac{5}{10}, \cdots \right\}.$$

We select $\frac{3}{1}$ as the representative of the set

$$\left\{ \frac{3}{1}, \frac{6}{2}, \frac{9}{3}, \frac{12}{4}, \frac{15}{5}, \cdots \right\}.$$

Whenever it is possible to select a representative with either its numerator or its denominator 1, we do so. When it is not possible to find a representative having 1 as one of its elements, we select the representative for which there are no positive integers k greater than 1 that divide both the numerator and denominator. For example, we select $\frac{2}{3}$ as the representative of the set

$$\left\{ \frac{2}{3}, \frac{4}{6}, \frac{6}{9}, \frac{8}{12}, \frac{10}{15}, \cdots \right\}.$$

The sum of any two rational numbers is defined to be a rational number:

$$\frac{a}{b} + \frac{c}{d} = \frac{ad + bc}{bd}$$

For example, $\frac{1}{3} + \frac{1}{2} = \frac{2 + 3}{6} = \frac{5}{6}$. This is consistent with the procedure

$$\frac{1}{3} = \frac{2}{6}, \qquad \frac{1}{2} = \frac{3}{6}, \qquad \frac{1}{3} + \frac{1}{2} = \frac{2}{6} + \frac{3}{6} = \frac{5}{6},$$

which we often justify by using the distributive property of multiplication with respect to addition (see §3-2):

$$\frac{1}{3} + \frac{1}{2} = \frac{1 \times 2}{3 \times 2} + \frac{1 \times 3}{2 \times 3} = \frac{2}{6} + \frac{3}{6} = \frac{1}{6}(2 + 3) = \frac{2 + 3}{6}$$

$$\frac{a}{b} + \frac{c}{d} = \frac{ad}{bd} + \frac{bc}{bd} = \frac{1}{bd}(ad + bc) = \frac{ad + bc}{bd}$$

The negative of a rational number $\frac{2}{3}$ may be expressed in any one of the following ways:

$$-\frac{2}{3}, \qquad \frac{-2}{3}, \quad \text{and} \quad \frac{2}{-3}$$

The form $\frac{-a}{b}$ is usually the most convenient. Notice that by the definition of the sum of two rational numbers

$$\frac{2}{3} + \frac{-2}{3} = \frac{2(3) + 3(-2)}{3 \times 3} = \frac{6 + (-6)}{9} = \frac{0}{9} = 0$$

and, in general,

$$\frac{a}{b} + \frac{-a}{b} = \frac{ab + b(-a)}{b^2} = \frac{ab + (-ab)}{b^2} = \frac{0}{b^2} = 0.$$

Then, as in the case of integers, we may define subtraction in terms of an equivalent addition:

$$\frac{a}{b} - \frac{c}{d} = \frac{a}{b} + \frac{-c}{d}$$

The product of any two rational numbers is defined to be a rational number:

$$\frac{a}{b} \times \frac{c}{d} = \frac{ac}{bd}$$

Note that $bd \neq 0$, since $b \neq 0$ and $d \neq 0$. Consider these examples:

$$\frac{2}{3} \times \frac{5}{6} = \frac{10}{18} = \frac{5}{9}; \qquad \frac{4}{5} \times \frac{25}{2} = \frac{100}{10} = \frac{10}{1} = 10$$

Just as the integers gave rise to integers when added, multiplied, or subtracted, so all sums, products, and differences of rational numbers are rational numbers. However, in the set of rational numbers we also obtain a rational number when we divide by any number different from zero. We define the **reciprocal** of any rational number $\frac{a}{b}$ different from zero to be the rational number $\frac{b}{a}$. Notice that

$$\frac{a}{b} \times \frac{b}{a} = \frac{ab}{ba} = 1.$$

That is, the reciprocal of a number is its inverse with respect to multiplication. Then we define **division** in terms of an equivalent multiplication; for any $\frac{c}{d} \neq 0$:

$$\frac{a}{b} \div \frac{c}{d} = \frac{a}{b} \times \frac{d}{c}$$

In other words, to divide by a number different from zero we multiply by its reciprocal. This is a formal statement of the common procedure described by "invert and multiply." This procedure may also be justified as follows:

$$\frac{\frac{a}{b}}{\frac{c}{d}} = \frac{\frac{a}{b} \times \frac{d}{c}}{\frac{c}{d} \times \frac{d}{c}} = \frac{\frac{a}{b} \times \frac{d}{c}}{1} = \frac{a}{b} \times \frac{d}{c}$$

The set of integers is a subset of the set of rational numbers. Thus we would expect the set of rational numbers to have many of the same properties as the set of integers. The set of rational numbers forms a commutative group under addition. That is, with respect to addition, the set of rational numbers is closed, associative, commutative, contains an identity element 0, and contains the inverses of each of its elements.

With respect to multiplication, the set of rational numbers is closed, associative, commutative, and contains an identity element 1. By expanding our number system from the set of integers to the set of rational numbers, we now have included the multiplicative inverses of each element except 0. Thus the inverse under multiplication of 3 is $\frac{1}{3}$, and of $-\frac{2}{3}$ is $-\frac{3}{2}$. However, the set of rational numbers does not form a group under multiplication because 0 has no inverse.

The set of rational numbers has one additional property of interest, namely, the density property. The set of rational numbers is said to be **dense,** since between any two elements of the set there is always another element of the set. Example 2 indicates how such numbers may be located.

EXAMPLE 2:   Locate a rational number between $\frac{17}{19}$ and $\frac{18}{19}$.

Solution: Change each fraction to one with a denominator of 38:

$$\frac{17}{19} = \frac{34}{38} \qquad \frac{18}{19} = \frac{36}{38}$$

We can see that $\frac{35}{38}$ lies between the two fractions given. Note that

$$\frac{35}{38} = \frac{1}{2}\left(\frac{17}{19} + \frac{18}{19}\right).$$

From Example 2 we see that we can always find a rational number between two given rational numbers by finding the average of the two given numbers. Furthermore, we can continue this process indefinitely so as to find as many rational numbers as desired between any two given numbers.

EXERCISES FOR SECTION 5-5

Use the definitions of this section and simplify:

1. $\frac{2}{3} + \frac{1}{2}$

2. $\frac{5}{6} + \frac{3}{4}$

3. $\frac{6}{18} \times \frac{10}{7}$

4. $\frac{12}{15} \times \frac{28}{10}$

5. $\frac{2}{3} \div \frac{4}{5}$

6. $\frac{7}{8} \div \frac{3}{4}$

7. $\frac{5}{12} \div \frac{10}{18}$

8. $\frac{17}{34} \div \frac{25}{10}$

9. $\frac{5}{6} - \frac{1}{3}$

10. $\frac{2}{5} - \frac{1}{4}$

11. $\frac{15}{8} - \frac{3}{4}$

12. $\frac{11}{9} - \frac{7}{5}$

Give an example illustrating each statement:

13. The sum of two fractions may be an integer. $\frac{1}{2} + \frac{2}{4} = \frac{4}{4} = 1$

14. The product of two fractions may be an integer.

15. The quotient of two fractions may be an integer.

Classify each statement as true or false:

16. Every integer is a rational number.

17. Every rational number may be expressed as an integer.

18. The set of integers is dense.

19. The multiplicative inverse of a positive rational number is a negative rational number.

20. Every rational number has an inverse under addition.

Copy the following table. Use "√" to show that the number listed at the top of a column is a member of the set listed at the side. Use "X" if the number is not a member of the set.

21. 22. 23. 24. 25.

Sets	3	-9	0	$\frac{3}{4}$	$-\frac{2}{3}$
Counting numbers	✓				
Whole numbers	✓		✓	✓	✓
Integers		✓	✓	✓	✓
Rational numbers				✓	✓

Find a replacement for n that will make each of the sentences below true where n must be a member of the set named at the top of the column. If there is no such replacement, write "none."

	Sentence	Counting numbers	Whole numbers	Integers	Rational numbers
26.	$n - 5 = 0$	5			
27.	$n + 2 = 2$	none	0		
28.	$n + 1 = 0$	none			
29.	$2n = 3$	none			
30.	$n \times n = 5$	none			

5-6 THE SET OF REAL NUMBERS

In mathematics we are concerned with the four fundamental operations $(+, -, \times, \div)$. The rational numbers have been introduced so
that these operations are always possible with the exception of
division by zero. However, using just the set of rational numbers, we
are still unable to find a replacement for n so as to make this sentence
true:

$$n^2 = 2$$

That is, we are unable to find a rational number a/b such that

$$\frac{a}{b} \times \frac{a}{b} = 2.$$

On the number line we have seen that the rational numbers are
dense, since there is a rational number between any two given rational
numbers. However, the appearance of a solid line of points with
rational numbers as coordinates is misleading. For example, if we
assume that there is a number that represents the length of a diagonal
of a unit square, the square of that number must be 2. We call the
number $\sqrt{2}$ and can locate a point with coordinate $\sqrt{2}$ on the number
line. However, the number $\sqrt{2}$ cannot be a rational number.

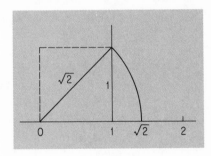

We use an **indirect proof** to prove that $\sqrt{2}$ cannot be a rational
number. That is, we assume that $\sqrt{2}$ is a rational number and show
that this leads to a contradiction. Thus suppose that a/b is a rational
number, where a and b are not both even numbers and

$$\frac{a}{b} \times \frac{a}{b} = 2; \quad \text{that is,} \quad \frac{a}{b} = \sqrt{2}.$$

Then $a^2 = 2b^2$ and a is an integer whose square is even. Therefore, as in §5-5, Exercise 29, a must be even; that is, $a = 2k$, where k stands for an integer. If we use $2k$ for a, we have

$$(2k)^2 = 2b^2;$$
$$4k^2 = 2b^2;$$
$$2k^2 = b^2.$$

Thus b is an integer whose square is even, and b must be an even integer. This is contrary to the assumption that a and b were not both even. Our assumption that there exists a rational number whose square is 2 has led to a contradiction. In other words, if there is a number whose square is 2, that number cannot be a rational number.

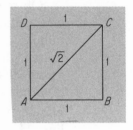

There exist line segments of length $\sqrt{2}$. For example, as we have observed, the diagonal $\overline{AC}$ of a square $ABCD$ with each side 1 unit long has length $\sqrt{2}$. We need numbers to represent lengths of line segments and thus need numbers that are not rational numbers. These numbers that are not rational numbers are called **irrational numbers.** We need irrational numbers such as $\sqrt{2}$ in order to have coordinates for each point on a line. We call the union of the set of rational numbers and the set of irrational numbers the set of **real numbers.**

There is a one-to-one correspondence between the elements of the set of real numbers and the set of points on the number line. Indeed, this is the distinguishing feature between the set of real numbers and the set of rational numbers. Thus every real number is the coordinate of a point on the number line, and every point on the number line is the graph of a real number. Accordingly, we refer to the number line as the real number line and we say that the number line is *complete*.

No further extension of the number system is necessary until one wishes to solve such equations as

$$n \times n = -1.$$

However, the solution of this problem, including the use of imaginary numbers and an extension to the set of complex numbers, is beyond the scope of this text.

Real numbers may be classified as being either rational or irrational by their decimal representations. Each real number may be represented by a decimal; each decimal represents a real number. Real numbers that are rational are represented by terminating decimals or by infinite repeating decimals such as the following:

$$\frac{1}{4} = 0.25; \qquad \frac{3}{8} = 0.375; \qquad \frac{1}{3} = 0.33\overline{3}; \qquad \frac{3}{11} = 0.2727\overline{27}.$$

Note the use of a bar to indicate that a sequence of digits repeats endlessly. The bar is used over the digit or digits that repeat. You may, if you wish, think of any terminating decimal as having repeated zeros and thus as being a repeating decimal. For example,

$$\frac{1}{4} = 0.25\overline{0}; \qquad \frac{3}{8} = 0.375\overline{0}.$$

Real numbers that are irrational are represented by nonterminating, nonrepeating decimals, such as

$$\sqrt{2} = 1.414214 \ldots ; \qquad \pi = 3.1415926 \ldots .$$

In each of these examples the digits exhibit no repeating pattern no matter how far they are extended. It is often convenient to represent irrational numbers by a sequence of digits that has a pattern but does not repeat any particular sequence of digits. For example, each of the following names an irrational number:

$$0.20220222022220222220 \ldots$$
$$0.305300530005300005 \ldots$$
$$0.404004000400004000004 \ldots$$

EXAMPLE 1:   How many zeros are there altogether between the decimal point and the one hundredth 5 in this sequence?

$$0.05005000500005 \ldots$$

Solution: There is one zero preceding the first 5, two zeros preceding the second five, etc. The total number of zeros is the sum

$$1 + 2 + 3 + \cdots + 100.$$

By the method of Exercise 9, §1-1, the sum is 5050.

In summary, every real number can be represented by a decimal. If the real number is a rational number, then it may be represented by a terminating or by a repeating decimal. If the real number is an irrational number, then it may be represented by a nonterminating, nonrepeating decimal.

It is easy to show that every rational number in fractional form can be represented as a repeating (or terminating) decimal. Consider, for example, any rational number such as $\frac{12}{7}$. When we divide 12 by 7, the possible remainders are 0, 1, 2, 3, 4, 5, 6. If the remainder is 0, the division is exact; if any remainder occurs a second time, the terms after it will repeat also. Since there are only 7 possible remainders when you divide by 7, the remainders must repeat or be exact by the seventh decimal place. Consider the determination of the decimal value of $\frac{12}{7}$ by long division:

$$
\begin{array}{r}
1.\overline{714285} \\
7\,\overline{)12.000000} \\
\underline{7} \\
\text{⑤}0 \\
\underline{49} \\
10 \\
\underline{7} \\
30 \\
\underline{28} \\
20 \\
\underline{14} \\
60 \\
\underline{56} \\
40 \\
\underline{35} \\
\text{⑤}
\end{array}
$$

The fact that the remainder 5 occurred again implies that the same steps will be used again in the long division process and the digits 714285 will be repeated over and over; that is, $\frac{12}{7} = 1.714285\overline{714285}$.

Similarly, any rational number $\frac{p}{q}$ can be expressed as a terminating or repeating decimal, and at most q decimal places will be needed to identify it.

We can also show that any terminating or repeating decimal can be written as a rational number in the form a/b.

If a decimal is terminating, you can write it as a fraction with a power of 10 as the denominator. For example, if $n = 0.75\overline{0}$, then

$100n = 75$, and $n = \frac{75}{100}$, which reduces to $\frac{3}{4}$. If a fraction can be expressed as a terminating decimal, its denominator must be a factor of a power of 10. If a decimal is repeating, it can be written as a rational number. For example, if a decimal n repeats one digit, we can find $10n - n$. Suppose $n = 3.244\overline{4}$; then $10n = 32.444\overline{4}$ and we have:

$$
\begin{aligned}
10n &= 32.444\overline{4} \\
n &= 3.244\overline{4} \\
\hline
9n &= 29.200\overline{0}
\end{aligned}
$$

$$n = \frac{29.2}{9} = \frac{292}{90} = \frac{146}{45}$$

We can avoid the use of decimals in common fractions:

$$
\begin{aligned}
100n &= 324.44\overline{4} \\
10n &= 32.44\overline{4} \\
\hline
90n &= 292
\end{aligned}
$$

$$n = \frac{292}{90} = \frac{146}{45}$$

If a decimal n repeats two digits, we find $10^2 n - n$; if it repeats three digits, we find $10^3 n - n$; and so forth.

EXAMPLE 2: Express $0.\overline{36}$ as a quotient of integers.

Solution: Let $n = 0.\overline{36}$; then $100n = 36.\overline{36}$ and we have:

$$
\begin{aligned}
100n &= 36.\overline{36} \\
n &= 0.\overline{36} \\
\hline
99n &= 36
\end{aligned}
$$

$$n = \frac{36}{99} = \frac{4}{11}$$

EXAMPLE 3: Express $0.78346\overline{346}$ as a quotient of integers.

Solution:

$$
\begin{aligned}
1000n &= 783.46346\overline{346} \\
n &= 0.78346\overline{346} \\
\hline
999n &= 782.68
\end{aligned}
$$

$$n = \frac{782.68}{999} = \frac{78,268}{99,900} = \frac{19,567}{24,975}$$

The real numbers may be classified in several ways. Any real number is

1. Positive, negative, or zero.
2. A rational number or an irrational number.
3. Expressible as a terminating, a repeating, or nonterminating, nonrepeating decimal.

The relationship of the set of real numbers to some of the other sets of numbers that we have studied is shown in the following array:

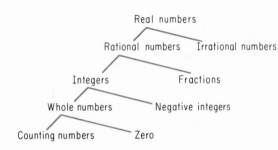

EXERCISES FOR SECTION 5-6

Tell whether or not each number is (**a**) *an integer;* (**b**) *a rational number;* (**c**) *an irrational number;* (**d**) *a real number:*

1. 5
2. 5.76
3. −3
4. 1.73$\overline{73}$
5. $\sqrt{2}$
6. 3.1415926 . . . ; i.e., π
7. 0.0027$\overline{27}$
8. $\frac{19}{31}$
9. $\sqrt{8}$
10. $\sqrt{9}$

Tell whether each number should be represented by a terminating, a repeating, or a nonterminating, nonrepeating decimal:

11. $\frac{3}{4}$
12. $\frac{2}{5}$
13. $\frac{2}{3}$
14. $\frac{5}{12}$
15. $\frac{13}{16}$
16. $\sqrt{3}$

Express each number as a decimal:

17. $\frac{3}{5}$
18. $\frac{1}{6}$
19. $\frac{27}{15}$
20. $\frac{1}{17}$

Express each number as a quotient of integers:

21. $0.\overline{45}$ **22.** $0.\overline{234}$

23. $0.5\overline{22}$ **24.** $0.\overline{9}$

25. $2.11\overline{1}$ **26.** $5.22\overline{2}$

27. $2.14\overline{14}$ **28.** $4.25\overline{25}$

29. $0.123\overline{123}$ **30.** $65.268\overline{268}$

Classify each of the statements in Exercises 31 through 35 as true or false:

31. Every rational number is a real number.

32. Every real number is a rational number.

33. Every repeating decimal is the name of a real number.

34. Every irrational number can be represented by a decimal.

35. The set of real numbers contains the additive inverse of each of its elements.

36. Write the first ten digits of the decimal (**a**) $0.\overline{37}$; (**b**) $0.4\overline{567}$.

37. Write the digit in the twentieth position to the right of the decimal point in the decimal (**a**) $0.3\overline{72}$; (**b**) $0.6\overline{89}$.

5-7 ORDER RELATIONS (Not on test).

The set of numbers $\{1, 3, 5\}$ is *equivalent* to the set of numbers $\{3, 1, 5\}$, since two sets are equivalent if they have the same members. However, we think of the elements of the set $\{1, 3, 5\}$ as being listed in their natural order, whereas the elements of the set $\{3, 1, 5\}$ are not listed in their natural order. The purpose of this section is to extend our intuitive concept of the order of numbers.

The integers are normally listed as

$$\{-3, -2, -1, 0, 1, 2, 3, \ldots\}$$

and this ordering of them is considered to be their **natural order.** Let a and b represent integers. We define a to be less than b if and only if there is a positive number c such that $a + c = b$. In other words, $a < b$ if and only if a precedes b when the integers are considered in their natural order. Then $2 < 5$ since $2 + 3 = 5$; $-2 < 3$ since $-2 + 5 = 3$.

We define $b > a$ if and only if $a < b$. Then $5 > 2$ since $2 < 5$; $3 > -2$ since $.-2 < 3$.

The following relations between numbers may now be defined:

$a = b$ if and only if a and b stand for the same number.

$a \neq b$ (read "a is not equal to b") if and only if a and b stand for different numbers.

$a < b$ (read "a is less than b") if and only if there exists a positive number c such that $a + c = b$.

$a \not< b$ (read "a is not less than b") if and only if there does not exist a positive number c such that $a + c = b$.

$b > a$ (read "b is greater than a") if and only if $a < b$.

$b \not> a$ (read "b is not greater than a") if and only if $a \not< b$.

$b \leq a$ (read "b is less than or equal to a") if and only if $b \not> a$.

$a \geq b$ (read "a is greater than or equal to b") if and only if $b \leq a$.

The last two relations are based upon a very important **trichotomy principle** of the set of real numbers: *if a and b stand for real numbers, then exactly one of the relations*

$$a < b, \qquad a = b, \qquad a > b$$

must hold. In other words, in the natural ordering of numbers a precedes b, a and b stand for the same number, or b precedes a. Then if $a \neq b$ either $a < b$ or $b < a$. This is often called the **comparison property** of the numbers. Here are a few examples of correct statements according to the natural order of the numbers:

$$2 < 5, \qquad 3 \leq 7, \qquad 4 \leq 4, \qquad 7 \geq 6, \qquad 7 \geq 7, \qquad 6 \neq 7.$$

Order relations for the rational numbers are defined in terms of the order relations for integers. First each rational number is expressed so that its denominator is positive; then $0 < b$, $0 < d$, and

$$\frac{a}{b} < \frac{c}{d} \quad \text{if and only if} \quad ad < bc.$$

Notice that under this definition

$$\frac{2}{1} < \frac{3}{1}, \qquad \frac{-4}{1} < \frac{-3}{1}, \qquad \frac{2}{3} < \frac{7}{8}.$$

We have seen that the set of real numbers is dense. Yet order prevails on the number line, and it is possible to locate both rational numbers and irrational numbers between any two given real numbers as in the examples that follow.

※※

EXAMPLE 1:   Find a rational number between 0.342 and 0.343.

Solution: There are many possible solutions; indeed, there are an infinite number of rational numbers between any two given real numbers. Think of the two given numbers as 0.3420 and 0.3430. Then several examples of rational numbers between the two are

$$0.3421, \qquad 0.3427, \qquad 0.\overline{3421}.$$

EXAMPLE 2:   Find a rational number between $0.\overline{23}$ and $0.\overline{24}$.

Solution: Here we need to find a decimal that repeats or terminates and that is greater than $0.\overline{23}$ but less than $0.\overline{24}$. Here are several possible answers:

$$0.234, \qquad 0.235, \qquad 0.\overline{238}.$$

It may be easier to see that these fall between the two given numbers by writing them out to several decimal places.

$$0.\overline{23} = 0.232323 \ldots$$
$$0.234000 \ldots$$
$$0.235000 \ldots$$
$$0.238238 \ldots$$
$$0.\overline{24} = 0.242424 \ldots$$

EXAMPLE 3:   Find an irrational number between 0.47 and 0.48.

Solution: Again there are many possible solutions, inasmuch as there are an infinite number of irrational numbers between any two given rational numbers. Several possible answers are

$$0.4724722472224722222 \ldots,$$
$$0.47505005000500005 \ldots.$$

※※

EXERCISES FOR SECTION 5-7

In Exercises 1 through 12 consider the natural order of the integers and insert the proper symbol $(<, =, $ *or* $>)$:

1. 3 ___ 6

2. -11 ___ 17

3. 7 ___ 11

4. 7 ___ -3

5. $3 + 4$ ___ 5

6. $3 + 4$ ___ 7

7. $3 - 2$ ___ $5 - 3$

8. $7 + 5$ ___ $5 + 7$

9. 5×6 ___ 6×5

10. $120 \div 30$ ___ $120 \div 40$

11. $720 \div 180$ ___ $720 \div 120$

12. 17×31 ___ 17×29

13. Repeat Exercises 1 through 12 using the symbols $=$ and $\neq$.

14. Repeat Exercises 1 through 12 using the symbols $<$ and $\geq$.

15. Repeat Exercises 1 through 12 using the symbols $>$ and $\leq$.

List each of the following sets of numbers in order from smallest to largest:

16. 0.35, $0.353553555\ldots$, 0.35355, $0.\overline{35}$, $0.3\overline{5}$.

17. 1.414, 1.4141, $1.\overline{41}$, $1.414114111\ldots$, 1.4.

18. 0.078, $0.07\overline{8}$, $0.0787887888\ldots$, 0.07, $0.\overline{07}$.

19. Which of the following names a rational number between 0.37 and 0.38? (**a**) 0.375; (**b**) $0.\overline{37}$; (**c**) $0.373773777\ldots$; (**d**) $0.37\overline{8}$.

20. Which of the following names an irrational number between 0.234 and 0.235? (**a**) 0.2345; (**b**) $0.\overline{234}$; (**c**) $0.234040040004\ldots$; (**d**) $0.23454554555\ldots$.

21. Name two rational numbers between 0.523 and 0.524.

22. Name two irrational numbers between 0.38 and 0.39.

23. Name two irrational numbers between $0.\overline{78}$ and $0.\overline{79}$.

24. Name two rational numbers between $0.\overline{356}$ and $0.\overline{357}$.

TEST FOR CHAPTER 5

1. Show a one-to-one correspondence between the set of whole numbers and the set of negative integers.

2. List the set of prime numbers that are less than 15.

3. Write the prime factorization of 300.

4. Find the greatest common factor of 120 and 140.

5. Find the least common multiple of 90 and 1500.

6. Classify each statement as true or false:
(a) Every counting number is a whole number.
(b) The opposite of every whole number is a negative integer.
(c) Every rational number may be expressed as the quotient of two integers.
(d) Every rational number may be expressed as a repeating or a terminating decimal.
(e) Between every two rational numbers there is only one other rational number.

7. Copy the following table. Use "√" to show that the number at the top of the column is a member of the set named at the side. Use "X" if the number is not a member of the set.

	(a) $\frac{3}{4}$	(b) -2	(c) 0	(d) $\sqrt{2}$	(e) $\sqrt{4}$
Set					
Counting numbers					
Whole numbers					
Integers					
Rational numbers					
Real numbers					

8. Express as a quotient of integers: (a) $0.\overline{27}$; (b) $0.\overline{612}$.

9. Name (a) a rational number and (b) an irrational number between 0.25 and 0.26.

10. List the following numbers in order from smallest to largest: $0.2\overline{3}$, $0.232332333\ldots$, 0.23, 0.2323, $0.\overline{23}$.

chapter 6

AN INTRODUCTION
TO GEOMETRY

Geometry has evolved from a concern for earth measure (geo-metry), through the use of line segments and other figures to represent physical magnitudes, to a study of properties of sets of geometric elements. The figures serve as the elements of geometry. Relations among these elements and proofs of their properties from given sets of postulates are considered in more advanced courses.

All geometric figures are usually considered to be sets of points. Although other basic elements are considered in abstract geometry, we shall restrict our consideration to points. This is not a serious restriction, since points may be *interpreted* in many ways. For example, we usually think of a point as a position on a line, on a plane, or in space. We may also think of a point on a number scale in terms of its coordinate. We may even think of cities as points on a map, with the air routes joining them considered as lines. This freedom to interpret points in a variety of ways provides a basis for more abstract geometries.

6-1 POINTS, LINES, AND PLANES

We have an intuitive idea of what is meant by a point, but we have not and shall not *define* a point. In order to define a term, we need to distinguish it from other terms. In doing this, we must describe our term in words that are already known to us (that is, in simpler terms) in such a way that whenever the description is applicable, the term being defined is also appropriate.

The early Greeks described a point as "that which has no part." Today we recognize such a description as an aid to our interpretations, but we do not consider it a definition. We object to it as a formal definition because the terms used are not simpler terms and, indeed, simpler terms are not available.

Lines also are left undefined. In any logical system there must be some undefined terms. In other words, it is not possible to define everything; we must start with something. In geometry we start with points and lines. Then we define other figures in terms of these.

Even though lines are undefined, they do possess certain properties. Here are four of these properties:

1. *A line is a set of points.* Each point of the line is said to be *on* the line.

2. *Any two distinct points determine a unique line.* In other words, there is one and only one line AB through any two given points A and B. Thus a line may be named by any two of its points. If C and D are points on the line AB, then the line CD is the same as the line AB.

$$
\begin{array}{cccc}
\bullet & \bullet & \bullet & \bullet \\
C & A & D & B
\end{array}
$$

3. *Every line is a real number line.* Then as in §5-6 each line is a dense set of points and has infinitely many points.

4. *Any point A on a line separates the line into three parts: the point A and two half-lines, one on each side of A.* Each half-line is a set of points. The point A is not a point (member) of either half-line.

Half-line on the left — • A — Half-line on the right

Three points A, B, C either lie on a line or do not lie on a line Note that we think of (interpret) a "line" as a "straight line." If the points do not lie on the same straight line, then, since any two points determine a unique line, the three points determine three lines AB, BC, and AC as in the figure.

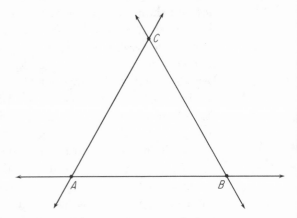

Each of the lines AB, BC, and AC is a set of points. Any two points on a line determine that line; for example, the points D and E on the line BC determine the line BC, and we say that BC and DE are two names for the same line. Any two points of the figure consisting of the lines AB, BC, and AC determine a line. If the points are not on the same one of these three lines, then the points determine a new line; for example, D and F determine a new line in the figure.

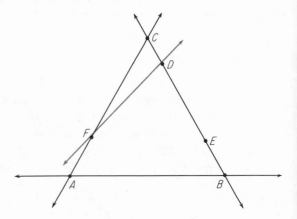

Many new lines can be determined in this way. A few such lines are shown in the next figure. The set of all points on such lines is the set of points of the plane determined by the three points A, B, and C.

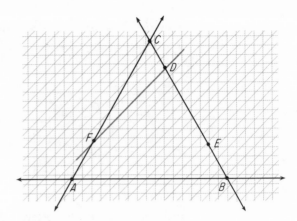

Planes are often accepted as undefined. However, all planes have certain basic properties. Here are five of these properties:

1. *A plane is a set of points.* Each point of the plane is said to be *on* the plane.

2. *Any three points that are not on the same line determine a unique plane.* In other words, there is one and only one plane through any three noncollinear points. For example, a piece of cardboard will balance firmly on the points of three thumbtacks; a three-legged stool is more stable than many four-legged chairs. We use this property when we name planes such as *ABC* by any three points that are on the plane but not on a straight line.

3. *If two distinct points of a line are on a plane, then every point of the line is on the plane.*

4. *Any line m on a plane separates the plane into three parts: the line m and two half-planes.* The points of the line *m* do not belong to either half-plane. However, the line *m* is often called the **edge** of both half-planes even though it is not a part of either.

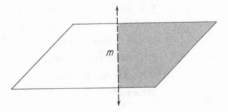

Note that we may think of the points of the plane that are on the right of *m* as forming one half-plane and the points of the plane that are on the left of *m* as forming the other half-plane.

5. *Two distinct planes have either a line in common or no points in common.* In other words, any two distinct planes either intersect in a line or are parallel.

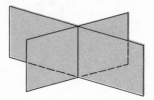 

In ordinary geometry (often called Euclidean geometry) it is possible for two planes to fail to have a point in common. Two planes that do not have any point in common are said to be **parallel.** A line is parallel to a plane if it does not have any point in common with the plane.

Think of an ordinary classroom. On any given wall the line along the ceiling and the line along the floor do not appear to intersect; that is, do not have any point in common no matter how far they are extended. The line along the ceiling and one wall also does not appear to intersect the line of intersection of two other walls. Any distinction between these two situations must take into consideration the fact that in the first case the two lines were on the same wall (plane), whereas in the second case there could not be a single plane containing both lines. In general, two lines that are on the same plane and do not have any point in common are also said to be **parallel lines;** two lines that are not on the same plane are called **skew lines;** two distinct lines that have a point in common are called **intersecting lines;** lines that have all their points in common may be visualized as two names for the same line and are called **coincident lines.**

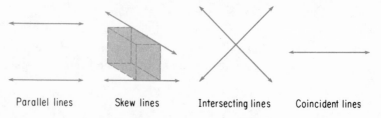

Parallel lines   Skew lines   Intersecting lines   Coincident lines

Note that the arrows indicate that the lines may be extended indefinitely; that is, that the figure involves representations for lines rather than actual lines. These representations are on the printed page and thus on a plane. Thus the figure for skew lines must be visualized as a "picture" on a plane of skew lines in space.

Points, lines, and planes are the building blocks of geometry. We use these elements and relations such as intersections, parallelism, coincidence, skewness, and separation as we define other geometric figures; that is, as we name other sets of points.

EXERCISES FOR SECTION 6-1

1. Label three points A, B, and C that are not on the same line. Draw and name each of the lines that are determined by these points.

2. Repeat Exercise 1 for four points A, B, C, and D such that no three of the points are on the same line.

3. Assume that the four points in Exercise 2 are not on the same plane. Name each of the planes that is determined by these points.

4. Assume that all of the given points are on the same plane and no three of the given points are on the same line. State how many lines are determined by the given number of points: **(a)** 2; **(b)** 3; **(c)** 4; **(d)** 5; **(e)** 6; *__(f)__ 10; *__(g)__ n.

5. Assume that all of the given lines are on the same plane, that each line intersects each of the other lines, and that no three of the given lines are on the same point. State how many points are determined by the given number of lines: **(a)** 2; **(b)** 3; **(c)** 4; **(d)** 5; **(e)** 6; *__(f)__ 10; *__(g)__ n.

6. Consider the lines along the edges of the rectangular solid shown in the given figure and state whether the specified lines are parallel lines, skew lines, or intersecting lines:

(a) $\overleftrightarrow{AB}$ and $\overleftrightarrow{CD}$ **(b)** $\overleftrightarrow{AB}$ and $\overleftrightarrow{EF}$

(c) $\overleftrightarrow{AB}$ and $\overleftrightarrow{EH}$ **(d)** $\overleftrightarrow{CD}$ and $\overleftrightarrow{FG}$

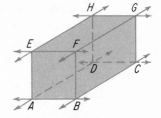

Use pencils, table tops, etc. to represent lines and planes and determine whether each statement appears to be true or false in Euclidean geometry:

7. Given any line m and any point P that is not a point of m, there is exactly one line t that is parallel to m and contains P.

8. Given any line m and any point P that is not a point of m, there is exactly one line q such that q contains P and m and q are intersecting lines.

9. Given any line m and any point P that is not a point of m, there is exactly one line s such that s contains P and s and m are skew lines.

10. Given any line m and any point P that is not a point of m, there is exactly one plane that is parallel to m and contains P.

11. Given any plane ABC and any point P that is not a point of ABC, there is exactly one plane that contains P and intersects ABC.

12. Given any plane ABC and any point P that is not a point of ABC, there is exactly one plane that contains P and is parallel to ABC.

13. Given any plane ABC and any point P that is not a point of ABC, there is exactly one line that contains P and intersects ABC.

14. Given any plane ABC and any point P that is not a point of ABC, there is exactly one line that contains P and is parallel to ABC.

15. Given any plane ABC and any line m that is parallel to ABC, there is exactly one plane that contains m and intersects ABC.

16. Given any plane ABC and any line m that is parallel to ABC, there is exactly one plane that contains m and is parallel to ABC.

17. Given any plane ABC and any line m that is parallel to ABC, there is for any given point P that is not on m and not on ABC exactly one line that is parallel to m and also parallel to ABC.

Many interesting figures may be obtained by paper folding. Wax paper is especially well suited for these exercises:

18. Draw a line m and select a point P that is not on m. Fold the point P onto points of m in at least 20 different positions spaced as evenly as possible. Describe the pattern formed by the folds.

19. Draw a circle C and select a point P outside the circle. Fold the point P onto points of C in at least 20 different positions spaced as evenly as possible. Describe the pattern formed by the folds.

20. Repeat Exercise 19 for a point P that is inside the circle but not at the center of the circle.

21. Repeat Exercise 19 for the point P at the center of the circle.

22. Repeat Exercise 19 for a point P on the circle.

6-2 RAYS, LINE SEGMENTS, AND ANGLES

Suppose that we are given a line m and two points A and B on m. There is one and only one line m on both A and B. We call this the line AB and writ . it as $\overleftrightarrow{BA}$. As in §6-1 the point A separates the line m into two half-lines. Note that one of these half-lines contains the point B and one does not.

The set of points consisting of the half-line $\overset{\circ\!\!\rightarrow}{AB}$ and the point A is called a **ray.** The point A is the **endpoint** of the ray. There is one and only one ray with endpoint A and containing the point B. We call this the ray AB and write it as $\overrightarrow{AB}$. There is also a ray BA with endpoint B and containing A.

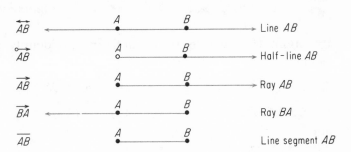

The **line segment** AB, written as $\overline{AB}$, consists of the points which $\overrightarrow{AB}$ and $\overrightarrow{BA}$ have in common. We may use the symbol $\cap$ for the intersection of two sets of elements (in this case, points) and write

$$\overline{AB} = \overrightarrow{AB} \cap \overrightarrow{BA}.$$

A line AB has no endpoints and may be named by any two of its points. A ray AB has one endpoint and may be named by that point A and any other point on the ray. A line segment AB has the two endpoints A and B and is named by those two points. However, for a line segment those two points may be stated in either order; that is, $\overline{AB} = \overline{BA}$.

When a direction, such as from A to B, is assigned to the points of a line segment, we obtain a **vector,** $\overrightarrow{AB}$. The vector AB has both direction and length. The direction is from A to B; the length is the same as the length of the line segment AB. Notice that a ray $\overrightarrow{AB}$ has only one endpoint A; a vector $\overrightarrow{AB}$ has two endpoints, an **initial point** A and a **terminal point** B.

$$\overrightarrow{AB} \quad \overset{A}{\bullet}\!\!\!-\!\!\!-\!\!\!-\!\!\!-\!\!\!-\!\!\!-\!\!\!-\!\!\!\overset{B}{\rightarrow} \quad \text{Vector } AB$$

Any point of a line segment AB that is not an **endpoint** (that is, any point that is distinct from A and B) is called an **interior point** of $\overline{AB}$. If E is an interior point of AB, then E is **between** A and B. Thus the line segment AB consists of the endpoints A and B and the points of the line AB that are between A and B. The interior points of a line segment AB form the **open line segment** AB:

$$\underset{AB}{\circ\!\!-\!\!-\!\!\circ} \quad \overset{A}{\circ}\!\!-\!\!-\!\!-\!\!-\!\!-\!\!-\!\!-\!\!\overset{B}{\circ} \quad \text{Open line segment } AB$$

EXAMPLE 1: Consider the given figure and identify each set of points:

(a) $\overline{PQ} \cup \overline{QS}$ (b) $\overline{PR} \cap \overline{QS}$

(c) $\overrightarrow{QR} \cup \overrightarrow{SR}$ (d) $\overrightarrow{PQ} \cap \overrightarrow{QS}$

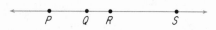

Solution: (a) $\overline{PS}$; (b) $\overline{QR}$; (c) $\overleftrightarrow{PQ}$ (any one of several names for the line may be used); (d) $\overrightarrow{QS}$ (this ray may also be named $\overrightarrow{QR}$).

Any line AB is a set of points. If C is a point of the line such that A is between C and B, then the line is the union of the rays AB and AC.

These two rays have a common endpoint A and are both on the line AB. Any figure formed by two rays that have a common endpoint is **a plane angle.** These rays may be on the same line but need not be on the same line. Each angle in the figure may be designated as $\angle BAC$; $\angle BAC = \overrightarrow{AB} \cup \overrightarrow{AC}$.

The rays AB and AC are called **sides** of $\angle BAC$. For the angle in the following figure there exist points P and Q of the angle such that the open line segment $\overset{\circ-\circ}{PQ}$ does not intersect the angle. All points of such open line segments are **interior points** of the angle.

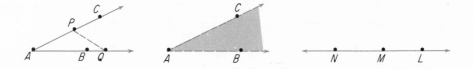

Notice that an angle such as $\angle LMN$ does not have any interior points, since $\overline{PQ} \subset \angle LMN$ for all points P and Q of the angle. Persons who have previously studied geometry may observe that any angle that has an interior has a measurement between $0°$ and $180°$. For this reason some elementary books consider only angles whose measurements are greater than $0°$ and less than $180°$.

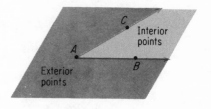

If an angle has an interior, then the angle separates the plane into three disjoint sets: the points of the angle, the interior points of the angle, and the **exterior points** of the angle.

EXAMPLE 2:   Consider the given figure and identify each set of points:

(a) $\overleftrightarrow{AB} \cap \overleftrightarrow{DE}$

(b) $\overrightarrow{BC} \cup \overrightarrow{BD}$

(c) $\angle CBD \cap \overrightarrow{ED}$

(d) $\overline{AF} \cap \overrightarrow{BD}$

(e) (Exterior $\angle ABE$) $\cap \overleftrightarrow{BD}$

(f) (Interior $\angle CBE$) $\cap \overleftrightarrow{AC}$

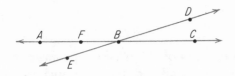

Solution: (a) B, the two lines intersect in the single point B;
(b) $\angle CBD$; (c) $\overrightarrow{BD}$; (d) $\varnothing$; (e) $\overset{\circ}{\overrightarrow{BD}}$; (f) $\varnothing$.

EXERCISES FOR SECTION 6-2

Consider the given figure and identify each set of points:

1. $\overline{AB} \cup \overline{BD}$

2. $\overline{AB} \cap \overline{CD}$

3. $\overline{AC} \cap \overline{BD}$

4. $\overline{AB} \cap \overline{BC}$

5. $\overline{AD} \cap \overline{BC}$

6. $\overline{AD} \cup \overline{BC}$

7. $\overleftrightarrow{AB} \cap \overline{BC}$

8. $\overleftrightarrow{AB} \cap \overrightarrow{BC}$

9. $\overrightarrow{BC} \cup \overrightarrow{CD}$

10. $\overrightarrow{BC} \cap \overrightarrow{CD}$

11. $\overrightarrow{BC} \cap \overrightarrow{BA}$

12. $\overrightarrow{DC} \cup \overrightarrow{CA}$

Consider the given figure and identify each set of points:

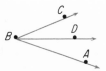

13. (Exterior ∠*ABC*) ∩ $\overrightarrow{BD}$

14. (Interior ∠*ABC*) ∩ $\overrightarrow{BD}$

15. (Interior ∠*ABC*) ∩ (exterior ∠*DBC*)

16. (Interior ∠*ABC*) ∪ (exterior ∠*ABC*) ∪ ∠*ABC*

17. (Exterior ∠*DBC*) ∩ $\overrightarrow{BA}$

18. (Exterior ∠*DBC*) ∩ $\overline{AB}$

Consider the given figure and identify each set of points:

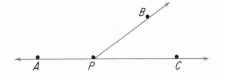

19. (Exterior ∠*BPC*) ∩ $\overrightarrow{CP}$

20. (Exterior ∠*BPA*) ∩ $\overleftrightarrow{AP}$

21. $\overrightarrow{PB}$ ∪ $\overrightarrow{PC}$

22. ∠*BPC* ∩ ∠*BPA*

23. ∠*BPC* ∪ ∠*BPA*

24. (Exterior ∠*BPC*) ∩ $\overline{AC}$

SUPPLEMENTARY EXERCISES FOR SECTION 6-2

Consider the given figure and identify each set of points:

1. $\overrightarrow{BC}$ ∩ $\overline{AD}$ 2. $\overline{BC}$ ∩ $\overrightarrow{AD}$

3. $\overline{BC}$ ∩ $\overline{AD}$ 4. $\overrightarrow{CA}$ ∪ $\overline{CD}$

5. $\overline{CA} \cup \overline{CD}$ **6.** $\overline{CA} \cap \overline{CD}$

7. $\overleftrightarrow{AB} \cap \overline{BD}$ **8.** $\overleftrightarrow{AB} \cap \overrightarrow{BD}$

9. $\overleftrightarrow{AB} \cup \overrightarrow{BD}$ **10.** $\overrightarrow{BD} \cup \overrightarrow{DB}$

11. $\overrightarrow{BD} \cap \overline{DB}$ **12.** $\overrightarrow{BD} \cap \overrightarrow{DB}$

Consider the given figure and identify each set of points:

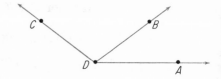

13. $\angle ADB \cap \angle BDC$

14. (Exterior $\angle ADB$) $\cap$ (exterior $\angle BDC$)

15. (Interior $\angle ADB$) $\cap$ (interior $\angle BDC$)

16. $\angle ADB \cap \overrightarrow{DB}$

17. $\angle ADB \cap \overrightarrow{BD}$

18. $\angle ADB \cap$ (exterior $\angle BDC$)

19. $\overrightarrow{DB} \cup$ (interior $\angle ADB$) $\cup$ (interior $\angle BDC$)

20. (Exterior $\angle ADC$) $\cap \overrightarrow{DB}$

21. (Exterior $\angle ADB$) $\cup$ (exterior $\angle ADC$)

6-3 PLANE FIGURES

We now continue our study of geometric figures on a plane; that is, sets of points on a plane. Consider the four figures in the accompanying diagram, where each is a union of line segments. Notice that in each case there seem to be three separate parts. A part may consist of

               (*a*)   (*b*)   (*c*)   (*d*) one line segment or be the union of two or more line segments. However, you could pick out the three parts of each figure. You recognized that any two distinct parts were not "connected"; that you could not draw them both without removing the point of the pencil from the paper to move from one to the other. We now assume that the word "connected" is understood even though it has not been defined.

Each of the three figures in the next diagram is a union of line segments, and each figure is connected. Each may be drawn by starting at one of the points A, B, and ending at the other.

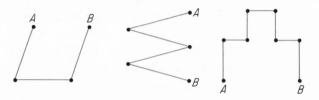

Each of the next five figures is a union of line segments, each is connected, each may be drawn as a continuous line by starting at one of the points R, S and ending at the other, and each differs from the figures A, B in the preceding set. See if you can identify that difference.

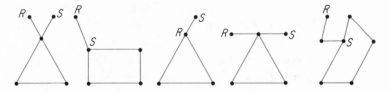

Any connected union of line segments is a broken line. Compare the three broken lines AB with the five broken lines RS. Each broken line AB may be drawn starting at A and ending at B without retracing any line segments or arriving at any point a second time. Each broken line RS may be drawn starting at R and ending at S without retracing any line segments, but for each broken line RS some point, possibly the starting point, must be used twice in the drawing. Briefly, we say that each broken line RS intersects itself. The word "simple" is used to distinguish between these two types of figures. A figure such as one of the broken lines AB which does not intersect itself is a **simple figure.** Figures such as triangles, squares, circles, and rectangles are also simple figures. A figure such as one of the broken lines RS that does intersect itself is *not a simple figure.*

The broken lines *AB* and *RS* differ from each of the next two figures. Each of these next figures is simple; each is connected; each is a union of line segments. Each differs from the previous figures in that when it is drawn one starts at a point and returns to that point. We say that such a figure is **closed**.

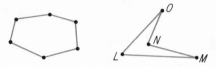

Figures may be either simple or not simple; they may also be either closed or not closed. For example, the figure *LMNO* is simple and closed; the figure *PQRS* is closed and not simple; the broken lines *AB* are simple and not closed; the broken lines *RS* are neither simple nor closed.

A simple closed broken line on a plane is called a **polygon**. The line segments are called **sides** of the polygon; the endpoints of the line segments are called **vertices** of the polygon. A polygon is a **convex polygon** if every line segment *PQ* with points of the polygon as endpoints is either a subset of a side of the polygon or has only the points *P* and *Q* in common with the polygon. A polygon that is not a convex polygon is a **concave polygon**.

Convex polygon   Concave polygon

If *P* and *Q* are points of a convex polygon and $\overline{PQ}$ is not a subset of a side of the polygon, then the points of the open line segment *PQ* are **interior points** of the convex polygon. The union of the points of a convex polygon and its interior points is a **polygonal region.** The points of the plane of a convex polygon that are not points of the polygonal region are **exterior points** of the polygon.

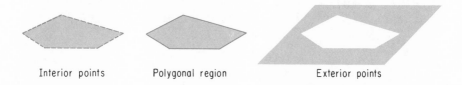

Interior points   Polygonal region   Exterior points

A polygon with three sides is a **triangle.** For example, triangle ABC consists of the points of $\overline{AB} \cup \overline{BC} \cup \overline{CA}$. The **interior** of triangle ABC consists of the points in the intersection of the interiors of the three angles, $\angle ABC$, $\angle BCA$, and $\angle CAB$. The **exterior** of triangle ABC consists of the points of the plane ABC that are neither points of the triangle nor points of the interior of the triangle.

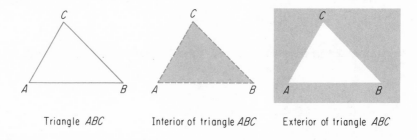

Triangle ABC Interior of triangle ABC Exterior of triangle ABC

In general, plane polygons are classified according to the number of sides. The common names are shown in this array:

Number of sides	Name of polygon
3	triangle
4	quadrilateral
5	pentagon
6	hexagon
7	heptagon
8	octagon
9	nonagon
10	decagon
12	dodecagon

EXAMPLE: Consider the given figure and identify each set of points: (a) $\overrightarrow{AB} \cap \overrightarrow{ED}$; (b) $\angle BAE \cap \angle BCD$; (c) (interior $\triangle ACE$) $\cap$ (exterior $\angle EFD$); (d) three angles such that the intersection of their interior points is the interior of $\triangle ABF$.

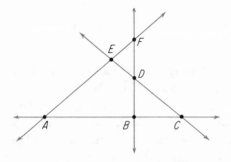

Solution :   (a) $\{C\}$; (b) $\overline{AC} \cup E$; (c) interior $\triangle BCD$; (d) $\angle ABF$, $\angle BFA$, and $\angle FAB$.

EXERCISES FOR SECTION 6-3

Sketch a union of line segments that is

    1. Connected.

    2. Not connected.

Sketch a broken line that is

    3. Simple but not closed.

    4. Closed but not simple.

    5. Simple and closed.

    6. Neither simple nor closed.

    7. A convex polygon of five sides.

    8. A concave polygon of six sides.

Consider the given figure and identify each set of points:

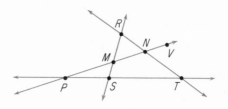

9. $\overrightarrow{MN} \cap \overrightarrow{TS}$ **10.** $\overrightarrow{SR} \cap \overrightarrow{ST}$

11. $\triangle RST \cap \overline{PM}$ **12.** (Exterior $\triangle RST$) $\cap \overline{MN}$

13. $\overrightarrow{TS} \cap \overline{PM}$ **14.** $\overline{PV} \cap \triangle RST$

15. (Interior $\triangle RST$) $\cap \overline{MN}$ **16.** $\overline{RS} \cap \overline{ST}$

17. $\overline{RM} \cup \overline{MN} \cup \overline{RN}$ **18.** (Exterior $\triangle RST$) $\cap \overrightarrow{NM}$

19. (Exterior $\triangle RST$) $\cap \overleftrightarrow{MN}$ **20.** $\overrightarrow{PM} \cup \overrightarrow{PS}$

21. $\overline{PV} \cap \triangle MRN$ **22.** $\angle SRT \cap \angle RTS$

23. (Interior $\triangle RST$) $\cap$ (interior $\triangle MRN$)

24. (Interior $\triangle RST$) $\cup$ (interior $\triangle MRN$)

25. (Interior $\angle VPT$) $\cap$ (interior $\triangle RST$)

26. (Interior $\angle SRT$) $\cap$ (interior $\angle RTS$)

27. (Interior $\angle RST$) $\cap$ (interior $\angle STR$) $\cap$ (interior $\angle TRS$)

28. (Interior $\triangle RMN$) $\cup$ (exterior $\triangle RMN$) $\cup \triangle RMN$

SUPPLEMENTARY EXERCISES FOR SECTION 6-3

Sketch a union of line segments that is:

1. Not a polygon.

2. A convex polygon of seven sides.

3. A concave polygon of seven sides.

4. Not simple, not closed, and not connected.

Consider the given figure and identify each set of points:

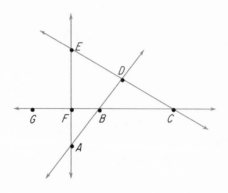

5. $\overrightarrow{GF} \cap \overrightarrow{DE}$

6. $\overrightarrow{CG} \cup \overrightarrow{CE}$

7. $\triangle CFE \cap \overrightarrow{AB}$

8. $\triangle ABF \cap \triangle BCD$

9. $\triangle ABF \cap \overrightarrow{CG}$

10. $\triangle CBD \cap \triangle CFE$

11. (Interior $\triangle CBD$) $\cap$ (interior $\triangle CFE$)

12. (Interior $\triangle ABF$) $\cap$ (exterior $\triangle CBD$)

13. (Exterior $\triangle ABF$) $\cap$ $\overrightarrow{BF}$

14. (Exterior $\triangle ABF$) $\cap$ $\overleftrightarrow{CD}$

15. (Interior $\triangle CFE$) $\cap$ $\overleftrightarrow{BD}$

6-4 SPACE FIGURES

Any two points A and B that are on a line but not on the same point determine a unique line segment AB. Any three points A, B, and C that are on a plane but not on the same line determine a unique

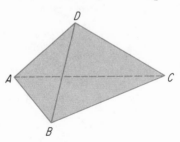

triangle ABC. Any four points A, B, C, and D that are in space but not on the same plane determine a unique **tetrahedron.** The four points A, B, C, D are the **vertices** of the tetrahedron; the six line segments $\overline{AB}$, $\overline{AC}$, $\overline{AD}$, $\overline{BC}$, $\overline{BD}$, $\overline{CD}$ are the **edges** of the tetrahedron.

The triangular regions of the four triangles ABC, BCD, CDA, and ABD are the **faces** of the tetrahedron. The **interior points** of the tetrahedron are the points of the open line segments PQ, where P and Q are points of the tetrahedron (points of the union of the faces of the tetrahedron) and $\overset{\circ\!-\!\circ}{PQ}$ does not intersect the tetrahedron.

A polygon is a simple, closed union of line segments; that is, a union of line segments (sides of the polygon) such that exactly two sides have each endpoint of a line segment (vertex of the polygon) in common and no side contains an interior point of another side. A **polyhedron** is a simple, closed union of polygonal regions (**faces** of the polyhedron) such that exactly two faces have each side of a polygonal region (**edge** of the polyhedron) in common and no face contains an interior point of another face. The vertices of the polygonal regions are also called **vertices** of the polyhedron. Cubes, pyramids, and prisms are considered in the exercises and are examples of polyhedrons.

EXERCISES FOR SECTION 6-4

1. The tetrahedron $MNOP$ is a **triangular pyramid.** Name its **(a)** vertices; **(b)** edges; **(c)** faces.

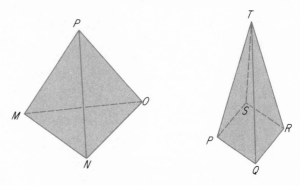

2. Repeat Exercise 1 for the **square pyramid** $PQRST$.

3. Repeat Exercise 1 for the **cube** *ABCDEFGH*.

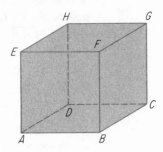

4. Think of the lines along the edges of the cube in Exercise 3 and identify the lines that appear to be (**a**) parallel to $\overleftrightarrow{AB}$; (**b**) skew to $\overleftrightarrow{AB}$; (**c**) parallel to the plane *ABFE*.

5. A cube has all of its vertices on two parallel planes and has square faces in those planes. Accordingly, a cube is an example of a **square prism.** Repeat Exercise 1 for the **triangular prism** *JKLMNO*.

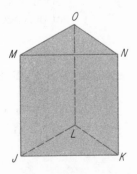

6. Let *V* be the number of vertices, *E* the number of edges, and *F* the number of faces. Then copy and complete the following table.

Figure	V	E	F
Triangular pyramid			
Square pyramid			
Cube			
Triangular prism			

In Exercises 7 through 13 extend the table in Exercise 6 for:

7. A pyramid with a pentagon as a base.

8. A prism with a pentagon as a base.

9. A prism with a hexagon as a base.

10. A pyramid with a hexagon as a base.

11. The given figure which represents two triangular pyramids with their common base removed.

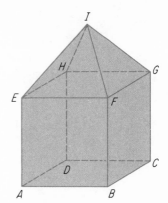

12. The given figure *FGHIJK* which represents two square pyramids with their common base removed.

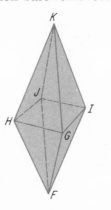
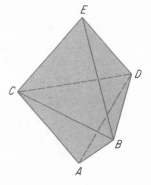

13. The given figure *ABCDEFGHI* which represents a cube with one face replaced by the four triangular faces of a square pyramid.

14. In the tables for Exercises 6 through 13 study the values of V, E, and F for each polyhedron. Compare the value of E with the value of $V + F$. Then conjecture a formula for E in terms of V and F. You should obtain the famous *Euler formula for polyhedrons*.

15. A three-inch cube (three inches long, three inches wide, and three inches high) is painted red and then cut into 27 one-inch cubes.

(a) What is the smallest number of cuts that can be used to divide the original cube into 27 pieces? (You are not allowed to move the pieces after you start to make a cut.)

(b) How many of these one-inch cubes will have red paint on none of their faces? On one of their faces? On two of their faces? On three of their faces? On more than three of their faces?

16. Answer the question in Exercise 15 (b) for a four-inch cube that is painted red and then cut into 64 one-inch cubes. Repeat the same procedure for a five-inch cube. Do you see any emerging pattern?

*17. The "pictures" (sketches, drawings) of space figures on a sheet of paper never completely represent the figure and are often hard to visualize. Consider the accompanying pattern and make a model of a tetrahedron.

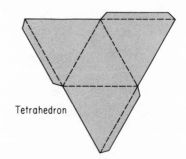

Tetrahedron

*18. As in Exercise 17 consider the pattern and make a model of a cube.

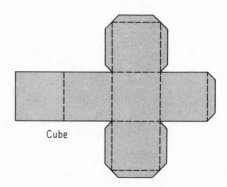

Cube

6-5 PLANE CURVES

Throughout this chapter we have considered points, lines, planes, rays, line segments, figures composed of line segments and rays, and regions of planes determined by line segments, rays, and half-planes. We now consider plane figures that may be approximated by broken lines and polygons; that is, we consider **plane curves.** Each of the following figures is a **simple closed curve.** Notice that a polygon is a special case of a simple closed curve.

Any two simple closed curves have a common property. Can you find that property? Size, shape, angles, and straight lines are certainly not common properties here. What is left to be considered? Some readers may consider the common property that we are seeking trivial because of its simplicity. We prefer to believe that the really basic properties of mathematics are inherently simple. The property that we have in mind may be stated very easily: Any simple closed curve has an inside and an outside.

In advanced mathematics we say that *any simple closed curve in a plane divides the plane into two regions.* This is the **Jordan curve theorem.** The curve is the common boundary of the two regions, and one cannot cross from one region to the other without crossing the curve. The Jordan curve theorem is a very powerful theorem and yet a very simple one. Notice that it is independent of the size or shape of the curve.

How can such a simple theorem have any significance? It provides a basis for Euclid's assumption that any line segment joining the center of a circle to a point outside the circle must contain a point of the circle. In more advanced courses it provides a basis for the existence of a zero of a polynomial on any interval on which the polynomial changes sign. It provides a basis for Euler diagrams and

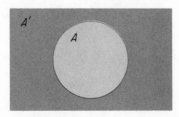

Venn diagrams in any two-valued logic. In §4-5 we assumed that all points of the universal set were either points of a circular region A or points of A', the complement of A.

In §4-6 we considered statements p that are either true or false (in which case $\sim p$ is true) but not both true and false. Because of the Jordan curve theorem we were able to represent the situations under which statements were true (or false) by Euler diagrams and by Venn diagrams.

This simple theorem regarding the existence of an inside and an outside of any simple closed curve may also be used to answer questions raised by the next problem. This problem is a popular one, and many people have spent hours working on it. (See §1-4, Exercise 4.) Consider three houses ($\times$) in a row and three utilities ($\circ$) in a second row on a plane surface. The problem is to join each house to each utility by an arc on the plane in such a way that no two arcs cross or pass through houses or utilities except at their endpoints. As in the figure on the left it is easy to designate paths from one house to each of the three utilities. One can also designate paths to each utility from the second house as in the second figure. Then one can designate two of the paths from the third house, but it is not possible on an ordinary plane to draw the path from the remaining house to the remaining utility. This assertion is based upon the fact that the simple closed curve indicated in the third figure divides the plane into two regions; the third house is inside the curve (shaded region), the remaining utility is outside the curve, and the two cannot be joined without crossing the curve.

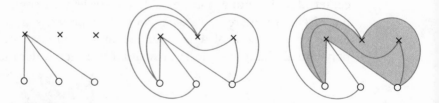

As in the case of broken lines, plane curves may be either simple or not simple and either closed or not closed. Each of the figures that follow is a plane curve that may be approximated by a closed broken line that is not simple. Each curve is a closed curve that is not simple.

Closed curves that are not simple divide the plane into three or more regions. The points at which a curve intersects itself are **vertices**; also, any other points may be designated as vertices. The simple curves with vertices as endpoints and not containing any other vertices are **arcs**. Each of the following curves has three points designated as vertices. The numbers V of vertices, A of arcs, and R of regions into which the plane is divided are shown below each figure. The last figure leaves the plane as a single region, since, for any two points P and Q that are points of the plane but not points of the figure, there is a simple plane curve (arc) with endpoints P and Q that does not intersect the given figure.

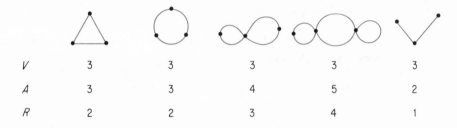

V	3	3	3	3	3
A	3	3	4	5	2
R	2	2	3	4	1

The next figures may be approximated by simple broken lines that are not closed. They are called simple curves that are not closed. Notice that a line and a ray are special cases of simple curves that are not closed; thus in geometry curves do not have to be "crooked."

The next figures may be approximated by a broken line that is neither simple nor closed; each is called a curve that is neither simple nor closed.

EXERCISES FOR SECTION 6-5

Sketch three curves that are different in appearance and are each

1. Simple and closed.   **2.** Simple and not closed.

3. Closed and not simple.   **4.** Neither simple nor closed.

Sketch a broken line that closely approximates a given

5. Simple closed curve.

6. Simple curve that is not closed.

7. Closed curve that is not simple.

8. Polygon.

In Exercises 9 through 14 find the numbers V of vertices, A of arcs, and R of regions for each figure:

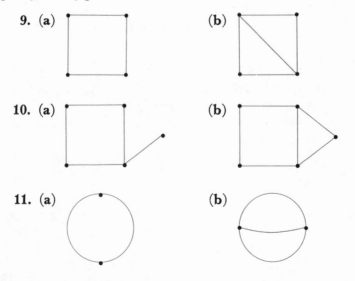

9. (a)   **(b)**

10. (a)   **(b)**

11. (a)   **(b)**

12. (a)   **(b)**

13. (a)   **(b)**

14. (a)   **(b)**

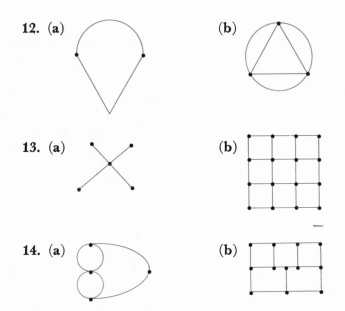

15. Study the values of V, A, and R obtained in Exercises 9 through 14 and find an expression for A in terms of V and R. You should obtain a form of the *Euler formula for networks*.

6-6 NETWORKS

Any set of line segments (or arcs) forms a **network.** If the network can be drawn by tracing each line segment exactly once without removing the point of the pencil from the paper, the network is **traversable.** For example, any connected simple network is traversable. If such a network is closed, any point may be selected as a starting point for the drawing and this point will also be the terminating point of the drawing. If the connected simple network is not closed, the drawing must start at one of the endpoints and terminate at the other.

The study of the traversability of networks probably stemmed from a problem concerning the bridges in the city of Königsberg. There was a river flowing through the city, two islands in the river, and seven bridges as in the figure. The people of Königsberg loved a Sunday stroll and thought it would be nice to take a walk that would take them across each bridge exactly once. They found that no matter where they started or what route they tried, they could not cross each bridge exactly once. Gradually it was observed that the

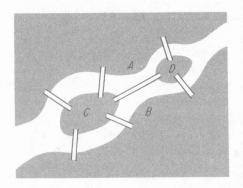

basic problem was concerned with paths between the two sides of the river *A*, *B*, and the two islands *C*, *D* as in the figure. With this representation of the problem by a network, it was no longer necessary to discuss the problem in terms of walking across the bridges. Instead one could discuss whether or not the network associated with the problem was traversable. The problem was solvable if and only if its network was traversable.

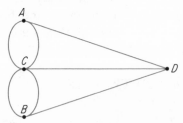

When is a network traversable? One can walk completely around any city block, and it is not necessary to start at any particular point to do so. In general, one may traverse any simple closed broken line in a single trip. We next consider walking around two blocks and down the street $\overline{BE}$ separating them. This problem is a bit more interesting in that it is necessary to start at *B* or *E*. Furthermore, if one starts at *B*, one ends at *E*, and conversely.

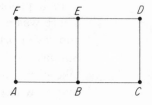

Note that it is permissible to pass through a vertex several times, but one may traverse a line segment only once. The peculiar property of the vertices B and E is based upon the fact that each of these endpoints is an endpoint of three line segments, whereas each of the other vertices is an endpoint of two line segments. A similar observation led a famous mathematician named Euler to devise a complete theory for traversable networks.

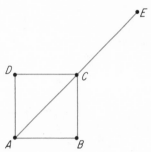

Euler classified the vertices of a network as odd or even. For example, in the given figure the vertex A is an endpoint of three arcs $\overline{AB}$, $\overline{AC}$, and $\overline{AD}$ and thus is an odd vertex; B is an endpoint of two arcs $\overline{BA}$ and $\overline{BC}$ and is an even vertex; C is an endpoint of four arcs $\overline{CB}$, $\overline{CA}$, $\overline{CD}$, and $\overline{CE}$ and is an even vertex; D is an endpoint of two arcs $\overline{DA}$ and $\overline{DC}$ and is an even vertex; E is an endpoint of one arc $\overline{EC}$ and is an odd vertex. Thus the figure has two odd vertices A and E and three even vertices B, C, and D. For any network a vertex that is an endpoint of an odd number of arcs is an **odd vertex;** a vertex that is an endpoint of an even number of arcs is an **even vertex.** Since each arc has two endpoints, there must be an even number of odd vertices in any network.

Any network that has only even vertices is traversable, and the trip may be started at any vertex. Furthermore, the trip will terminate at its starting point. If a network has exactly two odd vertices, it is traversable, but the trip must start at one of the odd vertices and will terminate at the other. If a network has more than two odd vertices, it is not traversable. In general, a network with $2k$ odd vertices may be traversed in k distinct trips. The network for the Königsberg bridge problem has four odd vertices and thus is not traversable in a single trip. Notice that the Königsberg bridge problem is independent of the size and shape of the river, bridges, or islands.

EXERCISES FOR SECTION 6-6

In Exercises 1 through 8 identify (**a**) *the number of even vertices;* (**b**) *the number of odd vertices;* (**c**) *whether or not the network is traversable and, if it is traversable, the vertices that are possible starting points.*

1.

2.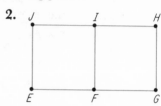

3.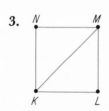

4.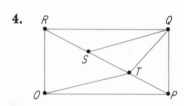

5.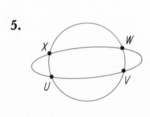

6.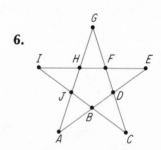

7. The network formed by the edges of a triangular pyramid.

8. The network formed by the edges of a cube.

9. Explain how a highway inspector can use a network to determine whether or not he can inspect each section of a highway without traversing the same section of the highway twice.

10. Use a related network to obtain and explain your answer to the following question: Is it possible to take a trip through a house with the floor plan indicated in the figure and pass through each doorway exactly once?

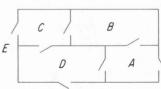

11. Explain whether or not it is possible to draw a simple connected broken line cutting each line segment of the given figure exactly once.

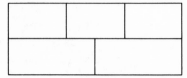

12. Consider the use of highway networks by a salesman who wants to visit each town exactly once. (**a**) Does the salesman always need to travel each highway at least once? (**b**) Consider each of the networks in Exercises 1 through 4 and indicate whether or not the salesman can visit each town exactly once without retracing any highway. (**c**) On the basis of your answer for part (b), does traversability of the network appear to be of interest to the salesman?

***13.** Describe a modification that would make the Königsberg bridge problem possible.

***14.** Describe a modification of the network for Exercise 11 such that the possibility of the desired construction is changed.

6-7 TOPOLOGY

The study of points, lines, plane curves, and space figures is part of geometry. Actually, there are several types of geometry. We shall mention only two types.

In Euclidean geometry line segments may be measured; angles may be measured; areas of triangles may be found. Two line segments of the same length are congruent; two angles of the same measure are congruent; two triangles of the same area are of equal size; two triangles of the same size and shape (each angle of one triangle may be matched with and is congruent to an angle of the other triangle) are congruent. You have probably studied this geometry of figures and their measurements before. Since it is a geometry involving measurements, it is called a **metric geometry.**

The study of simple closed curves, networks, and other plane curves that we have just considered did not involve measurement and is called a **nonmetric geometry.** Indeed, the topics that we considered were part of a particular geometry called **topology.**

We have selected topics that reflect the emphasis upon careful definitions and the use of sets of elements in both metric and nonmetric geometries. Several additional topics are considered in Chapter 10. Detailed study of geometry is regretfully left for future courses.

Let us continue our consideration of topology with a few comments on a surface that has several very unusual properties. This surface is one-sided. A fly can walk from any point on it to any other point without crossing an edge. Unlike a table top or a wall, it does not have a top and a bottom or a front and a back. This surface is called a **Möbius strip,** and it may be very easily constructed from a rectangular piece of paper such as a strip of gummed tape. Size is theoretically unimportant, but a strip an inch or two wide and about a foot long is easy to handle. We may construct a Möbius strip by twisting the strip of gummed tape just enough (one half-twist) to stick the gummed edge of one end to the gummed edge of the other end. If we cut across this strip, we again get a single strip similar to the one we started with. But if we start with a rectangular strip and cut around the center of the Möbius strip (see the dotted line in the second figure), we do not get two strips. Rather, we get one strip with two half-twists in it.

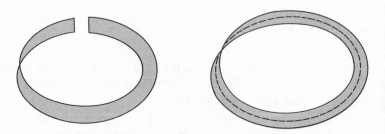

On one occasion one-sided surfaces of this sort were used as place cards at a seven-year-old's birthday party. While waiting for dessert, the youngsters were encouraged to cut the strip down the middle while guessing what the result would be. They were suitably impressed when they found only one piece, and were anxious to cut it again. Once more they were impressed when they found two pieces linked together. Almost a year after the party, one of the boys asked about the piece of paper that was in only one piece after it was cut in two.

When confronted with unusual properties such as those of the Möbius strip, both children and adults may ask questions that the nearest teacher cannot answer and that many college mathematics professors cannot answer. This is good for all concerned, since it impresses upon them that there is more to mathematics than formal algebraic manipulations and classical geometric constructions.

EXERCISES FOR SECTION 6-7

1. Construct a Möbius strip and cut around the center to obtain one strip with two half-twists in it.

2. Repeat Exercise 1 and then cut around the center again.

3. Construct a Möbius strip and cut along a path that is about one-third of the distance from one edge to the other.

4. Construct a Möbius strip, mark a point A on it, and draw an arc from A around the strip until you return to the point A.

5. Explain why a Möbius strip is called a one-sided surface.

6. Does a Möbius strip have one or two simple closed curves as its edge? Explain the reason for your answer.

TEST FOR CHAPTER 6

1. Consider the given figure and identify each set of points: (a) $\overline{BD} \cap \overline{CA}$; (b) $\overline{CD} \cup \overline{CB}$.

2. Sketch and label two rays $\overrightarrow{PQ}$ and $\overrightarrow{RS}$ such that $\overrightarrow{PQ} \cap \overrightarrow{RS}$ is (a) a line segment; (b) a ray.

3. Sketch (a) a simple curve that is not closed; (b) a convex polygon with five sides.

4. Consider the six lines along the edges of a triangular pyramid $ABCD$ as in the figure. Identify the lines that (**a**) intersect $\overleftrightarrow{AB}$ in a single point; (**b**) form skew lines with $\overleftrightarrow{AB}$.

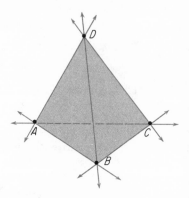

5. Consider the given figure and identify each set of points: (**a**) $\angle ABC \cap \angle CDE$; (**b**) (interior $\triangle ABC$) $\cap \overleftrightarrow{DE}$.

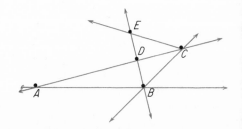

6. In the figure for Exercise 5, name (**a**) an angle that does not have any interior points; (**b**) two triangles such that the intersection of their interior points is the set of interior points of $\triangle BCD$.

7. Sketch a cube, label its vertices, and name its edges.

8. Think of a triangular prism and state the number of (**a**) vertices; (**b**) edges.

9. Sketch: (**a**) a curve that is neither simple nor closed; (**b**) a network with two odd vertices and two even vertices.

10. Consider the given figure and state whether or not each network is traversable. If a network is traversable, identify the vertices that are possible starting points.

(a)
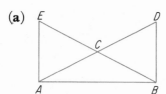

(b)
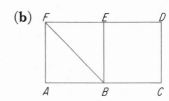

(c)
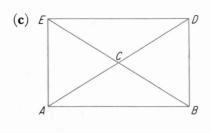

(d)
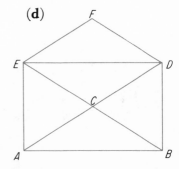

chapter 7

AN INTRODUCTION
TO ALGEBRA

Algebra is an extension of the arithmetic of the integers, rational numbers, and real numbers that we studied in Chapter 5. In our study of algebra we first consider statements. Statements involving only numbers and operations on numbers can be identified as true or as false. Algebra differs from arithmetic in that statements in algebra also include *variables;* that is, symbols that may be replaced by any member of a set of elements. Statements that involve variables may be true for some replacements for the variables and false for others.

Within this chapter we shall also see the interrelationship of algebra and geometry as we explore graphs of sentences. First we study graphs on a line, and then graphs in a plane. For the latter we are indebted to the discoveries of the French mathematician René Descartes (1596–1650), who provided a geometric interpretation for algebraic sentences in two variables and gave rise to the branch of mathematics known as analytic geometry.

7-1 SENTENCES AND GRAPHS

We assume that the reader understands from his study of English what is meant by a sentence. We shall consider two types of sentences. Sentences such as $2 + 3 = 5$, which can be identified as true, and such as $2 \times 3 = 7$, which can be identified as false, are called **statements.** Sentences such as $x + 2 = 5$, which cannot be identified as true or as false without the introduction of additional information, are called **open sentences.**

We also assume that a sentence cannot be both true and false. Here are some examples of statements; that is, sentences that are true and sentences that are false:

$$8 \times 2 = 16 \quad \text{(a true statement of equality)}$$
$$7 - 3 = 5 \quad \text{(a false statement of equality)}$$

Statements of equality, whether true or false, are called **equations.** We may also write **statements of inequality** using the symbolism introduced in §5-7. Consider these examples:

$$5 - 2 \neq 4 \quad \text{(a true statement of inequality)}$$
$$8 \times 3 \neq 24 \quad \text{(a false statement of inequality)}$$
$$12 > -3 \quad \text{(a true statement of inequality)}$$
$$-3 < -5 \quad \text{(a false statement of inequality)}$$

Below are some examples of open sentences (neither true nor false):

$$x + 2 = 7 \qquad x + 2 \neq 5$$
$$x - 3 = 4 \qquad x - 3 > 7$$

In the preceding examples of open sentences, each symbol x is called a *variable*. A **variable** is a placeholder for its replacements. In each case, the sentence is neither true nor false until a replacement is made for the variable. After such a replacement is made, we have a statement; that is, a sentence that can be classified as either true or false.

EXAMPLE 1:   Find a replacement for x that will make the open sentence $x - 1 = 3$ a true statement of equality.

Solution: When $x = 4$, we have the true statement $4 - 1 = 3$. For all other replacements of x we have a false statement of equality.

In Example 1 the replacement 4 for x is called the **solution** of the given open sentence.

EXAMPLE 2: Find all replacements for x that will make the sentence $x - 1 \leq 3$ a true statement of inequality if x is a whole number.

Solution: The sentence is true if x is replaced by 0, 1, 2, 3, or 4.

The set of solutions that make a sentence true is called the **solution set** of the given sentence for the given replacement set. In Example 2 the solution set is $\{0, 1, 2, 3, 4\}$. In the following examples note that for different replacement sets there may be different solution sets for a given sentence.

Sentence	Replacement set	Solution set
$x - 1 \leq 3$	Counting numbers	$\{1, 2, 3, 4\}$
$x - 1 \leq 3$	Whole numbers	$\{0, 1, 2, 3, 4\}$
$x - 1 \leq 3$	Integers	$\{\ldots, -2, -1, 0, 1, 2, 3, 4\}$
$x - 1 \leq 3$	Real numbers	All real numbers less than or equal to 4

Solution sets of open sentences may be graphed on a number line. We draw graphs to represent the set of points that correspond to the solution set of the sentence and refer to this simply as the **graph** of the equation or inequality. The examples that follow illustrate various types of graphs. In each one we are to graph the given open sentence for the stated replacement set.

EXAMPLE 3: $x + 3 = 5$, x an integer.

Solution: The solution set consists of a single element, $\{2\}$. We graph this solution set on a number line by drawing a solid dot at 2. The graph consists of a single point.

EXAMPLE 4: $x + 2 > 3$, x a real number.

Solution: The solution set consists of all the real numbers greater than 1. The graph of the solution set is drawn by placing a hollow dot at 1 on the number line to indicate that this is not a member of the solution set, and drawing a heavily shaded arrow to show that all numbers greater than 1 satisfy the given inequality. The graph is a *half-line*.

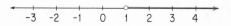

EXAMPLE 5: $x + 2 \geq 3$, x a real number.

Solution: This sentence is read "$x + 2$ is greater than or equal to 3." Thus it is true when $x = 1$, and it is true when $x > 1$. We recognize the graph of the sentence as a *ray*.

EXAMPLE 6: $-2 \leq x \leq 1$, x a real number.

Solution: This sentence is true when x is replaced by any real number *from* -2 *through* 1. The graph is a *line segment*.

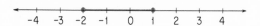

EXAMPLE 7: $-2 < x < 1$, x a real number.

Solution: The solution set consists of all real numbers *between* -2 and 1. The graph is often called an *open line segment* (or *open interval*); that is, a line segment without either of its endpoints.

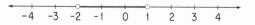

EXAMPLE 8: $-1 < x \leq 3$, x an integer.

Solution: This inequality states that x is greater than -1, but is less than or equal to 3. The solution set consists of the elements $\{0, 1, 2, 3\}$. The graph of the solution set follows:

For the replacement set given in this example, the solution set for $x \leq 3$ is $\{\ldots, -1, 0, 1, 2, 3\}$; the solution set for $-1 < x$ is $\{0, 1, 2, 3, 4, \ldots\}$. Then the solution set for $-1 < x \leq 3$ may be considered as the *intersection* of these two sets.

EXAMPLE 9: $-1 < x \leq 3$, x a real number.

Solution: This is the same sentence as in Example 8 but with a different replacement set. The graph of the solution set now includes all of the points on the number line between -1 and $+3$, including $+3$ but not -1. The graph consists of a line segment with one endpoint but not both. It is neither an open line segment (Example 7) nor a closed line segment (Example 6).

EXAMPLE 10: $x + 3 = 3 + x$, x a real number.

Solution: This sentence is true for all replacements of x. The solution set is the set of all real numbers; the graph of the solution set is the entire number line.

Any sentence that is true for all replacements of its variables is an **identity.** Thus the sentence in Example 10 is an identity.

EXAMPLE 11: $x + 2 = x$, x an integer.

Solution: There is no integer such that the sum of that integer and 2 is equal to the original integer. The solution set is the empty set and has no graph.

We now summarize the concepts considered in this section. An open sentence in one variable divides the replacement set of the variable into two *subsets:* one subset consists of replacements that make the sentence true; the other subset consists of the replacements that make the sentence false. A replacement that makes the sentence true is a *solution* of the sentence. The set of all solutions is the *solution set* of the sentence; the *graph* of an equation or an inequality is the graph of its solution set.

EXERCISES FOR SECTION 7-1

Tell whether each of the following is (**a**) *a statement of equality or a statement of inequality;* (**b**) *a true statement, a false statement, or an open sentence.*

1. $7 \times 8 = 54$

2. $17 + 13 = 30$

3. $\frac{2}{3} < \frac{5}{6}$

4. $\frac{1}{2} > \frac{4}{7}$

5. $\frac{9}{12} > \frac{2}{3}$

6. $\frac{24}{30} < \frac{5}{6}$

7. $7 \times 11 \neq 75$

8. $19 \times 21 = 20^2 - 1$

9. $39 \times 41 = 40^2 - 1$

10. $(x - 1)(x + 1) = x^2 - 1$

11. $8(5 + 3) = 8 \times 5 + 8$

12. $(3) - (2) = (-2) - (3)$

13. $7 - 3 \neq 9 - 5$

14. $\frac{2}{3} - \frac{1}{2} \neq 4\frac{2}{3} - 4\frac{1}{2}$

15. $\frac{432}{796} > \frac{432}{795}$

16. $-\frac{432}{796} < -\frac{432}{795}$

Identify the graph of the solution set of each sentence as a point, a half-line, a ray, a line segment, a line, or the empty set. In each case the replacement set is the set of real numbers.

17. $x - 1 = 3$

18. $x + 2 \leq 5$

19. $x + 2 = x$

20. $x + 5 = 5 + x$

21. $x - 3 > 2$

22. $-2 \leq x \leq 5$

23. $0 \leq x \leq 3$

24. $x + 2 < 7$

25. $x + 1 > x$

26. $5 \leq x + 1$

Graph each sentence for real numbers x:

27. $2x - 1 = 7$

28. $2x < 8$

29. $-3 < x < 2$

30. $-1 \leq x \leq 3$

31. $x + 3 < 7$ **32.** $x - 2 > 1$

33. $x - 1 \geq 2$ **34.** $x + 2 \leq 3$

35. $x - 1 < x$ **36.** $x + 1 \neq 1 + x$

37. $x + 2 \not< 3$ **38.** $-2 < x \leq 2$

***39.** $x^2 \leq 9$ ***40.** $x^2 \geq 9$

SUPPLEMENTARY EXERCISES FOR SECTION 7-1

Occasionally the symbolism $[a, b]$ is used to represent a set of points on a line in the interval from a to b, with both endpoints a and b included in the set. For integral points, $[2, 6] = \{2, 3, 4, 5, 6\}$. For an interval of real numbers, $[2, 6]$ represents all of the real numbers from 2 through 6 inclusive.

We use the symbolism (a, b) to represent the points on the interval from a to b, exclusive of these two endpoints. A combination of these symbols may be used to indicate that one endpoint is included but not the other. Thus $[a, b)$ is used to represent the points in the interval from a to b, including a but not including b. The symbol $[a, b]'$ is used to represent the complement of the interval $[a, b]$.

List and then show on a number line the integral elements in each set:

1. $[2, 4] \cup [1, 5]$ **2.** $[3, 7] \cup [1, 3]$

3. $[2, 5] \cap [3, 7]$ **4.** $[3, 5] \cap (5, 8]$

5. $(2, 5] \cup [3, 7)$ **6.** $[4, 9) \cap [8, 10)$

For each of the following, let $U = [-10, 10]$, an interval of real numbers. Draw the graph of each set and state the results, using the symbolism for intervals of real numbers.

7. $[-2, 3] \cup [2, 5]$ **8.** $[-3, 5] \cap [2, 7]$

9. $(-1, 5] \cap [0, 8)$ **10.** $[-5, 2) \cup [2, 4)$

11. $[-10, 3) \cup (5, 10]$ **12.** $[-5, 2]'$

13. $\{[-7, 2] \cap [3, 5]\}'$ **14.** $[-10, 10]'$

15. $\{[-2, 5] \cup [3, 8]\} \cap \{[-5, 7] \cap [-3, 3]\}$

16. $\{(3, 7] \cap [-1, 2)\} \cup \{[-1, 2] \cap [-2, 1]\}$

7-2 COMPOUND SENTENCES

In Chapter 4 (§4-7) we considered compound statements. Let us now turn our attention to compound sentences in algebra. For example, consider this compound sentence:

$$x + 1 > 2 \quad \text{and} \quad x - 2 < 1$$

The sentence $x + 1 > 2$ is true for all x greater than 1; the sentence $x - 2 < 1$ is true for all x less than 3. Recall that a compound sentence of the form $p \wedge q$ (p and q) is true only when both parts are true. Thus the given compound sentence is true for the set of elements in the *intersection* of the two sets. Graphically we can show this as follows:

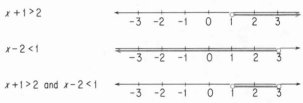

The graph of the compound sentence consists of an open interval and can be described as

$$1 < x < 3.$$

We can conveniently write the solution set of this compound sentence using **set-builder notation** as follows:

$$\{x \mid x > 1\} \cap \{x \mid x < 3\}$$

This is read as "the intersection of the set of all x such that x is greater than 1 and the set of all x such that x is less than 3." Note that no replacement set for x was specified here. When such is the case we shall assume the replacement set to be the set of real numbers.

EXAMPLE 1:   Find the solution set:

$$x \geq -2 \quad \text{and} \quad x + 1 \leq 4; \qquad x \text{ an integer.}$$

Solution: Here we want the set of integers that are greater than or equal to -2 but at the same time are less than or equal to 3. (If $x + 1 \leq 4$, then $x \leq 3$.) The solution set is $\{-2, -1, 0, 1, 2, 3\}$.

EXAMPLE 2:   Find the solution set for the replacement set of real numbers:

$$x + 3 < 5 \quad \text{and} \quad 3 < 1.$$

Solution: You will note that the second part of this sentence $(3 < 1)$ is false. If part of a sentence of the form $p \wedge q$ is false, then, as you may recall, the entire sentence is false. Thus the solution set is the empty set.

Next we consider a compound sentence involving use of the connective "or":

$$x + 1 < 2 \quad \text{or} \quad x - 2 > 1.$$

The sentence $x + 1 < 2$ is true for all x less than 1; the sentence $x - 2 > 1$ is true for all x greater than 3. Recall that a sentence of the form $p \vee q$ (p or q) is true unless both parts are false. Thus the given compound sentence is true for the set of elements in the *union* of the two sets. Graphically we have the following:

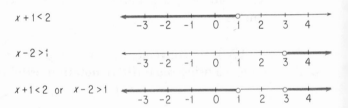

The graph of the compound sentence consists of the union of two half-lines and can be written in set-builder notation as follows:

$$\{x \mid x < 1\} \cup \{x \mid x > 3\}$$

This is read as "the union of the set of all x such that x is less than 1 and the set of all x such that x is greater than 3."

EXAMPLE 3:   Find the solution set for the replacement set of real numbers:

$$5 > 1 \quad \text{or} \quad x + 2 < 5.$$

Solution: Since the first part of this sentence is true, the whole sentence is true. The solution set is the entire set of real numbers.

EXAMPLE 4:   Graph the solution set:

$$x \leq -1 \quad \text{or} \quad x \geq 2.$$

Solution: The graph is the union of two rays.

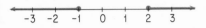

On the number line you should see that there are two points that are at a distance of 3 units from the origin; they have coordinates 3 and -3. We use the symbol $|x|$, read "the *absolute value* of x," to represent the distance of a point from the origin on the number line.

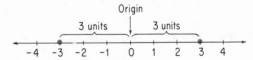

Thus for the diagram shown we may write

$$|3| = 3 \quad \text{and} \quad |-3| = 3.$$

In general, we define the **absolute value** of any real number k as follows:

$$|k| = k, \qquad \text{if } k \text{ is positive;}$$
$$|k| = -k, \qquad \text{if } k \text{ is negative;}$$
$$|k| = 0, \qquad \text{if } k = 0.$$

Notice in the second case that if k represents a negative number, then $-k$ represents a positive number. For example, if $x = -3$, $|-3| = -(-3) = 3$.

A sentence of the form $|x| = 2$ may now be written as a compound sentence:

$$x = 2 \quad \text{or} \quad x = -2.$$

The solution set of the statement $|x| = 2$ is the set of coordinates of points that are on a number line and at a distance of 2 units from the origin. Thus the solution set is $\{2, -2\}$ and is graphed as:

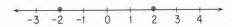

EXAMPLE 5:   Graph the solution set $|x| \geq 2$.

Solution: Here we are to find the set of all points on the number line that are two units or more than two units from the origin.

Note that the solution set of this example can be described by the compound sentence

$$x \leq -2 \quad \text{or} \quad x \geq 2.$$

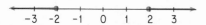

EXAMPLE 6:   Graph the solution set $|x| \leq 2$.

Solution: The graph consists of all the points on the number line that are two units or less than two units from the origin.

The solution set can be described by the compound sentence

$$x \geq -2 \quad \text{and} \quad x \leq 2.$$

EXAMPLE 7:   Find the solution set $|x - 1| = 2$.

Solution: If the absolute value of a number is 2, then that number must be equal to 2 or to -2. That is, the given sentence may be written as this compound sentence:

$$x - 1 = 2 \quad \text{or} \quad x - 1 = -2.$$

If $x - 1 = 2$, then $x = 3$; if $x - 1 = -2$, then $x = -1$. The solution set is $\{3, -1\}$.

EXAMPLE 8:   Find the solution set:

$$\{x \mid (x - 1)(x + 2) = 0\}$$

Solution: The product of two numbers is zero if and only if at least one of the numbers is zero. That is, for all real numbers a and b, if $a \times b = 0$ then $a = 0$, or $b = 0$, or $a = 0$ and $b = 0$. Therefore, if $(x - 1)(x + 2) = 0$, then $x - 1 = 0$ or $x + 2 = 0$. The solution set is $\{1, -2\}$.

EXERCISES FOR SECTION 7-2

List the elements in the solution set for integers x:

1. $x \geq -1$ and $x \leq 2$.   **2.** $x \leq 3$ and $x \geq -2$.

3. $x \leq 0$ or $x > 0$.   **4.** $x \geq -2$ and $x < 0$.

Graph the solution set for real numbers x:

5. $x \leq 2$ and $x \geq -1$.   **6.** $x \geq -2$ and $x \leq 3$.

7. $x > 1$ and $x < 3$.   **8.** $x < 2$ and $x > -3$.

9. $x + 1 < 5$ and $x - 1 > 2$.   **10.** $x + 2 > 2$ and $x - 1 < 3$.

11. $x \leq 0$ or $x \geq 3$.   **12.** $x \geq 2$ or $x \leq -1$.

13. $x > 2$ or $x < -1$.   **14.** $x < -3$ or $x > 1$.

15. $x - 1 > 3$ or $x + 2 < 3$.   **16.** $x + 2 < 0$ or $x - 2 > 1$.'

17. $7 > 5$ and $x - 1 < 2$.   **18.** $2 < 0$ and $x + 3 > 5$.

19. $5 < 0$ or $x \geq 2$.   **20.** $3 > -3$ or $x \leq 2$.

21. $\{x \mid x - 1 < 0\} \cup \{x \mid x + 2 > 5\}$

22. $\{x \mid x + 2 > 0\} \cap \{x \mid x - 2 < 3\}$

23. $\{x \mid (x - 2)(x - 1) = 0\}$ **24.** $\{x \mid (x + 3)(x - 2) = 0\}$

*25. $\{x \mid (x - 3)(x + 2) \geq 0\}$ ***26.** $\{x \mid (x + 2)(x - 3) \leq 0\}$

Evaluate:

27. $|-5|$ **28.** $|-3| + |-7|$

29. $|(-3) + (-7)|$ **30.** $-3 \times |-7|$

Write each sentence as a compound sentence and graph the solution set:

31. $|x| = 3$ **32.** $|x| = 5$

33. $|x| \leq 3$ **34.** $|x| \geq 5$

35. $|x - 2| = 3$ **36.** $|x + 1| = 2$

*37. $|x - 1| \leq 3$ ***38.** $|x + 2| \geq 2$

*39. $-2 < x < 1$ or $|x| = 3$.   ***40.** $1 \leq |x| \leq 5$

7-3 LINEAR SENTENCES IN TWO VARIABLES

An open sentence such as $x + y = 8$ remains an open sentence if a replacement is made for only one of the variables. For example, if x is replaced by 5, the sentence becomes $5 + y = 8$, which is an open sentence. Thus, a *pair* of replacements is needed for an open sentence in two variables before we can determine whether it is true or false for these replacements.

If x is replaced by 5 and y is replaced by 3, the sentence $x + y = 8$ is true. Usually we think of the variables as an *ordered pair* (x, y) and speak of the replacements as an ordered pair of numbers $(5, 3)$. By convention the variable x is assumed to be the first of the two variables, and the first number in the ordered pair of numbers is taken as the replacement for x; the variable y is then taken as the second variable, and the second number in the ordered pair is taken as the replacement for y. For example, the ordered pair $(3, 2)$ implies that $x = 3$ and $y = 2$; the ordered pair $(2, 3)$ implies that $x = 2$ and $y = 3$.

The sentence $x + y = 8$ is true or false for certain ordered pairs of numbers. It is true for $(5, 3)$; it is false for $(2, 7)$. The solution set for the sentence $x + y = 8$ is a set of ordered pairs of numbers for which the sentence is true. This solution set of the sentence may be indicated in the set-builder notation as follows:

$$\{(x, y) \mid x + y = 8\}$$

This is read as "the set of ordered pairs (x, y) such that $x + y = 8$:" The solution set for any sentence in two variables is a set of ordered pairs.

Just as was the case with sentences in one variable, the solution set of a sentence in two variables depends upon the replacement sets of the variables used. For example, if the replacement set for x and y is the set of counting numbers, then the solution set for $x + y$ is

$$\{(1, 7), (2, 6), (3, 5), (4, 4), (5, 3), (6, 2), (7, 1)\}.$$

EXAMPLE 1:   Find the solution set for the sentence $x + y \leq 2$ if the replacement set for x and for y is the set of whole numbers.

Solution: When $x = 0$, y must be less than or equal to 2. When $x = 1$, y must be less than or equal to 1. When $x = 2$, $y = 0$. Can $x = 3$? The solution set is $\{(0, 0), (0, 1), (0, 2), (1, 0), (1, 1), (2, 0)\}$.

A set of ordered pairs may be obtained from any set of numbers. For example, consider the set of numbers

$$U = \{1, 2, 3\}.$$

Then the set of all ordered pairs of numbers from U consists of those pairs of numbers whose members are both elements of U. This set of ordered pairs is called the **Cartesian product** of U and U, is written as $U \times U$, and is read "U cross U." The set of all ordered pairs whose coordinates belong to the given set U is

$$\{(1, 1), (1, 2), (1, 3), (2, 1), (2, 2), (2, 3), (3, 1), (3, 2), (3, 3)\}.$$

The graph of $U \times U$ is given by the nine points in the accompanying figure; such a set of points is sometimes called a **lattice**.

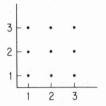

We may now use this figure to graph the solution sets of sentences for this given universe. For example, the solution set of $y = x$ for $U = \{1, 2, 3\}$ is $\{(1, 1), (2, 2), (3, 3)\}$. The graph of this solution set—that is, the graph of the sentence—is indicated by large dots at the points that correspond to these ordered pairs.

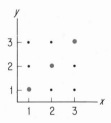

Graphs of sentences for other universal sets are discussed in the examples that follow. For each we are to draw the graph of the solution set.

EXAMPLE 2: $\{(x, y) \mid y = x + 1\}$; $U = \{1, 2, 3, 4\}$.

Solution: Here the set of possible replacements consists of a set of 16 ordered pairs of numbers; that is, a lattice of 16 points. The set of ordered pairs that make the sentence true, the solution set, is

$$\{(1, 2), (2, 3), (3, 4)\}.$$

These ordered pairs are indicated by large dots in the accompanying graph of the solution set.

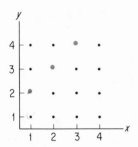

EXAMPLE 3: $\{(x, y) \mid x + y \geq 6\}$; $U = \{1, 2, 3, 4\}$.

Solution :   For $x = 1$, there is no value for y that is in the set U and such that this inequality is satisfied. For $x = 2$, $y = 4$; for $x = 3$, $y = 3$ or 4; and for $x = 4$, $y = 2, 3,$ or 4. The solution set is

$$\{(2, 4), (3, 3), (3, 4), (4, 2), (4, 3), (4, 4)\}.$$

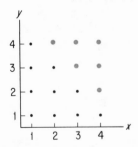

EXAMPLE 4: $\{(x, y) \mid y \geq x + 2\}$;

$$U = \{-3, -2, -1, 0, 1, 2, 3\}.$$

Solution: The set of ordered pairs $U \times U$ is represented by a lattice of 49 points. Before graphing the given inequality, it is helpful to consider first the corresponding statement of equality, $y = x + 2$. The solution set is $\{(x, y) \mid y = x + 2\} = \{(-3, -1), (-2, 0), (-1, 1), (0, 2), (1, 3)\}$.

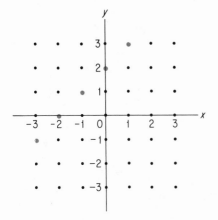

The graph of $y \geq x + 2$ consists of all the points that are solutions of $y = x + 2$, as well as all of the points in $U \times U$ that are above the points of the graph of $y = x + 2$.

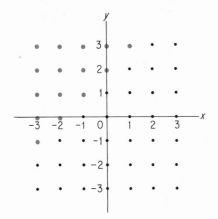

The lattice of points used need not be a square one. Thus, consider the following sets of numbers:

$$A = \{1, 2, 3\}$$
$$B = \{1, 2\}$$

Then $A \times B = \{(1, 1), (1, 2), (2, 1), (2, 2), (3, 1), (3, 2)\}$.

EXAMPLE 5: $\{(x, y) \mid y \geq x\}$; the replacement set for x is $\{1, 2, 3\}$ and the replacement set for y is $\{1, 2\}$.

Solution:

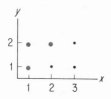

$$\{(x, y) \mid y \geq x\} = \{(1, 1), (1, 2), (2, 2)\}.$$

EXERCISES FOR SECTION 7-3

1. Let $U = \{1, 2\}$ and list the elements in $U \times U$.

2. Let $A = \{1, 2\}$ and $B = \{1, 2, 3\}$ and list the elements in $A \times B$.

Find the solution set for each sentence for the replacement set of whole numbers for x and for y:

3. $x + y = 3$ **4.** $x + y = 5$

5. $x + y < 3$ **6.** $x + y \leq 4$

List the elements in each solution set for $U = \{1, 2, 3\}$:

7. $y = x + 1$ **8.** $x + y = 3$

9. $y < x$ **10.** $y \geq x$

Graph each solution set on a plane lattice where $U = \{1, 2, 3, 4\}$:

11. $\{(x, y) \mid x + y = 5\}$ **12.** $\{(x, y) \mid y = x - 1\}$

13. $\{(x, y) \mid y \leq x - 1\}$ **14.** $\{(x, y) \mid y < x\}$

15. $\{(x, y) \mid y \geq x\}$ **16.** $\{(x, y) \mid y \geq x + 1\}$

Graph each solution set with $U = \{-3, -2, -1, 0, 1, 2, 3\}$:

17. $\{(x, y) \mid y = x\}$ 18. $\{(x, y) \mid y \leq x\}$

19. $\{(x, y) \mid x - y = 1\}$ 20. $\{(x, y) \mid y - x = 2\}$

21. $\{(x, y) \mid y < x - 1\}$ 22. $\{(x, y) \mid y \geq x\}$

23. $\{(x, y) \mid x + y = 7\}$ *24. $\{(x, y) \mid y \geq |x|\}$

7-4 GRAPHS ON A PLANE

In §7-3 we made use of finite coordinate systems to draw the graphs of linear sentences in two variables. Now we make the extension of U to the set of real numbers, and $U \times U$ becomes an infinite collection of ordered pairs of numbers. The graph of $U \times U$ consists of an entire plane and in honor of René Descartes is referred to as the **Cartesian plane.** Each point of a Cartesian plane can be represented by (has as its **coordinates**) an ordered pair of real numbers, and each ordered pair of real numbers can be used to identify (locate) a unique point of the plane. We speak of "the point with coordinates (x, y)" as "the point (x, y)."

For the universe of real numbers statements in one variable may be graphed on a line; statements in two variables may be graphed on a plane. Consider, for example, the sentence $y = x - 1$. We may list in a **table of values** several ordered pairs of numbers that are solutions of the sentence. Thus for $x = -1, y = -1 - 1 = -2$ and for $x = 3, y = 3 - 1 = 2$. Other pairs are given in the table.

$y = x - 1$:

x	-3	-2	-1	0	1	2	3
y	-4	-3	-2	-1	0	1	2

Each ordered pair of numbers (x, y) from the table can then be graphed and connected in the order of the x-coordinates. The graph of $y = x - 1$ is a straight line and extends indefinitely as indicated by the arrowheads, although often these arrowheads are omitted.

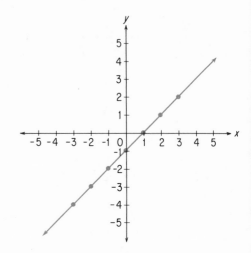

When the graph of a sentence is a straight line, the sentence is called a **linear equation** and may be expressed in the form

$$ax + by + c = 0,$$

where a and b are not both zero. Thus, for example, the sentence $y = x - 1$ may be written as $x - y - 1 = 0$ and is a linear equation.

Inasmuch as a straight line is determined by two points, we can graph a linear equation after locating just two of its points. (It is usually wise to locate a third point as a check of your work.) When $a \neq 0$ and $b \neq 0$ the most convenient points to locate are the points where the graph crosses the x-axis and crosses the y-axis. The graph of $y = x - 1$ crosses the x-axis when $y = 0$; that is, at the point A: $(1, 0)$, where 1 is the **x-intercept** of the graph. The graph of $y = x - 1$ crosses the y-axis when $x = 0$; that is, at the point B: $(0, -1)$, where -1 is the **y-intercept** of the graph.

EXAMPLE 1: Find the x-intercept and the y-intercept of the graph of $2x + 3y - 6 = 0$.

Solution: When $y = 0$, we have $2x - 6 = 0$ and $x = 3$. The x-intercept is 3, and the graph crosses the x-axis at the point $(3, 0)$. When $x = 0$, we have $3y - 6 = 0$ and $y = 2$. The y-intercept is 2, and the graph crosses the y-axis at the point $(0, 2)$.

EXAMPLE 2:   Graph $\{(x, y) \mid 2x + 3y - 6 = 0\}$.

Solution: Note that, as for statements in one variable, when no universal set is specified we assume the universe to be the set of real numbers. Using the information from Example 1, we have the following graph:

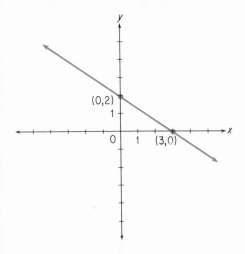

Statements of inequality can also be graphed for the universe of real numbers. Consider the sentence $y > x + 1$. It is helpful to draw first the graph of the corresponding statement of equality, $y = x + 1$. We draw this graph as a dotted line, since its points are not part of the graph of $y > x + 1$.

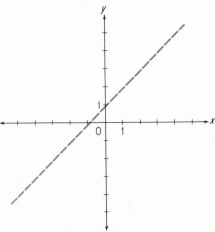

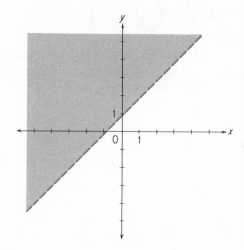

The line $y = x + 1$ divides the plane into two half-planes. Since we wish to show all the values of y *greater than* $x + 1$, we shade the half-plane that is *above* the line to represent the solution set.

To draw the graph of $y \geq x + 1$ we would have the same picture, except that the line $y = x + 1$ would then be drawn solid. The sentence $y \geq x + 1$ can be thought of as the compound sentence

$$y > x + 1 \quad \text{or} \quad y = x + 1$$

and is thus the union of the half-plane and the line.

EXAMPLE 3: Graph $y \leq x - 1$.

Solution: The graph of this statement consists of all the points on the line $y = x - 1$, as well as the points in the half-plane

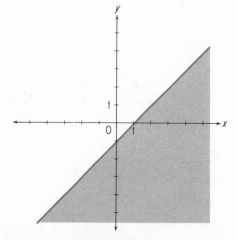

below the line, as indicated by the shaded portion of the graph. That is, the sentence $y \leq x - 1$ can be thought of as the compound sentence

$$y < x - 1 \quad \text{or} \quad y = x - 1.$$

Not all sentences with two variables have graphs that are straight lines—only those sentences that can be written in the form $ax + by + c = 0$. In §7-2 we considered graphs of sentences in one variable that involved absolute value. Now let us explore sentences with two variables that involve absolute value, such as $y = |x|$. As an aid to graphing this sentence for the universe of real numbers we first consider the graph for $U = \{-3, -2, -1, 0, 1, 2, 3\}$. The values to be graphed are summarized in this table of values.

x	-3	-2	-1	0	1	2	3
y	3	2	1	0	1	2	3

These ordered pairs (x, y) such that $y = |x|$ can be graphed on $U \times U$ as follows:

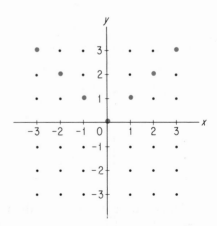

If U is the set of real numbers, our graph consists of an infinite collection of points. Using the preceding graph as a guide, we are now able to graph $y = |x|$ for the set of real numbers as follows:

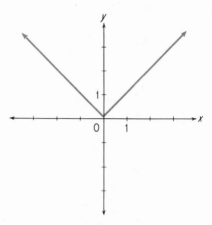

EXAMPLE 4:   Graph $\{(x, y) \mid y = |x + 1|\}$.

Solution: Recall that we assume the universal set to be the set of real numbers unless otherwise specified.

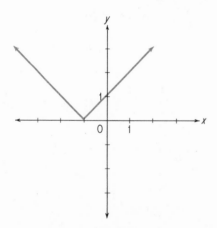

Notice that if $x = -1$, then $y = 0$; if $x = 0$ or -2, then $y = 1$; if $x = 1$ or -3, then $y = 2$; and so forth.

EXAMPLE 5:   Graph $\{(x, y) \mid y \geq |x + 1|\}$.

Solution: From Example 4 we know the graph of $y = |x + 1|$.
The graph of $y \geq |x + 1|$ is completed by shading in the portion
of the plane above the graph as shown.

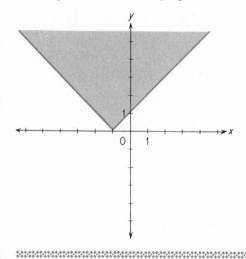

In summary, any sentence in two variables can be considered as
a *set selector*. The set of ordered pairs selected is a *subset* of $U \times U$.
If U is the set of real numbers, the solution set corresponds to the set
of points satisfying a given condition on a coordinate plane. Thus,
the graph of an equation or inequality is commonly called the **locus**
of the equation or inequality; that is, the locus is the set of points
that correspond to the solution set. Accordingly, we shall speak of
graphing a statement and mean thereby the graphing of the solution
set for the statement.

EXERCISES FOR SECTION 7-4

For the graph of each sentence, find (**a**) *the x-intercept;* (**b**) *the y-intercept:*

1. $x + y = 4$ 2. $x - y = 4$

3. $y = 2x + 4$ 4. $y = x - 2$

5. $2x + 3y = 12$ 6. $3x - 2y = 6$

7. $x + 2y - 4 = 0$ 8. $2x - y + 6 = 0$

Copy and complete each table of values for the given equations:

9. $y = x + 2$

x	-3	-2	-1	0	1	2	3
y							

10. $y = x - 2$

x	-3	-2	-1	0	1	2	3
y							

11. $y = |x| + 1$

x	-3	-2	-1	0	1	2	3
y							

12. $y = |x| - 1$

x	-3	-2	-1	0	1	2	3
y							

Graph each solution set for the universe of real numbers:

13. $y = x - 2$
14. $y = x + 2$
15. $x + y = 4$
16. $x - y = 4$
17. $x + y - 5 = 0$
18. $x - y + 5 = 0$
19. $2x + y - 4 = 0$
20. $x - 2y + 4 = 0$
21. $y \geq x$
22. $y \leq x - 2$
23. $y \leq x + 2$
24. $y \geq x + 3$
25. $\{(x, y) \mid y = |x - 1|\}$
26. $\{(x, y) \mid y = |x + 2|\}$
27. $\{(x, y) \mid y \leq |x|\}$
28. $\{(x, y) \mid y > |x|\}$
29. $\{(x, y) \mid y \geq |x| + 1\}$
30. $\{(x, y) \mid y \leq |x| - 2\}$
31. $\{(x, y) \mid y = 2\}$
32. $\{(x, y) \mid x = -3\}$

SUPPLEMENTARY EXERCISES FOR SECTION 7-4

Graph each statement on a plane lattice where $U = \{1, 2, 3, 4\}$:

1. $\{(x, y) \mid y = x^2\}$
2. $\{(x, y) \mid y > x^2\}$
3. $\{(x, y) \mid y < (x + 1)^2\}$
4. $\{(x, y) \mid y < x^3 - 1\}$

Graph each statement when U *is the set of real numbers:*

5. $\{(x, y) \mid y = x^2\}$
6. $\{(x, y) \mid y = x^2 + 2\}$
7. $\{(x, y) \mid y = x^2 - 1\}$
8. $\{(x, y) \mid y \geq x^2\}$

9. $\{(x, y) \mid x^2 + y^2 = 9\}$ 10. $\{(x, y) \mid x^2 + y^2 = 25\}$

*11. $\{(x, y) \mid y > x^2 \text{ and } x \geq 0\}$

*12. $\{(x, y) \mid x^2 + y^2 \leq 9 \text{ and } y \geq 0\}$

7-5 RELATIONS AND FUNCTIONS

A **relation** may be defined as any subset of $U \times U$; thus, a relation is a set of ordered pairs of numbers. It is most often defined as a rule. Consider, for example, $\{(x, y) \mid y > x - 1\}$, where $U = \{1, 2, 3\}$. This solution set, which *is* the relation, is $\{(1, 1), (1, 2), (1, 3), (2, 2), (2, 3), (3, 3)\}$. It may be graphed as in the accompanying figure.

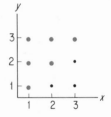

The relation may be defined by the rule, by the graph, or by a table of values for the variable:

x	1	1	1	2	2	3
y	1	2	3	2	3	3

Here is the table and graph for another relation:

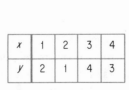

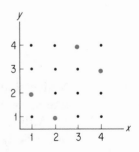

x	1	2	3	4
y	2	1	4	3

This relation is the set of ordered pairs $\{(1, 2), (2, 1), (3, 4), (4, 3)\}$. Note that this second relation differs from the first in that, for any

value of x, there is at most one value for y. We call this special type
of relation a *function*.

A **function** is a set of ordered pairs (x, y) such that for each value
of x there is at most one value of y; that is, no first element appears
with more than one second element. You may think of the first
element as the **independent variable** and the second element as the
dependent variable. Each variable has a set of possible values. The
set of all first elements of the ordered pairs of numbers is called the
domain of the function; the set of all second elements is called the
range of the function. In terms of its graph, any vertical line drawn
meets the graph of a function in at most one point.

Here are the graphs of two relations that are also functions:

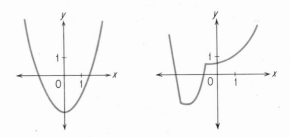

Notice that no vertical line intersects the graph in more than one
point.

Here are the graphs of two relations that are not functions:

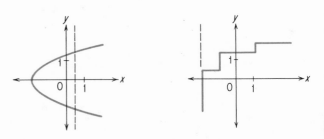

Notice that in each case there exists at least one vertical line that
intersects the graph in two or more points.

Although formulas such as $y = x^2$ may *define* a function, they are
not strictly functions. We have defined the function to be a set of
ordered pairs (x, y), such as those obtained from the formula $y = x^2$
for the real variable x. Thus, a formula may provide a rule by which
the function may be determined. In other words, a formula may

provide a means for associating a unique element in the range with each element in the domain.

When a formula such as $y = x^2 - 2x + 3$ is used to define a function, it is customary to think of y as *a function of* x and to write the formula in **functional notation**:

$$y = f(x)$$

where

$$f(x) = x^2 - 2x + 3.$$

Then the value of y for any value b of x may be expressed as $f(b)$. For example,

$$\begin{aligned}
f(2) &= 2^2 - 2(2) + 3 = 3; \\
f(-1) &= (-1)^2 - 2(-1) + 3 = 6; \\
f(0) &= 0^2 - 2(0) + 3 = 3; \\
f(1) &= 1^2 - 2(1) + 3 = 2.
\end{aligned}$$

Notice that for the function $f(x) = (x - 1)^2 + 2$, the domain of the function is the set of all real numbers, and the range of the function is the set of real numbers greater than or equal to 2. The range may be determined from the graph of the function or from the observation that since $(x - 1)^2 \geq 0$ we must have $(x - 1)^2 + 2 \geq 2$. Other letters, as in $g(x)$ and $h(y)$, may be used in designating functions.

EXAMPLE 1:   Graph the function $y = x^2 - 1$ and identify the domain and range of this function.

Solution: The variable x may assume any real number as a value. Thus the domain is the set of real numbers. The range is the set of real numbers greater than or equal to -1; that is, as in the graph, $y \geq -1$.

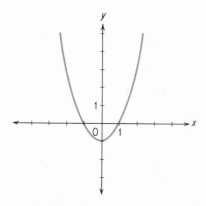

EXAMPLE 2: Find the domain and range of $y = |x|$.

Solution: Domain: set of real numbers. Range: set of non-negative real numbers; that is, $y \geq 0$.

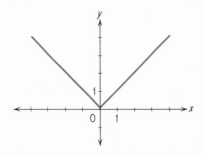

EXAMPLE 3: Which of these formulas define functions? (a) $y = x^3$; (b) $x = y^2$; (c) $x^2 + y^2 = 9$; (d) $y = (x + 1)^2$.

Solution: From the graphs we note that the formulas in (a) and (d) define functions.

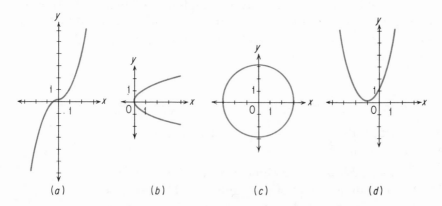

Given any relation, the **inverse relation** is the set of ordered pairs obtained by interchanging the elements of each of the ordered pairs of the given relation. Thus, suppose we are given the relation

$$R = \{(2, 1), (3, 2), (4, 3), (4, 5)\}.$$

The inverse relation of R then consists of the set of ordered pairs

$$\{(1, 2), (2, 3), (3, 4), (5, 4)\}.$$

In a similar manner, we may find the inverse of a function, inasmuch as a function is nothing more than a special type of relation. That is, the inverse of a function is obtained by interchanging the elements of each of the ordered pairs of numbers that comprise the function. The inverse of a function is a relation; however, it may or may not be a function. It will be a function if and only if, for each y of the original function, we have at most one x.

EXAMPLE 4:   Find the inverse of the function
$$F = \{(1, 2), (2, 3), (3, 4)\}.$$
Solution: The inverse of this function is another function F', where
$$F' = \{(2, 1), (3, 2), (4, 3)\}.$$

EXAMPLE 5:   Find the inverse of the function
$$A = \{(1, 3), (2, 4), (3, 4), (4, 7)\}.$$
Solution: The inverse A' of this function is a relation, but it is not a function;
$$A' = \{(3, 1), (4, 2), (4, 3), (7, 4)\}.$$

If a relation is given by a formula, then a formula for its inverse may be obtained by interchanging the variables.

EXAMPLE 6:   Find a formula for the inverse of the function
$$F = \{(x, y) \mid y = 2x\}.$$
Solution: The inverse of F is $F' = \{(x, y) \mid x = 2y\}$. We may also write it as $F' = \left\{(x, y) \mid y = \dfrac{x}{2}\right\}$. Here the inverse of the given function is also a function.

EXAMPLE 7:   Find the inverse of $F = \{(x, y) \mid y = x^2\}$.

Solution: $\{(x, y) \mid x = y^2\}$. We may also write the solution as $\{(x, y) \mid y = \pm\sqrt{x}\}$. Note that the inverse of the given function is a relation but it is not a function. Explain why not.

EXERCISES FOR SECTION 7-5

1. If $f(x) = x - 2$, find **(a)** $f(1)$; **(b)** $f(2)$; **(c)** $f(17)$.
2. If $f(x) = x^2 - 4x + 5$, find **(a)** $f(0)$; **(b)** $f(2)$; **(c)** $f(-3)$.
3. If $g(x) = x^3 - 7$, find **(a)** $g(2)$; **(b)** $g(-1)$; **(c)** $g(-2)$.
4. If $f(x) = |x| + x$, find **(a)** $f(-2)$; **(b)** $f(0)$; **(c)** $f(3)$.

Graph each relation, identify the relations that are functions, and state the domain and range for each one that is a function. In each case $U = \{1, 2, 3\}$.

5. $y = x$ 6. $y = x + 1$
7. $y < x$ 8. $y < x + 1$

Proceed as in Exercises 5 through 8 for the universe of real numbers:

9. $y = x + 1$ 10. $y = x - 1$
11. $y \geq |x - 1|$ 12. $y = |x + 1|$
13. $y = |x| + 1$ 14. $y = |x| - 1$
15. $y \geq x$ 16. $y \leq x - 1$
*17. $y = -x^2$ *18. $y = (x + 1)^2$

Find the inverse of each function. Tell whether or not the inverse is a function.

19. $F = \{(1, 1), (2, 2), (3, 3)\}$ 20. $F = \{(1, 2), (2, 2), (3, 2)\}$
21. $F = \{(1, 3), (2, 4), (3, 4)\}$ 22. $F = \{(1, 3), (2, 2), (3, 1)\}$
23. $F = \{(x, y) \mid y = x + 1\}$ 24. $F = \{(x, y) \mid y = x - 2\}$

Graph each function as a dotted curve and the inverse of the function as a solid curve. State whether or not the inverse of each function is a function.

25. $y = x + 2$ 26. $y = x - 2$
27. $y = x$ 28. $y = 2x$
*29. $y = x^2$ *30. $y = |x|$

7-6 LINEAR PROGRAMMING

Graphs of linear statements in two variables provide a very important tool for solving modern problems. Although mathematicians are developing theories for statements that are not necessarily linear, we shall consider only the linear case. Thus we assume that the conditions of a problem have been represented by or approximated by linear statements. Then the solution of the problem depends upon the solution of a system (that is, a set) of linear statements. The usual method of solution is by graphing; that is, the method is geometrical. Accordingly, we first consider two examples of graphs of systems of linear statements in two real variables.

EXAMPLE 1:   Graph the system $x \geq 0, y \geq 0, y \geq x - 1$.

Solution: The solution set of the given system consists of the ordered pairs of real numbers (x, y) that satisfy all three of the statements. To graph the system, we graph each one of the three statements and then take the intersection of their graphs.

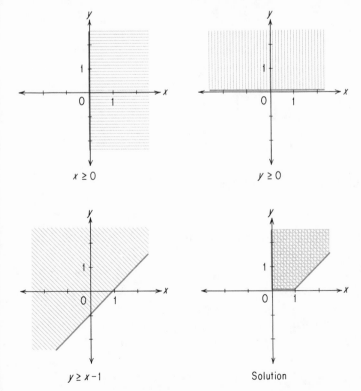

$x \geq 0$

$y \geq 0$

$y \geq x - 1$

Solution

As in §7-4 we graph an inequality by first graphing the equality (using a solid line if its graph is part of the solution set, a dashed line otherwise).

EXAMPLE 2:   Graph the system

$$x \geq 0; y \geq 0; x \leq 6; y \leq 7; x + y \leq 10.$$

Solution:

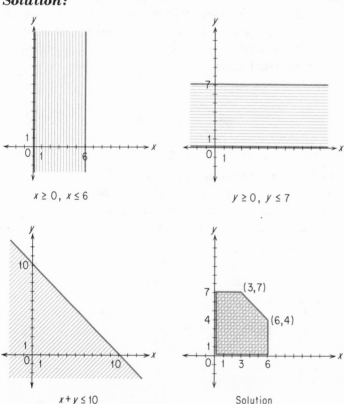

In Examples 1 and 2 the solutions of the systems of statements are known as **polygonal convex sets.**

In a linear programming problem we not only must set up our conditions, but we also must maximize or minimize an expression for profit, cost, or other quantity. Suppose the conditions for Example 2 represent the manufacture of x metal boxes and y glass jars in a given time, and $x + 2y$ represents the manufacturer's profit. If the manu-

facturer wishes to have a profit of $14, we then graph the equation
$x + 2y = 14$ over the conditions of Example 2.

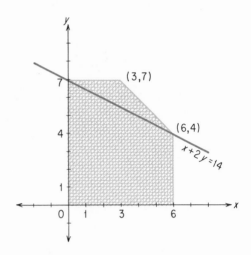

Note that there are now many ways in which the manufacturer
can earn a profit of $14. In particular, consider the points $(0, 7)$ and
$(6, 4)$. Thus he can earn $14 by manufacturing 0 metal boxes and
7 glass jars, or 6 metal boxes and 4 glass jars. Indeed, any point on
the line $x + 2y = 14$ that is within the polygonal region represents an
ordered pair (x, y) under the stated restrictions, and such that the
profit is $14.

Next consider the same example, but this time we wish the profit
to be k. For each value k the graph of $x + 2y = k$ is a straight line.
As k takes on different values, we have a set of parallel lines. When
several of these lines are graphed with the solution of the conditions
in Example 2, we see that under these conditions k may have any
value from 0 to 17 inclusive. The maximum (largest) value that is
possible for k under these conditions is 17 and occurs at $(3, 7)$. The
minimum (smallest) possible value for k is 0 and occurs at $(0, 0)$.
Recall that the conditions are for the manufacture of x metal boxes
and y glass jars in a given time and that $x + 2y$ represents the manufacturer's profit. Then if we assume that the manufacturer can sell
all that he can make, he would make the most profit by manufac-
turing 3 boxes and 7 jars per unit of time.

In any linear programming problem the maximum and minimum
always occur at a vertex (possibly at two vertices; that is, along a
side) of the polygonal region. Intuitively, the reason is that the region
is convex and thus the lines of a set of parallel lines first intersect the

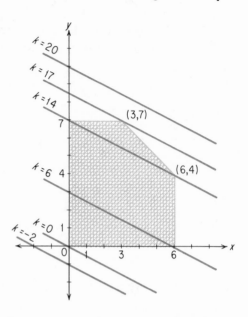

region either by passing through a vertex, as in our example, or by passing along a side of the region. Accordingly, in our example, we could have found the maximum value of $x + 2y$ for points of the region by testing the values corresponding to the vertices $(0, 0)$, $(6, 0)$, $(6, 4)$, $(3, 7)$, and $(0, 7)$ of the region. The corresponding values of $x + 2y$ are 0, 6, 14, 17, and 14, respectively. Thus, as we observed before, the minimum value of $x + 2y$ is 0 and occurs as $(0, 0)$; the maximum value of $x + 2y$ is 17 and occurs at $(3, 7)$.

EXAMPLE 3: Graph the system

$$x \geq 0; \; x \leq 3; \; y \leq 0; \; x - y \leq 5.$$

Solution:

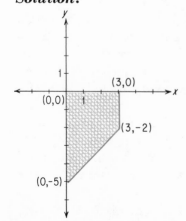

EXAMPLE 4:   Find the minimum and maximum values of the function $2x + y$ defined over the system of Example 3.

Solution: Call the function f. Then at $(0, 0)$, $f = 0$; at $(0, -5)$, $f = -5$; at $(3, 0)$, $f = 6$; at $(3, -2)$, $f = 4$. The minimum value, -5, occurs at $(0, -5)$. The maximum value, 6, occurs at $(3, 0)$.

EXAMPLE 5:   A manufacturer produces gidgets and gadgets, and has his machines in operation 24 hours a day. To produce a gidget requires 2 hours of work on machine A and 6 hours of work on machine B. It takes 6 hours of work on machine A and 2 hours on machine B to produce a gadget. The manufacturer earns a profit of \$5 on each gidget and \$2 on each gadget. How many of each should he produce each day in order to earn the maximum profit possible?

Solution: If we let x represent the number of gidgets to be produced, and y the number of gadgets, then the conditions of the problem may be stated and graphed as follows:

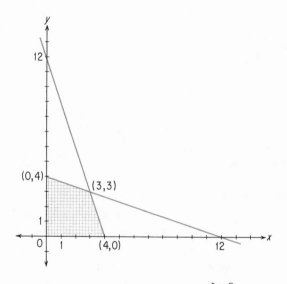

$$x \geq 0$$
$$y \geq 0$$
$$2x + 6y \leq 24$$
$$6x + 2y \leq 24$$
$$\text{Profit} = P = 5x + 2y$$

We test the profit expression, $5x + 2y$, at the vertices of the polygon. At $(0, 0)$, $P = 0$; at $(0, 4)$, $P = 8$; at $(3, 3)$, $P = 21$; and at $(4, 0)$, $P = 20$. Thus to insure a maximum profit, the manufacturer should produce 3 gidgets and 3 gadgets daily.

EXERCISES FOR SECTION 7-6

Graph each system:

   1. $x \geq 2$; $x \leq 4$; $y \geq 0$; $x + y \leq 5$.

   2. $x \geq 0$; $y \geq 0$; $x + 3y \leq 9$; $2x + y \leq 8$.

Find the values of x and y such that under the set of conditions in the specified exercise the given expression has (**a**) *a maximum value;* (**b**) *a minimum value:*

   3. $x + 2y$; Exercise 1.

   4. $3x + y$; Exercise 1.

   5. $x + y$; Exercise 2.

   6. $x + 5y$; Exercise 2.

Use linear programming to solve these hypothetical problems:

   7. A college is experimenting with a combination of teaching methods, using both teachers in the classroom and closed-circuit television. The college has facilities for handling five sections of a class at once using closed-circuit television. For the five sections of a class that meets three clock hours per week, the conditions appear to be as follows: The cost per minute of regular teaching is $5; the cost per minute of closed-circuit television is $3. For a certain week at most $750 can be spent on the instruction of these classes. Assume that the class hour can be spent in part with a teacher and in part with television. When neither the teacher nor the television is on, the students are free to discuss anything they wish. If the value to the students of x minutes of regular teaching and y minutes of closed-circuit television may be expressed as $3x + 2y$, how many minutes of regular teaching and how many minutes of closed-circuit television would be best for the students during the week?

   8. Repeat Exercise 7 with the additional condition that the instructor must be present at least 30 minutes each week.

9. Use the conditions as for Exercise 8 and find the number of minutes of regular teaching and of closed-circuit television when the value to the students may be expressed as $x + 2y$.

10. Repeat Exercise 9 when the value to the students may be expressed as $2x + y$.

TEST FOR CHAPTER 7

1. Identify the graph of the solution set as a point, a half-line, a line segment, a line, or the empty set.

(a) $x + 2 > 5$ (b) $x + 3 > x$
(c) $-2 \leq x \leq 1$ (d) $x - 3 \leq 5$

Graph the solution set for real numbers x:

2. (a) $x - 2 \geq 1$ (b) $-2 < x \leq 3$
3. (a) $x \leq 1$ and $x \geq -2$ (b) $x \leq -2$ or $x > 1$
4. (a) $|x| = 4$ (b) $|x| \leq 1$
5. Graph each solution set for $U = \{1, 2, 3\}$:

(a) $\{(x, y) \mid y = x + 1\}$ (b) $\{(x, y) \mid y > x\}$

Graph each solution set for the universe of real numbers:

6. (a) $y = x - 3$ (b) $x + y = 1$
7. (a) $y \geq x - 2$ (b) $y < |x|$

8. If $f(x) = x^2 + 2x - 3$, find (a) $f(-2)$; (b) $f(1)$.

9. Find the inverse of each function. Tell whether or not the inverse is a function.

(a) $F = \{(1, 3), (2, 5), (3, 5)\}$
(b) $F = \{(1, 4), (2, 3), (3, 2)\}$

10. Graph each function and tell its domain and range:

(a) $y = x - 1$ (b) $y = |x - 1|$

chapter 8

AN INTRODUCTION
TO PROBABILITY

We make frequent reference to probability in everyday language. For example, we say, "It probably will rain," "The odds are in his favor," and make similar comments about many things.

Ever since the fifteenth century, mathematicians have been exploring the topic of probability. Interestingly enough, the subject is said to have had its foundation in the realm of gambling and to have arisen from a discussion of the distribution of stakes in an unfinished game. Probabilities are still used to understand games of chance such as the tossing of coins, throwing of dice, or drawing of lottery tickets. Probabilities are also used extensively by persons who are concerned with the cost of insurance (based upon rates of mortality), the construction of various polls such as the Gallup Poll to appraise public opinion, and numerous other types of statistical studies. The topics in this chapter provide a basis for understanding probabilities and their applications to real life situations.

8-1 COUNTING PROBLEMS

Many problems depend for their solution upon an enumeration of all possible outcomes. Thus, the simple task of counting becomes an important one in the study of probability. To illustrate various problems in this chapter, we shall invent a fictitious club consisting of a set M of members:

$$M = \{\text{Betty, Doris, Ellen, John, Tom}\}$$

Let us form a committee that is to consist of one boy and one girl, each selected from the set M of club members. How many such committees are possible? One way to answer this question is by means of a tree diagram, which helps list each of the possibilities.

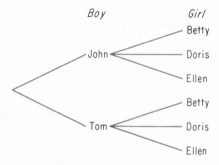

For each of the two possible choices of a boy, there are three possible choices of a girl. Thus the following six distinct possible committees can be formed and can be read from the tree diagram:

John–Betty	Tom–Betty
John–Doris	Tom–Doris
John–Ellen	Tom–Ellen

Suppose that we had selected a girl first. Then the **tree diagram** would be as shown in the next figure and there would still be six possibilities, the same six committees as before.

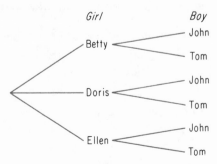

EXAMPLE 1: In how many different ways can two officers, a president and a vice-president, be elected from the set M of club members?

Solution: Let us select the officers in two stages. There are five possible choices for the office of president. Each of these five selections may be paired with any one of the remaining four members. Thus there are 20 possible choices in all, which can be read from the following diagram.

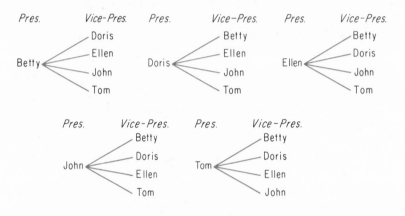

In general, if one task can be performed in m different ways and a second task can be performed in n different ways, then the first and second tasks together can be performed in $m \times n$ different ways. This general principle can be extended if there are additional tasks:

$$m \times n \times r \times \cdots \times t$$

EXAMPLE 2: The club members M must send a delegate to a meeting tomorrow and also a delegate to a different meeting next week. In how many ways may these delegates be selected if any member of the club may serve as a delegate to each meeting?

Solution: There are five possible choices of a delegate to the first meeting. Since no restriction is made, we assume that the same member may attend each of the two meetings. Thus, there are five choices for the delegate to next week's meeting. In all, there are 5×5; that is, 25 choices. A tree diagram may be used to show this.

EXAMPLE 3:   How many three-letter "words" may be formed from the set of vowels $V = \{a, e, i, o, u\}$ if no letter may be used more than once? (A word in this sense is any arrangement of three letters, such as aeo, iou, etc.)

Solution: There are five choices for the first letter, four for the second, and three for the third. In all, there are $5 \times 4 \times 3$; that is, 60 possible "words." Notice that 125 words would be possible if repetitions of letters were permitted.

EXERCISES FOR SECTION 8-1

1. How many three-letter "words" may be formed from the set $R = \{m, a, t, h, s\}$ if (**a**) no letter may be used more than once? (**b**) repetitions of letters are permitted?

2. Repeat Exercise 1 for four-letter words.

3. Bob has four sport shirts and three pairs of slacks. Assuming that he can wear any combination of these, how many different outfits can he assemble?

4. Jane has five dresses, three hats, and four pairs of shoes. Assuming that she can wear any combination of these, how many different outfits can she assemble?

5. A baseball team has six pitchers and four catchers. How many different batteries consisting of a pitcher and a catcher can they form?

6. Show, by means of a tree diagram, the number of different routes from New York to Los Angeles, via Chicago, if you can go from New York to Chicago by one train or one plane, and from Chicago to Los Angeles by one train, one plane, or one bus.

7. How many different two-digit numbers may be formed from the set of digits $D = \{1, 2, 3, 4, 5\}$ if repetitions of digits are allowed? How many numbers of two different digits can be formed from the set D?

8. Repeat Exercise 7 for $D = \{1, 2, 3, 4, 5, 6, 7\}$.

9. The Jonesboro Swim Club has 12 members. How many different sets of officers consisting of a president, a vice-president, and a secretary-treasurer can it form? No person can hold more than one of these three offices.

10. The Portland Swim Club has 250 members with 200 of these members eligible to hold any office. Repeat Exercise 9 for the Portland Swim Club.

11. How many five-digit numbers can be formed using the ten decimal digits if zero is not to be used as the first digit?

12. How many two-digit even numbers can be formed from the set $I = \{1, 2, 3, \ldots, 9\}$?

13. Find the number of "words" of three different letters that may be formed from the set $V = \{a, e, i, o, u\}$ if (**a**) the first letter must be i; (**b**) the first letter must be e and the last letter must be i.

14. How many license plates can be made using a letter from our alphabet followed by three decimal digits if the first digit must not be zero? How many are possible if the first digit must not be zero and no digit may be used more than once?

*15. Find the number of three-digit numbers that may be formed from the set $W = \{0, 1, 2, \ldots, 9\}$ if zero is not an acceptable first digit and (**a**) the number must be even; (**b**) the number must be divisible by 5; (**c**) no digit may be used more than once; (**d**) the number must be odd and less than 500.

*16. In a certain so-called "combination" lock there are 50 different positions. To open the lock you move to a certain number in one direction, then to a different number in the opposite direction, and finally to a third number in the original direction. What is the total number of such "combinations":
    (**a**) If the first turn must be clockwise?
    (**b**) If the first turn may be either clockwise or counterclockwise?

*17. Find the number of different possible license plates if each one is to consist of two letters of the alphabet followed by three decimal digits, the first digit may not be zero, and no repetitions of letters or numbers are permitted.

*18. Repeat Exercise 17 for license plates consisting of three consonants followed by three decimal digits.

8-2 PERMUTATIONS

Let us return to the set of club members M introduced in the previous
section and consider again the election of two officers discussed in
Example 1. We found that there were 20 possible sets of officers. Of
course, we could have obtained this answer by asserting that there are
five possible choices for the office of president, each of which can be
matched with any one of four choices of a vice-president.

We say that there are 5×4 (that is, 20) *permutations* of the set M,
using two elements at a time. In each of the 20 cases the first person
named would be president and the second person named would be
vice-president; thus, the *order* in which two people are named is
significant. A **permutation** of a set of elements is an arrangement of
certain of these elements in a specified order. In the problem just
discussed, the number of permutations of 5 things taken 2 at a time is
20. In symbols we write

$$_5P_2 = 20.$$

($_5P_2$ is read: "The permutations of 5 things taken 2 at a time.")

In general, we wish to find a formula for $_nP_r$; that is, the permutations of n things taken r at a time. To do this we note that we can fill
the first of the r positions in any one of n different ways. Then the
second position can be filled in $n - 1$ different ways, and so on.

Position: 1   2   3   4   . . . r
                       ↓   ↓   ↓   ↓   ↓
Number of choices: n $n-1$ $n-2$ $n-3$ . . . $n-(r-1)$
                                                  (i.e., $n-r+1$)

The product of these r factors gives the number of different ways of
arranging r elements selected from a set of n elements; that is, the
permutation of n things taken r at a time.

$$_nP_r = (n)(n-1)(n-2) \ldots (n-r+1),$$

where n and r are integers and $n \geq r$.

EXAMPLE 1:   Find $_8P_4$.

Solution: Here $n = 8$, $r = 4$, and $n - r + 1 = 5$. Thus

$$_8P_4 = 8 \times 7 \times 6 \times 5 = 1680.$$

Note that there are r, in this case 4, factors in the product.

EXAMPLE 2: How many different three-letter "words" can be formed from the 26 letters of the alphabet if each letter may be used at most once?

Solution: We wish to find the number of permutations of 26 things taken 3 at a time.

$$_{26}P_3 = 26 \times 25 \times 24 = 15,600.$$

A special case of the permutation formula occurs when we consider the permutations of n things taken n at a time. For example, let us see in how many different ways we may arrange the 5 members of set M in a row. Here we have the permutation of 5 things taken 5 at a time:

$$_5P_5 = 5 \times 4 \times 3 \times 2 \times 1$$

In general, for n things n at a time, $n = n$, $r = n$, and $n - r + 1 = 1$;

$$_nP_n = (n)(n - 1)(n - 2) \ldots (3)(2)(1).$$

We use a special symbol, $n!$, read "n factorial," for this product of integers from 1 through n. The following examples should illustrate the use of the new symbol:

$1! = 1$ $5! = 5 \times 4 \times 3 \times 2 \times 1$
$2! = 2 \times 1$ $6! = 6 \times 5 \times 4 \times 3 \times 2 \times 1$
$3! = 3 \times 2 \times 1$ $7! = 7 \times 6 \times 5 \times 4 \times 3 \times 2 \times 1$
$4! = 4 \times 3 \times 2 \times 1$ $8! = 8 \times 7 \times 6 \times 5 \times 4 \times 3 \times 2 \times 1$

Also, we *define* $0! = 1$ so that $(n - r)!$ may be used when $r = n$.

Using this factorial notation, we are now able to provide a different, but equivalent, formula for $_nP_r$:

$$_nP_r = n(n - 1)(n - 2) \ldots (n - r + 1)$$

$$\times \frac{(n - r)(n - r - 1)(n - r - 2) \ldots (3)(2)(1)}{(n - r)(n - r - 1)(n - r - 2) \ldots (3)(2)(1)} = \frac{n!}{(n - r)!}$$

EXAMPLE 3: Evaluate $_7P_3$ in two different ways.

Solution:

(a) $_7P_3 = 7 \times 6 \times 5.$

(b) $_7P_3 = \dfrac{7!}{4!} = \dfrac{7 \times 6 \times 5 \times 4 \times 3 \times 2 \times 1}{4 \times 3 \times 2 \times 1} = 7 \times 6 \times 5.$

EXAMPLE 4:   A certain class consists of 10 boys and 12 girls. They wish to elect officers in such a way that the president and treasurer are boys and the vice-president and secretary are girls. In how many ways can this be done?

Solution: The number of different ways of selecting the president and treasurer is $_{10}P_2$. The number of ways of selecting the vice-president and secretary is $_{12}P_2$. The total number of ways of choosing officers is

$$(_{10}P_2) \times (_{12}P_2) = (10 \times 9) \times (12 \times 11) = 11{,}880.$$

EXERCISES FOR SECTION 8-2

Evaluate:

   1. $5!$

   2. $6!$

   3. $\dfrac{8!}{6!}$

   4. $\dfrac{11!}{7!}$

   5. $_7P_2$

   6. $_7P_3$

   7. $_{10}P_1$

   8. $_{10}P_{10}$

   9. $_{12}P_{12}$

   10. $_{12}P_3$

  11. $_6P_2$

  12. $_6P_4$

  13. $_{10}P_3$

  14. $_{10}P_7$

Solve for n:

  15. $_nP_1 = 6$

  16. $_nP_2 = 6$

  17. $_nP_2 = 20$

  18. $_nP_3 = 24$

Find:

  19. The number of different arrangements of the set of letters $V = \{a, e, i, o, u\}$ if they are taken (**a**) two at a time; (**b**) five at a time.

20. The number of four-digit numbers that can be formed using the digits 1, 2, 3, 4, 5 if no digit may be used more than once in a number. How many of these numbers will be even?

21. The number of different signals that can be formed by running up three flags on a flagpole, one above the other, if seven different flags are available.

22. The number of different ways that a disc jockey can arrange a musical program of seven selections.

23. The number of different ways that a manager of a nine-man baseball team can arrange his batting order.

Find for any positive integer n a formula for:

24. $_nP_r \times (n - r)!$ **25.** $_nP_0$

8-3 COMBINATIONS

In each of the problems that we solved concerning permutations, the order of the objects involved was important. For example, the number of ways of selecting a president and a vice-president from the set M was found to be $_5P_2$. Here order is important in that Betty as president and Doris as vice-president is a different set of officers than Doris as president and Betty as vice-president.

Now, suppose we wish to select a committee of two members from set M without attaching any meaning to the order in which the members are selected. Then the committee consisting of Betty and Doris is certainly the same as the one consisting of Doris and Betty. In this case, we see that order is not important, and we call such an arrangement a **combination**. One way to determine the number of possible committees of two to be formed from the set M is by enumeration. We find that there are 10 possible committees, as follows:

Betty–Doris	Doris–John
Betty–Ellen	Doris–Tom
Betty–John	Ellen–John
Betty–Tom	Ellen–Tom
Doris–Ellen	John–Tom

We summarize this discussion by saying that the number of combinations of 5 things, taken 2 at a time, is 10. In symbols we write

$$_5C_2 = 10.$$

In general, we wish to find a formula for $_nC_r$; that is, the combinations of n things taken r at a time. This is written in symbols in the form

$$_nC_r \quad \text{or} \quad \binom{n}{r}.$$

To find a formula for $_nC_r$ let us first consider a specific problem, that of selecting committees of three from the set M. There are 10 such possibilities, and we list them below, using the first initial of each name only:

$$
\begin{array}{lll}
B, D, E & B, J, T & M = \{B, D, E, J, T\} \\
B, D, J & D, E, J & {}_5C_3 = 10 \\
B, D, T & D, E, T & \\
B, E, J & D, J, T & \\
B, E, T & E, J, T &
\end{array}
$$

Note that selecting committees of three is equivalent to selecting groups of two to be omitted. That is, omitting J and T is the same as selecting B, D, and E. Therefore, we find that $_5C_3 = {}_5C_2 = 10$.

Inasmuch as we wanted only committees, and assigned no particular jobs to the members of each committee, we see that order is not important. However, suppose that each committee is now to elect a chairman, secretary, and historian. In how many ways can this be done within each committee? This is clearly a problem in which order is important, involving permutations. The number of such possible arrangements within each committee is $_3P_3$; that is, $3!$. For example, the committee consisting of B, D, and E can rearrange themselves as chairman, secretary, and historian, respectively, as follows:

$$B, D, E; \quad B, E, D; \quad D, E, B; \quad D, B, E; \quad E, B, D; \quad E, D, B.$$

All six of these permutations constitute only one combination.

We know that $_5C_3 = 10$. If each of these combinations is multiplied by $3!$ we then will have the total number of permutations of five things taken three at a time:

$$_5C_3 \times 3! = {}_5P_3 \quad \text{and} \quad {}_5C_3 = \frac{{}_5P_3}{3!}.$$

In general, consider $_nC_r$. Each of these combinations, consisting of r elements each, may be used to form $r!$ permutations. Thus the number of combinations of n things taken r at a time is given by the formula

$$_nC_r \times r! = {_nP_r} \quad \text{and} \quad {_nC_r} = \frac{_nP_r}{r!}.$$

Since

$$_nP_r = (n)(n-1)(n-2)\ldots(n-r+1) = \frac{n!}{(n-r)!},$$

we also have the formula

$$_nC_r = \frac{(n)(n-1)(n-2)\ldots(n-r+1)}{r!} = \frac{n!}{r!(n-r)!}.$$

EXAMPLE 1:   Evaluate $_7C_2$ in two ways.

Solution:

(a) $_7C_2 = \dfrac{_7P_2}{2!} = \dfrac{7 \times 6}{2 \times 1} = 21.$

(b) $_7C_2 = \dfrac{7!}{2!\,5!} = \dfrac{7 \times 6 \times 5 \times 4 \times 3 \times 2 \times 1}{2 \times 1 \times 5 \times 4 \times 3 \times 2 \times 1} = 21.$

EXAMPLE 2:   In how many different ways can a hand of five cards be dealt from a deck of 52 cards?

Solution: The order of the five cards is unimportant, so this is a problem involving combinations.

$$_{52}C_5 = \frac{52!}{5!\,47!} = \frac{52 \times 51 \times 50 \times 49 \times 48 \times (47!)}{5! \qquad (47!)} = 2{,}598{,}960.$$

EXERCISES FOR SECTION 8-3

In Exercises 1 through 5 evaluate:

1. (a) $\dfrac{6!}{4!\,2!}$ **(b)** $\dfrac{8!}{5!\,3!}$

2. (a) $\dfrac{10!}{4!\,6!}$ **(b)** $\dfrac{12!}{7!\,5!}$

3. (a) $_7C_2$ (b) $_7C_3$

4. (a) $_8C_3$ (b) $_9C_4$

5. (a) $_{11}C_2$ (b) $_{15}C_3$

6. List the $_3P_2$ permutations of the elements of the set $\{a, b, c\}$. Then identify the permutations that represent the same combinations and find $_3C_2$.

7. List the $_4P_3$ permutations of the elements of the set $\{p, q, r, s\}$. Then identify the permutations that represent the same combinations and find $_4C_3$.

8. List the elements of each combination of $_4C_3$ for the set $\{w, x, y, z\}$. Then match each of these combinations with a combination of $_4C_1$ and thereby illustrate the fact that $_4C_3 = _4C_1$.

9. Find a formula for $_nC_n$ for any positive integer n.

10. Find the value and give an interpretation of $_nC_0$ for any positive integer n.

11. Evaluate $_3C_0$, $_3C_1$, $_3C_2$, $_3C_3$ and check that the sum of these combinations is 2^3, the number of possible subsets that can be formed from a set of three elements.

12. Evaluate $_5C_0$, $_5C_1$, $_5C_2$, $_5C_3$, $_5C_4$, $_5C_5$ and check the sum as in Exercise 11.

13. Use the results obtained in Exercises 11 and 12 and conjecture a formula for any positive integer n for

$$_nC_0 + _nC_1 + _nC_2 + _nC_3 + \cdots + _nC_{n-1} + _nC_n.$$

14. How many sums of money (include the case of no money) can be selected from a set of coins consisting of a penny, a nickel, a dime, a quarter, and a half-dollar?

15. A man has a penny, a nickel, a dime, a quarter, and a half-dollar in his pocket. In how many different ways can he give a tip if he wishes to use exactly two coins?

16. A class consists of 10 boys and 12 girls. How many different committees of four can be selected from the class if each committee is to consist of two boys and two girls?

17. In how many ways can a hand of 13 cards be selected from a bridge deck of 52 cards?

18. In how many ways can one choose a set of 3 books to read from a set of 7 books?

19. Explain why a so-called "combination" lock should really be called a permutation lock.

20. Urn A contains 5 balls and urn B contains 10 balls. In how many ways can 10 balls be selected if 3 are to be drawn from urn A and 7 from urn B?

21. An urn contains 7 black and 3 white balls. In how many ways can 4 balls be selected from this urn? How many of these selections will include exactly 3 black balls?

22. Repeat Exercise 21 for an urn that contains 10 black balls and 5 white balls.

*23. Give an algebraic proof that $_nC_r = {_nC_{n-r}}$.

SUPPLEMENTARY EXERCISES FOR SECTION 8-3

State whether each question involves a permutation, a combination, or a permutation and a combination. Then answer each question.

1. The 20 members of the Rochester Tennis Club are to play on a certain Saturday evening. In how many ways can pairs be selected for playing "singles"?

2. In how many different ways can a disc jockey with 10 records: (**a**) Select 4 records to be used for a program? (**b**) Present a program in which 4 records are played?

3. Students taking a certain examination are required to answer 4 out of 8 questions. In how many ways can a student select the 4 questions that he tries to answer?

4. In how many ways can 7 people line up at a single theater ticket window?

5. How many lines are determined by 10 points if no 3 points are collinear?

6. In how many ways can the 15 boys in a certain class be selected in a group of 9 to play baseball?

7. How many different hands can be dealt from a deck of 52 bridge cards if each hand contains: (**a**) 4 cards? (**b**) 7 cards?

8. In how many different ways may 5 guests be seated in the 5 seats of a six-passenger car after the driver is seated?

9. In how many ways can 4 pictures be arranged with one in each of 4 given places on the walls of a room?

10. A class is to be divided into 2 committees. In how many different ways can some or all of 8 of the students be assigned to one of the committees?

11. In how many different ways can a group of 8 students be divided into 2 groups of 4 students each?

12. In how many different ways can a group of 8 students be divided into 2 groups of students?

8-4 DEFINITION OF PROBABILITY

When an ordinary coin is tossed, we know that there are two distinct and equally likely ways in which it may land, heads or tails. We say that the probability of getting a head is one out of two, or simply $\frac{1}{2}$.

In rolling one of a pair of ordinary dice, there are six equally likely ways in which the dice may land. We say that the probability of rolling a 5 on one toss of a die is one out of six, or $\frac{1}{6}$.

In each of these two examples, the events that may occur are said to be **mutually exclusive.** That is, one and only one of the events can occur at any given time. When a coin is tossed, there are two possible events (heads and tails); one and only one of these may occur. When a single die is rolled, there are six events (1, 2, 3, 4, 5, 6); one and only one of these may occur. We may now define probability in general as follows:

If an event can occur in any one of n mutually exclusive and equally likely ways, and if m of these ways are considered favorable, then the **probability** $P(A)$ that a favorable event A will occur is given by the formula

$$P(A) = \frac{m}{n}.$$

The probability $\frac{m}{n}$ satisfies the relation $0 \leq \frac{m}{n} \leq 1$, since m and n are integers and $m \leq n$. When success is inevitable, $m = n$ and the probability is 1; when an event cannot possibly succeed, $m = 0$ and the probability is 0. For example, the probability of getting either a head or a tail on a single toss of a coin is 1, assuming that the coin does not land on an edge. The probability of tossing a sum of 13 with a single toss of a pair of ordinary dice is 0. (Here, and in all future work, assume that normal dice are used unless otherwise instructed.)

The sum of the probability of an event's occurring and the probability of that same event's not occurring is 1.

$$\text{If} \quad P(A) = \frac{m}{n}, \quad \text{then} \quad P(\text{not } A) = 1 - \frac{m}{n}.$$

EXAMPLE 1:   A single card is selected from a deck of 52 bridge cards. What is the probability that it is a spade? What is the probability that it is not a spade? What is the probability that it is an ace or a spade?

Solution: Of the 52 cards, 13 are spades. Therefore, the probability of selecting a spade is $\frac{13}{52}$; that is, $\frac{1}{4}$. The probability that the card selected is not a spade is $1 - \frac{1}{4}$; that is, $\frac{3}{4}$. There are 4 aces and 12 spades besides the ace of spades. Therefore, the probability that the card selected is an ace or a spade is $(4 + 12)/52$; that is, $\frac{16}{52}$, which we express as $\frac{4}{13}$.

EXAMPLE 2:   A committee of two is to be selected from the set

$$M = \{\text{Betty, Doris, Ellen, John, Tom}\}$$

by drawing names out of a hat. What is the probability that both members of the committee will be girls?

Solution: This problem involves combinations, since the order in which the names are drawn is not important. The total number of ways in which 2 persons can be selected from a set of 5 is $_5C_2$. The number of ways in which two girls can be selected is $_3C_2$, since there are three girls in set M.

$$_3C_2 = \frac{3 \times 2}{2 \times 1} = 3; \qquad _5C_2 = \frac{5 \times 4}{2 \times 1} = 10.$$

The probability that both members selected are girls is

$$\frac{_3C_2}{_5C_2} = \frac{3}{10}.$$

Note that our knowledge of combinations made Example 2 easy to set up in symbols. We could also have solved the problem by actually listing all of the possibilities, although this process can become quite tedious. As in §8-3 the set of all possible committees of 2 from the set M is

Betty–Doris	Doris–John
Betty–Ellen	Doris–Tom
Betty–John	Ellen–John
Betty–Tom	Ellen–Tom
Doris–Ellen	John–Tom

Of the ten possible committees, there are three (those boxed) that consist of two girls. What is the probability of selecting a committee to consist of two boys?

EXERCISES FOR SECTION 8-4

What is the probability of tossing on a single toss of one die:

1. An even number?   **2.** An odd number?

3. A number greater than 3?

4. A number less than 5?

5. A number different from 5?

6. A number different from 7?

7. The number 7?

8. An even number or a number greater than 3?

9. An odd number or a number less than 5?

10. An odd number or a number greater than 4?

11. An even number or a number greater than 6?

12. An odd number or a number greater than 10?

13. An odd number or a number less than 6?

14. An even number or a number less than 10?

In Exercises 15 through 18 what is the probability of drawing on a single draw from a deck of 52 bridge cards:

15. An ace?   **16.** A king?

17. A spade?   **18.** A red card?

19. The probability of obtaining all heads in a single toss of three coins is $\frac{1}{8}$. What is the probability that not all three coins are heads on such a toss?

20. What is the probability that the next person you meet was not born on a Sunday?

8-5 SAMPLE SPACES

It is often convenient to solve problems of probability by making a list of all possible outcomes. Such a listing is called a **sample space.** Consider first the problem of tossing two coins. The sample space for this problem is given by the following set of all possible outcomes:

$$\{HH, HT, TH, TT\}$$

We may also summarize these data by means of a chart:

First coin	Second coin
H	H
H	T
T	H
T	T

Another convenient way to list all of the logical possibilities is by means of a tree diagram, where the branches represent the possible choices. The set of possible outcomes, $\{HH, HT, TH, TT\}$, may be read from the diagram. Note that there are four possible events: two heads occur in one event, one head and one tail occur in two events, no heads (that is, two tails) occur in one event. Thus we may list various probabilities regarding the tossing of two coins as follows:

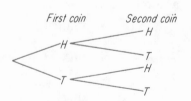

First coin   Second coin

Event	Probabilty
2 heads	$\frac{1}{4}$
1 head	$\frac{2}{4}$
0 heads	$\frac{1}{4}$

Since all possibilities have been considered, the sum of the probabilities should be 1; $\frac{1}{4} + \frac{2}{4} + \frac{1}{4} = 1$. This provides a check on our computation. The list of probabilities is sometimes called a **probability distribution.**

For the case of three coins, the following tree diagram and array may be made.

First coin	Second coin	Third coin	First coin	Second coin	Third coin
		H	H	H	H
	H	T	H	H	T
		H	H	T	H
H	T	T	H	T	T
		H	T	H	H
	H	T	T	H	T
T		H	T	T	H
	T	T	T	T	T

From the tree diagram, we may list the probabilities of specific numbers of heads by means of the following distribution.

Event	Probabilty
0 heads	$\frac{1}{8}$
1 head	$\frac{3}{8}$
2 heads	$\frac{3}{8}$
3 heads	$\frac{1}{8}$

In each case, both for two coins and for three coins, the sum of the probabilities is 1; that is, all possible events have been listed and these events are mutually exclusive. Note also that for two coins there were four possible outcomes, for three coins there were eight possible outcomes, and, in general, for n coins there would be 2^n possible outcomes.

Each of the preceding distributions is an example of a **binomial distribution,** since each is based upon the occurrence of one of *two* possibilities, in this case heads or tails.

EXAMPLE 1: A box contains 2 red and 3 white balls. Two balls are drawn in succession without replacement. List a sample space for this experiment.

Solution: To identify individual balls, we denote the red balls as R_1 and R_2; the white balls as W_1, W_2, W_3. Then the sample space is as follows:

$$
\begin{array}{lllll}
R_1R_2, & R_2R_1, & W_1R_1, & W_2R_1, & W_3R_1 \\
R_1W_1, & R_2W_1, & W_1R_2, & W_2R_2, & W_3R_2 \\
R_1W_2, & R_2W_2, & W_1W_2, & W_2W_1, & W_3W_1 \\
R_1W_3, & R_2W_3, & W_1W_3, & W_2W_3, & W_3W_2
\end{array}
$$

EXAMPLE 2: Use a tree diagram to show the possible selections for Example 1.

Solution:

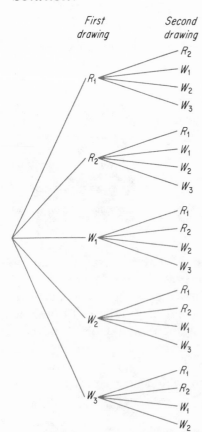

EXERCISES FOR SECTION 8-5

Use the sample space of Example 1 to find the probability that:

1. Both balls are red.

2. Both balls are white.

3. The first ball is red.

4. The first ball is red and the second ball is white.

5. One ball is red and the other is white.

In Exercises 6 through 8 use the sample space for the outcomes when three coins are tossed to find the probability that:

6. All three coins are heads.

7. At least two coins are heads.

8. At most one coin is tails.

9. List a sample space for the outcomes when four coins are tossed.

In Exercises 10 through 12 use the sample space for the outcomes when four coins are tossed (Exercise 9) to find the probability that:

10. All four coins are heads.

11. At least three coins are heads.

12. At most two coins are tails.

13. List a sample space for the outcomes when a pair of dice is tossed. Represent each outcome by an ordered pair of numbers. For example, let (1, 3) represent a 1 on the first die and a 3 on the second die.

In Exercises 14 through 22 use the sample space for the outcomes when a pair of dice is tossed (Exercise 13) to find the probability that:

14. The number on the first die is 2.

15. The number 2 is on both dice.

16. The same number is on both dice.

17. The sum of the numbers obtained is 11.

18. The sum of the numbers obtained is not 11.

19. The sum of the numbers obtained is 7.

20. The sum of the numbers obtained is not 7.

21. The number on one die is twice the number on the other die.

22. The number on one die is three more than the number on the other die.

23. A box contains 2 red balls R_1 and R_2 and 2 white balls W_1 and W_2. List a sample space for the outcomes when 2 balls are drawn in succession without replacement. Find the probability that both balls are red.

24. Repeat Exercise 23 for the case in which the first ball is replaced before the second ball is drawn.

25. Repeat Exercise 23 for a box that contains 3 red balls and 2 white balls.

*26. Consider a World Series baseball contest between the Dodgers D and the Yankees Y. Assume that each team is equally likely to win each game. Remember that 4 victories are needed to win the series, each game must be won by one of the teams, and thus at most 7 games will be needed. Make a tree diagram for the entire series under the assumption that the Dodgers win the first two games. Circle the entry and assign a probability to each position in the diagram that represents a completion (winning) of the series. Find the probability of the Dodgers' winning the series on the fourth game, on the fifth game, on the sixth game, and on the seventh game. Find the probability of the Yankees' winning the series on each of these games. Check your work by being sure that the sum of the probabilities of someone winning the series is 1.

*27. Three cards are in a box. One is red on both sides, one is white on both sides, and one is red on one side and white on the other. A card is drawn at random and placed on a table. It has a red side showing. What is the probability that the side not showing is also red? [*Hint*: The answer is not $\frac{1}{2}$.]

8-6 COMPUTATION OF PROBABILITIES

If A and B represent two mutually exclusive events, then

$$P \ (A \text{ or } B) = P(A) + P(B).$$

That is, the probability that one event or the other will occur is the sum of the individual probabilities. Consider, for example, the probability of drawing an ace or a picture card (that is, a jack, queen, or king) from an ordinary deck of 52 bridge cards.

The probability of drawing an ace, $P(A)$, is $\frac{4}{52}$.
The probability of drawing a picture card, $P(B)$, is $\frac{12}{52}$.
Then $P(A \text{ or } B) = \frac{4}{52} + \frac{12}{52} = \frac{16}{52} = \frac{4}{13}$.

EXAMPLE 1:   A bag contains 3 red, 2 black, and 5 yellow balls. Find the probability that a ball drawn at random will be red or black.

Solution: The probability of drawing a red ball, $P(R)$, is $\frac{3}{10}$. The probability of drawing a black ball, $P(B)$, is $\frac{2}{10}$. Then

$$P(R \text{ or } B) = P(R) + P(B) = \frac{5}{10} = \frac{1}{2}.$$

This process can be extended to find the probability of any finite number of mutually exclusive events.

$$P(A \text{ or } B \text{ or } C \text{ or } \ldots) = P(A) + P(B) + P(C) + \cdots$$

EXAMPLE 2:   A single die is tossed. What is the probability that either an odd number or a number greater than 3 appears?

Solution: There are three odd numbers possible, (1, 3, 5), so the probability of tossing an odd number is $\frac{3}{6}$. The probability of getting a number greater than 3 (that is, 4, 5, 6) is also $\frac{3}{6}$. Adding these probabilities gives $\frac{3}{6} + \frac{3}{6} = 1$. Something is obviously wrong, since a probability of 1 implies certainty and we can see that an outcome of 2 is neither odd nor greater than 3. The difficulty lies in the fact that the events are *not* mutually exclusive; a number may be both odd and also greater than 3 at the same time. In particular, 5 is both odd and greater than 3 at the same time. Thus $P(5)$ has been included twice. Since $P(5) = \frac{1}{6}$, our answer should be $\frac{3}{6} + \frac{3}{6} - \frac{1}{6}$; that is, $\frac{5}{6}$.

In situations like that of Example 2 we need to subtract the probability that both events occur at the same time. Thus, where A and B are not mutually exclusive events, we have

$$P(A \text{ or } B) = P(A) + P(B) - P(A \text{ and } B).$$

Note that in Example 2, we had the following probabilities:

$P(A)$, the probability of an odd number, is $\frac{3}{6}$.

$P(B)$, the probability of a number greater than 3, is $\frac{3}{6}$.

$P(A \text{ and } B)$, the probability that a number (in this case 5) is odd and greater than 3, is $\frac{1}{6}$.

$P(A \text{ or } B) = \frac{3}{6} + \frac{3}{6} - \frac{1}{6} = \frac{5}{6}$.

By an actual listing we can see that five of the six possible outcomes in Example 2 are either odd or greater than 3, namely 1, 3, 4, 5, and 6. The only "losing" number is 2. Thus the probability $P(A \text{ or } B)$ must be $\frac{5}{6}$.

These two situations $P(A \text{ or } B)$ and $P(A \text{ and } B)$ that we have considered can also be described by means of Euler diagrams (see §4-5) where the points of the circular regions represent probabilities of events.

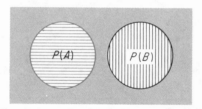 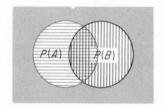

The first of the two accompanying figures shows mutually exclusive events:

$$P(A \text{ or } B) = P(A) + P(B)$$

In the second figure, the region that is shaded both horizontally and vertically represents $P(A \text{ and } B)$, $P(A \text{ and } B) \neq 0$, the events are **dependent events** (not mutually exclusive), and

$$P(A \text{ or } B) = P(A) + P(B) - P(A \text{ and } B).$$

We must subtract $P(A \text{ and } B)$, since we have counted it twice in the sum $P(A) + P(B)$.

Next we turn our attention to the probability that several events will occur, one after the other. Consider the probability of tossing a coin twice and obtaining heads on the first toss and tails on the second toss. From a sample space we see that the probability is $\frac{1}{4}$.

$$\{HH, \; (HT), \; TH, \; TT\}$$

Furthermore, we see that the probability $P(A)$ that the first coin is heads is $\frac{1}{2}$. The probability $P(B)$ that the second coin is tails is $\frac{1}{2}$. Then $P(A \text{ and } B) = \frac{1}{2} \times \frac{1}{2} = \frac{1}{4}$. Note that these events are **independent**; that is, the outcome of the first toss does not affect the second toss.

In general, let the probability that an event A occurs be $P(A)$. Let the probability that an independent second event occurs, after A has occurred, be $P(B)$. Then

$$P(A \text{ and } B) = P(A) \times P(B).$$

This can be extended to any finite number of independent events.

$$P(A \text{ and } B \text{ and } C \text{ and } \ldots) = P(A) \times P(B) \times P(C) \times \cdots.$$

EXAMPLE 3:   Urn A contains 3 white and 5 red balls. Urn B contains 4 white and 3 red balls. One ball is drawn from each urn. What is the probability that they are both red?

Solution: Let $P(A)$ be the probability of drawing a red ball from urn A and $P(B)$ be the probability of drawing a red ball from urn B. Then

$$P(A) = \tfrac{5}{8}; \qquad P(B) = \tfrac{3}{7}; \qquad P(A \text{ and } B) = \tfrac{5}{8} \cdot \tfrac{3}{7} = \tfrac{15}{56}.$$

EXAMPLE 4:   Two cards are selected in succession, without replacement, from an ordinary bridge deck of 52 cards. What is the probability that they are both aces?

Solution: The probability that the first is an ace is $\frac{4}{52}$. Now the probability of success depends on the drawing of the first card. If it is an ace, then the probability that the second card is an ace is $\frac{3}{51}$. The probability that both cards are aces is $\frac{4}{52} \times \frac{3}{51}$, that is, $\frac{1}{221}$. This problem can also be solved by noting that $_{52}C_2$ is the total number of ways of selecting two cards from a deck of 52 cards. Also $_4C_2$ is the total number of ways of selecting two aces from the four aces in a deck. The required probability is then given as

$$\frac{_4C_2}{_{52}C_2} = \frac{\dfrac{4!}{2!2!}}{\dfrac{52!}{2!50!}} = \frac{4 \times 3}{52 \times 51} = \frac{1}{221}.$$

EXERCISES FOR SECTION 8-6

A single card is drawn from a deck of 52 bridge cards. In Exercises 1 through 7 find the probability that the card selected is:

1. An ace or a king.

2. A spade or a heart.

3. A spade or a king.

4. A spade and a king.

5. A spade and a queen.

6. A heart or a king or a queen.

7. A club or an ace or a king.

8. Two cards are drawn in succession from a deck of 52 bridge cards without the first card's being replaced. Find the probability that (**a**) both cards are spades; (**b**) both cards are aces of spades; (**c**) the first card is a spade and the second card is a heart; (**d**) the first card is an ace and the second card is the king of hearts; (**e**) both cards are of the same suit.

9. Repeat Exercise 8 if the first card is replaced in the deck after the first drawing.

10. A coin is tossed 5 times. What is the probability that all 5 tosses are heads?

11. A coin is tossed 5 times. What is the probability that at least one head is obtained? [*Hint*: First find the probability of getting no heads.]

12. A coin is tossed and then a die is rolled. Find the probability of obtaining (**a**) a head and a 3; (**b**) a head and an even number; (**c**) a head or a 3; (**d**) a head or an even number.

13. A bag contains 3 red balls and 7 white balls. (**a**) If one ball is drawn at random, what is the probability that it is white? (**b**) If two balls are drawn at random, what is the probability that they are both white?

14. Five cards are drawn at random from an ordinary bridge deck of 52 cards. Find the probability that (**a**) all 5 cards drawn are spades; (**b**) the 4 aces are drawn.

15. A box contains 3 red, 4 white, and 5 green balls. Three balls are drawn in succession, without replacement. Find the probability that (**a**) all three are red; (**b**) the first is red, the second is white, and the third is green; (**c**) none are green; *(**d**) all three are of the same color.

16. Repeat Exercise 15 if each ball is replaced after it is drawn.

17. A die is tossed three times. Find the probability that (**a**) a 6 is tossed on the first toss; (**b**) a 6 is tossed on the first two tosses; (**c**) a 6 is tossed on all three tosses; (**d**) a 6 is tossed on the first toss and not tossed on the second or third toss.

18. A die is tossed three times. Find the probability that (**a**) an even number is tossed on all three tosses; (**b**) an even number is tossed on the first two tosses and an odd number on the third toss; (**c**) an odd number is tossed on the first toss and an even number on the second and third tosses; (**d**) exactly one even number is tossed.

*****19.** A die is tossed three times. Find the probability that (**a**) at least one 6 is tossed; (**b**) exactly one 6 is tossed.

*****20.** Five cards are dealt from an ordinary deck of 52 bridge cards. Find the probability that the hand consists of 3 aces and 2 kings.

8-7 ODDS AND MATHEMATICAL EXPECTATION

One often reads statements in the sports section of the daily newspaper concerning "odds" in favor of, or against, a particular team or individual's winning or losing some encounter. For example, we may read that the odds in favor of the Cardinals' winning the pennant are "4 to 1." In this section we shall attempt to discover just what such statements really mean.

Consider the problem of finding the odds against obtaining a 3 in one toss of a die. Since the probability of obtaining a 3 is known to be $\frac{1}{6}$, most people would say that the odds are therefore 6 to 1 against rolling a 3. This is not correct—because out of every six tosses of the die, in the long run, one expects to toss one 3. The other five tosses are not expected to be 3's. Therefore, the correct odds against rolling a 3 in one toss of a die are 5 to 1. The odds in favor of tossing a 3 are 1 to 5. Formally we define odds as follows:

The **odds in favor** of an event are defined as the ratio of the probability that an event will occur to the probability that the event will not occur. The reciprocal of this ratio gives the **odds against** the occurrence of the event.

Thus the odds in favor of an event that may occur in several equally likely ways is the ratio of the number of favorable ways to the number of unfavorable ways.

EXAMPLE 1: Find the odds in favor of drawing a spade from an ordinary deck of 52 bridge cards.

Solution: Since there are 13 spades in a deck of cards, the probability of drawing a spade is $\frac{13}{52} = \frac{1}{4}$. The probability of failing to draw a spade is $\frac{3}{4}$. The odds in favor of obtaining a spade are $\frac{1}{4} \div \frac{3}{4}$; that is, $\frac{1}{3}$.

The odds in favor of drawing a spade are stated as $\frac{1}{3}$. They may also be stated as "1 to 3" or as "1:3." Similarly, the odds against drawing a spade are $\frac{3}{1}$, which may be written as "3 to 1" or "3:1."

Mathematical expectation is closely related to odds and is defined as the product of the probability that an event will occur and the amount to be received upon such occurrence. Suppose that you are to receive $2.00 each time you obtain two heads on a single toss of two coins. You do not receive anything for any other outcome. Then your mathematical expectation will be one-fourth of $2.00; that is, $0.50. This means that you should be willing to pay $0.50 each time you toss the coins if the game is to be a fair one. In the long run, both you and the person who is running the game would break even. For example, if you played the game four times it would cost you 4 × $0.50; that is, $2.00. You expect to win, in the long run, once out of every four games played. Assuming that you do so, you will win $2.00 once every four times and thus be even.

If an event has several possible outcomes that occur with probabilities p_1, p_2, p_3, and so forth, and for each of these outcomes one may expect the amounts m_1, m_2, m_3, and so on, then the mathematical expectation E may be defined as

$$E = m_1 p_1 + m_2 p_2 + m_3 p_3 + \cdots.$$

Whenever this formula is used, it is worthwhile to check that all possible outcomes have been considered by checking that the sum of the probabilities is 1.

:::

EXAMPLE 2:   Suppose that you play a game wherein you are to toss a coin twice and are to receive 10 cents if two heads are obtained, 5 cents if one head is obtained, and nothing if both tosses produce tails. What is your expected value in this game?

Solution: The probabilities of obtaining two, one, and no heads, respectively, are $\frac{1}{4}$, $\frac{1}{2}$, and $\frac{1}{4}$. Therefore, the expected value E, in cents, is found to be

$$E = (10)(\tfrac{1}{4}) + (5)(\tfrac{1}{2}) + (0)(\tfrac{1}{4}) = 5.$$

This solution may be interpreted in several ways. For one thing, it is the price you should be willing to pay for the privilege of playing this game. It may also be interpreted as the average amount of winnings per game that one may expect when one is playing a large number of games.

:::

EXERCISES FOR SECTION 8-7

What are the odds in favor of obtaining:

   1. Two heads in a single toss of two coins?

   2. At least two heads in a single toss of three coins?

   3. Two heads when a single coin is tossed twice?

   4. At least two heads when a single coin is tossed three times?

In Exercises 5 through 8 what are the odds against obtaining:

   5. Two heads in a single toss of two coins?

   6. An ace in a single draw from a deck of 52 bridge cards?

   7. An ace or a king in a single draw from a deck of 52 bridge cards?

   8. A 7 or an 11 in a single toss of a pair of dice?

9. What are the odds in favor of rolling a 7 or an 11 in a single toss of a pair of dice?

10. One hundred tickets are sold for a lottery. The grand prize is $1000. What is a fair price to pay for a ticket?

11. Repeat Exercise 10 for the case in which 250 tickets are sold.

12. What is your mathematical expectation when you buy one of 300 tickets for a single prize worth $750?

13. What is your mathematical expectation in a game in which you will receive $10 if you toss a "double" (the same number on both dice) on a single toss of a pair of dice?

14. A box contains 3 dimes and 2 quarters. You are to reach in and select one coin, which you may then keep. Assuming that you are not able to determine which coin is which by its size, what would be a fair price for the privilege of playing this game?

15. There are three identical boxes on a table. One contains a five-dollar bill, one contains a one-dollar bill, and the third is empty. A man is permitted to select one of these boxes and to keep its contents. What is his expectation?

16. Three coins are tossed. What is the expected number of heads?

17. Two bills are to be drawn from a purse that contains three five-dollar bills and two ten-dollar bills. What is the mathematical expectation for this drawing?

18. Three cards are dealt from a deck of 52 bridge cards. What are the odds against their all being of the same suit?

19. If there are two pennies, a nickel, a dime, a quarter, and a half-dollar in a hat, what is the mathematical expectation of the value of a random selection of a coin from the hat?

8-8 PASCAL'S TRIANGLE

The final problem that we shall consider in this chapter is that of finding the number of different subsets of various sizes that can be formed from a given set. To illustrate this we return to our original set M:

$$M = \{\text{Betty, Doris, Ellen, John, Tom}\}$$

We wish to know the number of different committees that can be formed consisting of 0, 1, 2, 3, 4, and 5 members. Each of these can be found:

$$_5C_0 = 1; \quad _5C_1 = 5; \quad _5C_2 = 10; \quad _5C_3 = 10; \quad _5C_4 = 5; \quad _5C_5 = 1.$$

Recall that the notation $_nC_r$ may also be written in the form $\binom{n}{r}$. The preceding results may then be written in the form

$$\binom{5}{0} = 1; \qquad \binom{5}{1} = 5; \qquad \binom{5}{2} = 10;$$

$$\binom{5}{3} = 10; \qquad \binom{5}{4} = 5; \qquad \binom{5}{5} = 1.$$

We shall use the form $\binom{n}{r}$ to simplify the arrays in this section. In any case, the total number of subsets of a set of five elements is $1 + 5 + 10 + 10 + 5 + 1$; that is, 32.

In like manner, if our original set had consisted of only four members, the number of different committees of 0, 1, 2, 3, and 4 members each would be found as

$$\binom{4}{0} = 1; \quad \binom{4}{1} = 4; \quad \binom{4}{2} = 6; \quad \binom{4}{3} = 4; \quad \binom{4}{4} = 1.$$

Notice that $1 + 4 + 6 + 4 + 1 = 16$.

There is a convenient way to summarize these data for sets of n elements, where $n = 1, 2, 3, \ldots$:

$$n = 1: \qquad \binom{1}{0} \quad \binom{1}{1}$$

$$n = 2: \qquad \binom{2}{0} \quad \binom{2}{1} \quad \binom{2}{2}$$

$$n = 3: \qquad \binom{3}{0} \quad \binom{3}{1} \quad \binom{3}{2} \quad \binom{3}{3}$$

$$n = 4: \qquad \binom{4}{0} \quad \binom{4}{1} \quad \binom{4}{2} \quad \binom{4}{3} \quad \binom{4}{4}$$

$$n = 5: \quad \binom{5}{0} \quad \binom{5}{1} \quad \binom{5}{2} \quad \binom{5}{3} \quad \binom{5}{4} \quad \binom{5}{5}$$

$\cdot \quad \cdot \quad \cdot \quad \cdot \quad \cdot \quad \cdot \quad \cdot \quad \cdot \quad \cdot \quad \cdot \quad \cdot \quad \cdot \quad \cdot \quad \cdot \quad \cdot \quad \cdot \quad \cdot \quad \cdot$

If we replace each symbol by its equivalent number, we may write the following array, known as **Pascal's triangle.** Generally ascribed to the French mathematician Blaise Pascal (1623–1662), this array of numbers is said to have been known to the Chinese in the early fourteenth century.

$n = 1$:   1   1
$n = 2$:   1   2   1
$n = 3$:   1   3   3   1
$n = 4$:   1   4   6   4   1
$n = 5$:   1   5   10   10   5   1
. . . .

We read each row of this array by noting that the first entry in the nth row is $\binom{n}{0}$, the second is $\binom{n}{1}$, the third is $\binom{n}{2}$, and so on until the last entry, which is $\binom{n}{n}$. Since $\binom{n}{0} = \binom{n}{n} = 1$, each row begins and ends with 1.

There is a simple way to continue the array with very little computation. In each row the first number is 1 and the last number is 1. Each of the other numbers may be obtained as the sum of the two numbers appearing in the preceding row to the right and left of the position to be filled. Thus, to obtain the sixth row, begin with 1. Then fill the next position by adding 1 and 5 from the fifth row. Then add 5 and 10 to obtain 15, add 10 and 10 to obtain 20, and so forth as in this diagram:

$n = 5$:   1   5   10   10   5   1
$n = 6$:   1   6   15   20   15   6   1

Let us see if we can find out why this pattern works as it does. To do so, consider the rows for $n = 4$ and $n = 5$:

$n = 4$:   1   4   6   4   1

$n = 5$:   1   5   10   10   5   1

We will consider the fourth entry in row 5 and give an example of why it is equal to the sum of the third and fourth entries in row 4. That is, we shall show that

$$\binom{5}{3} = \binom{4}{2} + \binom{4}{3}.$$

Consider our original set M and the problem of selecting different committees of three. Each of these committees either will or will not include Betty. First, we shall assume that Betty *is* to be included.

Then the other two members of the committee will be selected from the remaining four members of M in $\binom{4}{2}$ different ways. If Betty is *not* to be included on the committee, then the committee of three will be selected from the other four members of M in $\binom{4}{3}$ different ways. Together, $\binom{4}{2} + \binom{4}{3}$, we have the total number of ways in which a committee of three can be selected from the set M. But this is given as $\binom{5}{3}$, which illustrates the relationship that we set out to demonstrate. This relationship and, in general,

$$\binom{n}{r} = \binom{n-1}{r-1} + \binom{n-1}{r}$$

can be formally proved by using the formula for $_nC_r$ (Exercise 20).

Pascal's triangle may be used mechanically to compute probabilities as follows:

The elements of the second row are the numerators for the probabilities when two coins are tossed; the elements of the third row are the numerators when three coins are tossed; and so on. The denominator in each case is found as the sum of the elements in the row used. For example, when three coins are tossed, we examine the third row (1, 3, 3, 1). The sum is 8. The probabilities of 0, 1, 2, and 3 heads are then given as $\frac{1}{8}$, $\frac{3}{8}$, $\frac{3}{8}$, $\frac{1}{8}$, as in §8-5.

Note that the sum of the entries in the second row is 4, the sum in the third row is 2^3 or 8, the sum in the fourth row is 2^4 or 16, and, in general, the sum in the nth row will be 2^n.

EXAMPLE: Use the fourth row of Pascal's triangle to find the probability of 0, 1, 2, 3, 4 heads in a single toss of four coins.

Solution: The numerators of the fractions for the probabilities are the entries

$$1, \quad 4, \quad 6, \quad 4, \quad 1$$

from the fourth row of Pascal's triangle. The denominators are each 16; that is, 2^4, where

$$2^4 = 1 + 4 + 6 + 4 + 1.$$

Thus we have

Number of heads	0	1	2	3	4
Probability	$\frac{1}{16}$	$\frac{4}{16}$	$\frac{6}{16}$	$\frac{4}{16}$	$\frac{1}{16}$

These probabilities may be checked as in §8-5. The method may be used also for numbers of tails.

EXERCISES FOR SECTION 8-8

In Exercises 1 through 10 use Pascal's triangle to find for a single toss of five coins the probability of:

1. 0 heads.

2. 1 head.

3. 2 heads.

4. 3 heads.

5. 4 heads.

6. 5 heads.

7. 1 tail.

8. 3 tails.

9. At least 2 tails.

10. More than 2 tails.

11. Construct Pascal's triangle for $n = 1, 2, 3, \ldots, 10$.

12. List the entries in the eleventh row of Pascal's triangle, using the notation

$$\binom{n}{r}.$$

13. Repeat Exercise 12 for the twelfth row.

14. Make a table of probabilities for all of the possible outcomes of heads when 6 coins are tossed.

15. What is the probability of obtaining at least four heads on a single toss of (**a**) 6 coins? (**b**) 7 coins?

16. What is the probability of obtaining at least three heads on a single toss of (**a**) 7 coins? (**b**) 10 coins?

17. What is the probability of obtaining more than three heads on a single toss of (**a**) 6 coins? (**b**) 8 coins?

*18. Pascal's triangle may be used to determine the coefficients in the binomial expansion of $(a + b)^n$. For example,

$$(a + b)^4 = \underline{1}a^4 + \underline{4}a^3b + \underline{6}a^2b^2 + \underline{4}ab^3 + \underline{1}b^4.$$

Note the pattern exhibited by the variables a and b, and use the results of Exercise 11 to write the expansion of $(a + b)^6$.

*19. Repeat Exercise 9 for $(a + b)^7$.

*20. Use the definition $\dbinom{n}{r} = \dfrac{n!}{r!(n - r)!}$ and prove that

$$\binom{n}{r} = \binom{n - 1}{r - 1} + \binom{n - 1}{r}.$$

TEST FOR CHAPTER 8

1. Evaluate: **(a)** $_8P_2$; **(b)** $_9C_3$.

2. A certain florist has 5 different kinds of roses. In how many ways can one each of 3 different kinds be selected?

3. Seven boys apply for two identifiably different vacancies at a store. In how many ways can the vacancies be filled?

4. A man has a nickel, a dime, a quarter, and a half-dollar. In how many ways can he leave a tip of exactly two coins?

5. Use a sample space to represent the possible outcomes described in Exercise 4 and find the probability that the tip is at least thirty cents when the selection of the two coins is at random.

6. What is the probability of tossing on a single toss of two dice **(a)** a 7? **(b)** a number greater than 7?

7. What are the odds in favor of obtaining an ace when one card is drawn from a deck of 52 bridge cards?

8. What is your mathematical expectation when you buy 3 tickets out of a total of 6000 tickets for a single prize worth $1000?

9. A hat contains 3 slips of paper labeled a, e, and t respectively. If the slips are drawn one at a time, what is the probability that the letters will spell "eat" in that order?

10. A disc jockey has 25 records. In how many ways can he **(a)** select 5 records to be used in a program? **(b)** arrange a program of 5 records?

chapter 9

CONCEPTS
OF LOGIC

You undoubtedly make numerous conscious and subconscious
decisions. Many of these decisions are based upon reasoning. Your
satisfactions from your decisions often depend upon the validity of
your reasoning and thus upon logical concepts. In this sense an
understanding of logical concepts can improve your personal oppor-
tunities to find the kind of life that you want and to enjoy the kind of
life that you find.

Reasoning is based upon the handling of facts, usually in the form
of statements. You may think of reasoning as an "algebra" of statements with the operations of conjunction, disjunction, negation, and
implication that we considered in Chapter 4. In this chapter truth
values of statements are considered in an effort to recognize relations
among statements. Then some of these relations are selected to
provide the basis for the discussion of valid arguments, logical reasoning, and proofs. In the process you will learn how to recognize

several different forms of the same statement in the English language. Many people feel that the study of logical concepts is worthwhile solely for the purpose of increasing their facility with the English language.

9-1 UNIVERSAL QUANTIFIERS

Many statements can be identified as true or false and are thus **decidable statements.** For example,

$$2 \times 3 = 5$$

is a false statement;

$$2 + 3 = 5$$

is a true statement. In general, any *arithmetic statement* is a decidable statement.

A statement that involves a variable may be considered to be an **algebraic statement.** These are examples of algebraic statements:

$$x + 1 = 1 + x$$
$$x + 1 \neq x$$
$$x + 2 = 5$$

Are these algebraic statements decidable? We think of the first statement as true, since $x + 1 = 1 + x$ for all real numbers x. Logicians include the *quantifier* "for all real numbers x" with the statement before considering the statements decideable. Consider the statements:

For all real numbers x, $x + 1 = 1 + x$.
For all real numbers x, $x + 1 \neq x$.
For all real numbers x, $x + 2 = 5$.

Each of these statements is decidable. The first two are true; the third is false. The necessity of the quantifier may be recognized for the second statement by recalling from §5-1 that

$$\aleph_0 + 1 = \aleph_0.$$

The quantifier "for all real numbers x" identifies the universal set (in this case the set of real numbers) of values of x that are to be considered. Any quantifier of the form

For all _____,

or equivalent to this form, is called a **universal quantifier.**

We use universal quantifiers when we say

For all integers n, $n = \dfrac{n}{1}$.

For all integers n, n is a rational number.

Every integer is a rational number.

For all right angles A and B, $\angle A \cong \angle B$.

Any two right angles are congruent.

All right angles are congruent.

For all real numbers x and all y, $x + y = y + x$.

We frequently assert that statements are universally true by statements of the form:

For all x, _____ .

Every x is _____

For all x and all y, _____ .

Any two x and y are _____ .

All x and all y are _____ .

Each of these universal quantifiers can be considered in one of the forms:

For all x.

For all x and all y.

These quantifiers may be expressed in symbols:

$\forall_x$ read as "For all x."

$\forall_x \forall_y$ read as "For all x and all y."

When it is necessary to specify the universal set, we write the universal quantifier in the form

$\forall_x$, x a real number, _____ .

::

EXAMPLE 1: Give an appropriate symbol to identify the universal quantifier in each statement:

(a) For all real numbers x, $x \times 1 = x$.

(b) All squares are rectangles.

(c) Every integer is a real number.

Solution: (a) $\forall_x$, x a real number; (b) $\forall_x$, x a square; (c) $\forall_x$, x an integer.

::

Consider the statement

$$\text{If } x = 2, \quad \text{then} \quad x + 3 = 5.$$

This statement appears to have its own "built-in" quantifier for x, since the variable x is simply another name for the number 2. In this sense the variable x is not a **free variable.** The variable x is free in each of these statements, and each statement is not decidable:

$$x + 2 = 5$$
$$x < 1$$
$$x \neq 7$$

A variable is not a free variable when it has an assigned value, as in the statement

$$\text{If } x = 2, \quad \text{then} \quad x + 3 = 5.$$

A variable is not a free variable when it is restricted by a universal quantifier, as in the statement

$$\forall x, \ x \text{ a real number}, \ x + 3 = 5.$$

Also, a variable is not a free variable when it is restricted by an *existential quantifier* (§9-2), as in the statement

There exists a real value of x such that $x + 3 = 5$.

We assume, as in the formal study of logic, that

Each statement that involves a free variable is not decidable.
Each statement that does not involve a free variable is decidable.

We may restrict a free variable in a statement and thereby make the statement decidable in any one of these three ways:

Assign a value to the variable.
Use a universal quantifier.
Use an existential quantifier (§9-2).

EXAMPLE 2: Make each sentence false (therefore decidable) by assigning a value to the free variable:

(a) $x^2 + 1 = 10$;   (b) $m(\angle A) = 90$ and $\angle A \cong \angle B$.

Solution: (a) $x = 5$; any value different from 3 and -3 may be used to make the sentence false as requested. (b) $\angle B$ is a straight angle; other procedures may be used to assert that B is not a right angle. Note that A is not a free variable.

EXAMPLE 3:   Use universal quantifiers to make each statement decidable for real variables x, y, and z:

(a) $x + 2 = 5$;   (b) $x(y + z) = xy + xz$.

Solution: (a) $\forall_x: x + 2 = 5$; (b) $\forall_x \forall_y \forall_z: x(y + z) = xy + xz$.

In Example 3(a) the given statement $x + 2 = 5$ is true if $x = 3$ and false if $x \neq 3$; that is, the statement is neither true nor false as originally stated. The statement $\forall_x: x + 2 = 5$ is false for the real variable x, since a **counterexample** (an example for which the statement is false) may be found; for example,

$$\text{If } x = 5, \quad \text{then} \quad x + 2 \neq 5.$$

Any value different from 3 can be used for x to obtain a counterexample for the statement $\forall_x: x + 2 = 5$. Any universal statement for which at least one counterexample can be found is false.

EXAMPLE 4:   Identify as true or false for a real variable x:

(a) $\forall_x: \ x + 2 = 2 + x$;   (b) $\forall_x: \ x - 2 = 2 - x$.

Solution: (a) True by the commutative property of addition; (b) false, since for $x = 1$ the statement $1 - 2 = 2 - 1$ is false.

Notice in Example 4(b) that a single example such as $x = 2$ for which the statement is true, $2 - 2 = 2 - 2$, is not enough to prove that a universal statement is true.

EXERCISES FOR SECTION 9-1

Give an appropriate symbol to identify the universal quantifier used in each statement:

   1. For all real numbers x, $x + 1 = 1 + x$.

2. For all integers y, $y - 1 = 1 - y$.

3. For all integers t, $[t] = t$.

4. All integers are real numbers.

5. Every real number is a complex number.

6. Every rectangle is a parallelogram.

7. All triangles are polygons.

8. Any even integer is divisible by 2.

9. Any house is a building.

10. Triangles are plane figures.

11. If x is an integer, then x is even.

12. If x is a rational number, then x is a whole number.

Assign a value to the variable to make each statement (a) true: (b) false:

13. $x - 2 = 7$ 14. $2x + 3 = 15$

15. $2 - 3x = 20$ 16. $5 - 2x = 35$

Use universal quantifiers to make each statement decidable for real variables x, y, and z:

17. $x + 2y = 2x + y$ 18. $2x + 6 = 2(x + 3)$

19. $x + yz = (x + y)z$ 20. $xy + yz = y(x + z)$

Identify as true or false for a real variable x:

21. $\forall_x$: $x^2 - 1 = (x - 1)(x + 1)$

22. $\forall_x$: $x(1 - x) = x - x^2$

23. $\forall_x$: $x^x \neq 1$ 24. $\forall_x$: $x^x \neq 4$

25. $\forall_x$: $\dfrac{x}{x} = 1$ 26. $\forall_x$: $\dfrac{2x - 2}{x - 1} = 2$

9-2 EXISTENTIAL QUANTIFIERS

There are several ways in which we may assert the existence of at least one value of the real variable x in the sentence $x^2 < 5$. For example, we may say:

There exists a real number x such that $x^2 < 5$.

There is at least one real number x such that $x^2 < 5$.
$x^2 < 5$ for some real number x.

Each of these statements may be written as

$$\exists_x, x \text{ a real number}: x^2 < 5.$$

For real numbers x we write simply

$$\exists_x: \quad x^2 < 5.$$

We read the **existential quantifier** $\exists_x$ as "there exists at least one x such that."

EXAMPLE 1:   Use existential quantifiers to make each statement a true statement for real variables x, y, and z:

(a) $2x + 3 = 17$;   (b) $x^2 - 1 \neq 8$;
(c) $x + y = y - x$;   (d) $x^2 = xyz$.

Solution: (a) $\exists_x: \quad 2x + 3 = 17$;   (b) $\exists_x: \quad x^2 - 1 \neq 8$;
(c) $\exists_x\exists_y: \quad x + y = y - x$; (d) $\exists_x\exists_y\exists_z: \quad x^2 = xyz$.

The statement (a) is true for $x = 7$. The selection of values for which the other statements are true may be done in many ways. For example, consider for (b) $x = 2$; for (c) $x = 0$ and $y = 5$; for (d) $x = 6, y = 2$, and $z = 3$.

EXAMPLE 2:   Give an appropriate symbol for the existential quantifier in each statement:

(a) There exist positive integers greater than 7.
(b) The equation $x^3 + 7x^2 + x = 9$ has an integral solution.

Solution: (a) $\exists_x$, x a positive integer: (b) $\exists_x$, x an integer.

The close relationship between existential quantifiers and universal quantifiers is evident when we consider negations of statements. As in §4-7, we use $\sim p$ to represent the negation of any statement p.

If p is true, then $\sim p$ is false; if p is false, then $\sim p$ is true. Consider these statements:

p: All triangles are isosceles.

$\sim p$:   Not all triangles are isosceles; that is, there exists a triangle that is not isosceles.

q: There exists a mortal who does not live on earth.

$\sim q$:   It is not true that there exists a mortal who does not live on earth; that is, all mortals live on earth.

Notice that the statement p has the form $V_x: r$, and the negation of p has the form $\exists_x: \sim r$; the statement q has the form $\exists_x: s$, and the negation of q has the form $V_x: \sim s$. In general, the negation of any statement of the form

$$V_x: \quad r \qquad \text{(for all } x)$$

is the corresponding statement

$$\exists_x: \quad \sim r \qquad \text{(there exists at least one } x \text{ such that);}$$

the negation of any statement of the form

$$\exists_x: \quad s \qquad \text{(there exists at least one } x \text{ such that)}$$

is the corresponding statement

$$V_x: \quad \sim s \qquad \text{(for all } x).$$

EXAMPLE 3:   State in words the negation of each statement:
(a) There is a rectangle that is not a square.
(b) All triangles are right triangles.

Solution: (a) All rectangles are squares. (b) There exists a triangle that is not a right triangle.

EXAMPLE 4:   State in symbols the negation of each statement:

(a) $V_x: x^2 > 1$;   (b) $\exists_x: x = |x|$.

Solution: (a) $\exists_x: x^2 \leq 1$; (b) $V_x: x \neq |x|$.

EXERCISES FOR SECTION 9-2

Give an appropriate symbol for the existential quantifier in each statement:

1. There exists a nonnegative number.

2. There exist negative numbers.

3. The equation $x - 5 = 7$ has an integral solution.

4. The equation $x^3 = -8$ has an integral solution.

5. Some real numbers are positive.

6. Some real numbers are negative.

7. There is at least one real number that is neither positive nor negative.

8. The equation $x^{31} - 17 = 0$ has at least one real root.

Use an existential quantifier to make each statement a true statement for a real variable x:

9. $2x - 5 = 11$ **10.** $2 - x = 8 + x$

11. $x^2 - x - 6 = 0$ **12.** $x^2 - 75 = 0$

State in words the negation of each statement:

13. All apples are pieces of fruit.

14. All numbers are real numbers.

15. Any whole number is positive.

16. Any fraction represents a rational number.

17. There exist rational numbers that are not integers.

18. There exist real numbers that are not rational numbers.

19. Some complex numbers are real numbers.

20. Some rational numbers are integers.

In Exercises 21 through 24 state in symbols the negation of each given statement:

21. V_x: $x = 2$ **22.** $\exists_x$: $x + 1 = 1 + x$

23. $\exists_x$: $x^2 \leq 0$ **24.** V_x: $x + 1 = 1 + x$

25. There are also symbols for specifying the exact number of values of x that exist for a given statement. For example, we may write for a real variable x:

$\exists_{1x}$: $x + 2 = 5$.   There exists exactly one value of x such that $x + 2 = 5$.

$\exists_{2x}$: $x^2 = 7$.   There exist exactly two values of x such that $x^2 = 7$.

Identify each statement as true or false for a real variable x:

(a) $\exists_{1x}$: $x^2 = 9$ (b) $\exists_{2x}$: $x^2 = 1$

(c) $\exists_{2x}$: $x^2 = |x|$ (d) $\exists_{2x}$: $x = |x|$

9-3 DEPENDENT STATEMENTS

There are four possible combinations of truth values that may arise for any statements p and q. We denote these combinations by TT, TF, FT, and FF as in the following array:

	TT	TF	FT	FF
p:	T	T	F	F
q:	T	F	T	F

Two statements are **independent statements** if all four possible combinations of their truth values arise (occur). Two statements are **dependent statements** if they are not independent statements; that is, if at least one of the combinations of truth values fails to occur. In the following array we use "$\checkmark$" to show that a specified combination of truth values can be satisfied (occurs) for the given statements and "$\times$" to show that the specified combination does not occur. We number the examples so that we may refer to them later as "Case 1," "Case 2," and so forth. The sixteen cases are arranged in the same order as we would use for a truth table for four statements. Any two statements provide an example of exactly one of the sixteen cases. Two statements are independent if and only if they illustrate Case 1 as shown by the four check marks in the chart on page 288.

	TT	TF	FT	FF	Example
1.	✓	✓	✓	✓	p: It is eight o'clock in the evening here. q: It is quiet outside now.
2.	✓	✓	✓	✗	p: $x^2 = 9$, x real. q: $x \neq 3$, x real.
3.	✓	✓	✗	✓	p: It is a citrus fruit. q: It is an orange.
4.	✓	✓	✗	✗	p: $x + 1 = x + 1$. q: $x + 2 = 5$.
5.	✓	✗	✓	✓	p: It is an orange. q: It is a citrus fruit.
6.	✓	✗	✓	✗	p: $x + 2 = 5$. q: $x + 1 = x + 1$.
7.	✓	✗	✗	✓	p: $x = 2$. q: $3x = 6$.
8.	✓	✗	✗	✗	p: $x + 2 \leq x + 2$. q: $x = x$.
9.	✗	✓	✓	✓	p: This car is a Ford. q: This car is a Chevrolet.
10.	✗	✓	✓	✗	p: This car is a Ford. q: This car is not a Ford.
11.	✗	✓	✗	✓	p: $x + 2 = 5$. q: $x + 1 \neq x + 1$.
12.	✗	✓	✗	✗	p: $x + 1 = x + 1$. q: $2x \neq x + x$.
13.	✗	✗	✓	✓	p: $x + 1 \neq x + 1$. q: $x + 2 = 5$.
14.	✗	✗	✓	✗	p: $2x \neq x + x$. q: $x + 1 = x + 1$.
15.	✗	✗	✗	✓	p: $x + 1 \neq x + 1$. q: $2x \neq x + x$.
16.	✗	✗	✗	✗	Impossible.

As you read the examples in the array you undoubtedly noticed that

1. There exist statements t such as

$$x + 1 = x + 1$$
$$x = x$$
$$2x = x + x$$
$$x + 2 \leq x + 2$$

that are always true; that is, $\mathbf{V}_x: \quad t$.

2. There exist statements s such as

$$x + 1 \neq x + 1$$
$$2x \neq x + x$$

that are always false; that is, $\mathbf{V}_x: \quad \sim s$.

3. There exist statements r such as

> It is eight o'clock in the evening here.
> It is an orange.
> $x + 2 = 5$.

that may be either true or false; that is,

$$(\exists_x: \quad r) \wedge (\exists_x: \quad \sim r).$$

Various selections of statements have been used to illustrate each of the first fifteen possible cases of pairs of truth values for p and q. Our failure to find an example for Case 16 is based upon the fact that we consider only statements p, q that are either true or false. Accordingly, it is not possible to find statements p and q that are neither true nor false; that is, statements such that none of the combinations of truth values TT, TF, FT, FF occur.

Two statements p and q are **consistent statements** if the combination of truth values TT may occur (Cases 1 through 8). Thus any two independent statements are consistent; also, any two dependent statements of the kinds represented in Cases 2 through 8 are consistent.

Two statements p and q are **contrary statements** if they are not consistent; that is, if the combination of truth values TT fails to occur (Cases 9 through 15). The two statements are **contradictory statements** if and only if both the combinations TT and FF fail to occur and both the combinations TF and FT occur (Case 10). Thus any two contradictory statements are contrary statements; any two contrary statements are dependent statements.

Examples of independent, dependent, consistent, contrary, and contradictory statements are given for the various cases cited. To determine whether or not the statements of a given pair are independent, dependent, consistent, contrary, or contradictory, we first identify the combinations of truth values that may occur and thus the case that the two statements illustrate.

EXAMPLE: Determine whether or not the given statements are independent, dependent, consistent, contrary, or contradictory:

$$p: \quad x < 5, x \text{ real}$$
$$q: \quad x^2 = 36, x \text{ real}$$

Solution: The combination of truth values

TT: occurs if $x = -6$;
TF: occurs if, for example, $x = 2$;
FT: occurs if $x = 6$;
FF: occurs if, for example, $x = 7$.

The given statements illustrate Case 1 and thus are independent, not dependent, consistent, not contrary, and not contradictory.

EXERCISES FOR SECTION 9-3

1 through **15.** Give three additional examples of pairs of statements p and q for Cases 1 through 15 of possible combinations of truth values considered in this section.

Identify the combinations of truth values that may arise and thus the particular case that is illustrated by each pair of statements:

16. p: The car is a Buick.
    q: The car is not a Cadillac.

17. p: x is a positive number.
    q: x is a negative number.

18. p: $x < 7$.
    q: $x \geq 7$.

19. p: $x < 6$.
    q: $x = 7$.

20. p: $x^2 = 25$.
    q: $x \neq 5$.

21. p: $x \neq x + 1$.
    q: $x^2 > 0$.

Identify the pairs of statements in Exercises 16 through 21 that are:

22. Independent.   23. Dependent.

24. Consistent.   25. Contrary.

26. Contradictory.

9-4 EQUIVALENT STATEMENTS

Two statements are **equivalent statements** if they are either both true or both false as in Case 7 of §9-3. If p and q are equivalent statements, we write

$$p \leftrightarrow q \qquad \text{read as "}p\text{ is equivalent to }q\text{."}$$

Notice that two statements p and q are contradictory (§9-3) if and only if $p \leftrightarrow (\sim q)$.

EXAMPLE 1:   Show by means of a truth table that

$$(p \to q) \leftrightarrow [(\sim q) \to (\sim p)]$$

Solution:

p	q	$[p \to q]$	$\longleftrightarrow$	$[(\sim q)$	$\longrightarrow$	$(\sim p)]$
T	T	T	T	F	T	F
T	F	F	T	T	F	F
F	T	T	T	F	T	T
F	F	T	T	T	T	T
		(a)	(e)	(b)	(d)	(c)

The desired equivalence is always true, as indicated in column (e).

The following pairs of equivalent statements (see §4-7 for the meanings of the symbols used) are considered in Exercises 1 through 4:

1. $\sim(p \wedge q)$ and $(\sim p) \vee (\sim q)$
2. $\sim(p \vee q)$ and $(\sim p) \wedge (\sim q)$
3. $p \rightarrow q$ and $q \vee (\sim p)$
4. $(\sim p) \rightarrow (\sim q)$ and $q \rightarrow p$

The first two of these pairs of equivalent statements correspond to properties of sets and their complements

$$(A \cap B)' = A' \cup B'$$
$$(A \cup B)' = A' \cap B'$$

and thus are sometimes called *De Morgan's laws for statements*. The third pair of equivalent statements enables us to replace any statement of implication by a disjunction.

∷∷∷

EXAMPLE 2:   Rephrase as a disjunction:

If a triangle is equilateral, then it is isosceles.

Solution: Any triangle is either isosceles or not equilateral.

∷∷∷

Each statement $p \rightarrow q$ has a **converse statement** $q \rightarrow p$; an **inverse statement** $(\sim p) \rightarrow (\sim q)$; and a **contrapositive statement** $(\sim q) \rightarrow (\sim p)$. Frequently these dependent statements are presented as in this array:

Statement:	$p \rightarrow q$
Converse:	$q \rightarrow p$
Inverse:	$(\sim p) \rightarrow (\sim q)$
Contrapositive:	$(\sim q) \rightarrow (\sim p)$

The statement proved in Example 1 may now be expressed in the form:

Any statement of implication is equivalent to its contrapositive.

Similarly, the equivalence to be proved in Exercise 4 may be expressed in the form:

The inverse of any given statement of implication is equivalent to the converse of the given statement.

Here are five examples of statements of implication with their converses, inverses, and contrapositives:

1. *Statement:* If it is snowing, I leave my car in the garage.
   Converse: If I leave my car in the garage, it is snowing.
   Inverse: If it is not snowing, I do not leave my car in the garage.
   Contrapositive: If I do not leave my car in the garage, it is not snowing.
2. *Statement:* If $\triangle ABC \cong \triangle XYZ$, then $\triangle ABC \sim \triangle XYZ$.
   Converse: If $\triangle ABC \sim \triangle XYZ$, then $\triangle ABC \cong \triangle XYZ$.
   Inverse: If $\triangle ABC$ is not congruent to $\triangle XYZ$, then $\triangle ABC$ is not similar to $\triangle XYZ$.
   Contrapositive: If $\triangle ABC$ is not similar to $\triangle XYZ$, then $\triangle ABC$ is not congruent to $\triangle XYZ$.
3. *Statement:* If x is negative, then $x \neq 0$.
   Converse: If $x \neq 0$, then x is negative.
   Inverse: If x is not negative, then $x = 0$.
   Contrapositive: If $x = 0$, then x is not negative.
4. *Statement:* If $x + 2 = 5$, then $x = 3$.
   Converse: If $x = 3$, then $x + 2 = 5$.
   Inverse: If $x + 2 \neq 5$, then $x \neq 3$.
   Contrapositive: If $x \neq 3$, then $x + 2 \neq 5$.
5. *Statement:* $p \rightarrow (\sim q)$.
   Converse: $(\sim q) \rightarrow p$.
   Inverse: $(\sim p) \rightarrow \sim (\sim q)$, which can be simplified as $(\sim p) \rightarrow q$.
   Contrapositive: $\sim (\sim q) \rightarrow (\sim p)$, or simply $q \rightarrow (\sim p)$.

The following truth tables for these variants of a conditional statement $p \rightarrow q$ summarize this discussion and specify the truth values for each statement:

		Statement	Converse	Inverse	Contrapositive
p	q	$p \rightarrow q$	$q \rightarrow p$	$(\sim p) \rightarrow (\sim q)$	$(\sim q) \rightarrow (\sim p)$
T	T	T	T	T	T
T	F	F	T	T	F
F	T	T	F	F	T
F	F	T	T	T	T

EXERCISES FOR SECTION 9-4

Show by means of truth tables that the following statements are equivalent:

1. $\sim(p \wedge q)$ and $(\sim p) \vee (\sim q)$.

2. $\sim(p \vee q)$ and $(\sim p) \wedge (\sim q)$.

3. $p \rightarrow q$ and $q \vee (\sim p)$.

4. $(\sim p) \rightarrow (\sim q)$ and $q \rightarrow p$.

Write the converse, inverse, and contrapositive of each statement:

5. If we can afford it, then we buy a new car.

6. If we play pingpong, then you win the game.

7. If two sides and the included angle of one triangle are congruent to two sides and the included angle of another triangle, then the triangles are congruent.

8. If $x > 2$, then $x \neq 0$.

9. If $x(x - 1) = 0$, then $x = 1$.

10. $(\sim p) \rightarrow q$.

Exercises 11, 12, 13, and 14 refer to the statements given in Exercises 7, 8, and 9. Tell whether or not you accept as always true:

11. The given statement.

12. The converse of the given statement.

13. The inverse of the given statement.

14. The contrapositive of the given statement.

9-5 FORMS OF STATEMENTS

Any two equivalent statements (§9-4) may be considered as different forms of the same statement. The recognition of different forms of a statement is particularly useful when statements of implication (conditional statements, §4-8) are under consideration. Frequently the words *necessary* and *sufficient* are used in conditional statements. For example, consider the statement:

Working hard is a sufficient condition for passing the course.

Let us use p to mean "work hard" and q to represent "pass the course." We need to decide whether the given statement means "if p, then q" or "if q, then p." The word sufficient can be interpreted to mean that working hard is adequate or enough—but not necessary—for passing. That is, there may be other ways to pass the course, but working hard will do it. Thus we interpret the statement to mean:

> If you work hard, then you will pass the course.

The symbolic statement $p \rightarrow q$ may thus be used for each of these statements:

> If p, then q.
> p is a sufficient condition for q.

Next consider the statement:

> Working hard is a necessary condition for passing the course.

Here you are told that working hard is necessary or essential in order to pass. That is, regardless of what else you do, you had better work hard if you wish to pass. However there is no assurance that working hard alone will do the trick. It is necessary, but not sufficient. (You may also have to get good grades.) Therefore, we interpret the statement to mean:

> If you pass the course, then you have worked hard.

The symbolic statement $q \rightarrow p$ may thus be used for each of these statements:

> If q, then p.
> p is a necessary condition for q.

Still another form to consider is the statement "q, only if p." In terms of the example used in this section we may write this as:

> You will pass the course only if you work hard.

Note that this does *not* say that working hard will insure a passing grade. It does mean that if you have passed, then you have worked hard. That is, "q, only if p" is equivalent to the statement "if q, then p."

We can also interpret this in another way. This statement "q, only if p" means "if not p, then not q." The contrapositive of this last statement, however, is "if q, then p." In terms of our illustration this means that if you do not work hard, then you will not pass. Therefore, if you pass, then you have worked hard.

To summarize our discussion to date, each of the following statements represents an equivalent form of writing the statement $p \rightarrow q$:

If p, then q.

q, if p.

p implies q.

q is implied by p.

p is a sufficient condition for q.

q is a necessary condition for p.

p, only if q.

The last form is probably the hardest to use. It should appear reasonable when considered as a restatement of the fact that if $p \rightarrow q$, then it is impossible to have p without having q.

The seven ways of asserting that a statement p implies a statement q illustrate the difficulty of understanding the English language. We shall endeavor to reduce the confusion by considering statements of implication in the form

$$p \rightarrow q$$

when stated in symbols and in the form

If p, then q

when stated in words.

EXAMPLE 1:   Write each statement in if-then form:
  (a) Right angles are congruent.
  (b) $x > 5$, only if $x \geq 0$.

Solution: (a) If two angles are right angles, then they are congruent. (b) If $x > 5$, then $x \geq 0$.

EXAMPLE 2:   Translate into symbolic form, using

  p: I will work hard.
  q: I will get an A.

  (a) I will get an A only if I work hard.
  (b) Working hard will be a sufficient condition for me to get an A.

(c) If I work hard then I will get an A and if I get an A then
I will have worked hard.

Solution: (a) $q \rightarrow p$; (b) $p \rightarrow q$; (c) $(p \rightarrow q) \wedge (q \rightarrow p)$.

The statement $(p \rightarrow q) \wedge (q \rightarrow p)$ in Example 2(c) is one way of
stating that p and q are equivalent, $p \leftrightarrow q$. Any statement of implication is sometimes called a conditional statement (§4-8); any statement
of the equivalence of two statements is then called a **biconditional
statement.** The symbol $\leftrightarrow$ is referred to as the **biconditional symbol**
or the **equivalence symbol.**
      Any biconditional statement

$$p \leftrightarrow q$$

is a statement that p is a sufficient condition for q and also p is a
necessary condition for q. We may condense this by saying that p is a
necessary and sufficient condition for q. The biconditional statement may be stated in any one of these forms:

p if and only if q; that is, p **iff** q.
p implies and is implied by q.
p is a necessary and sufficient condition for q.

EXAMPLE 3:   Complete a truth table for the statement:
$$(p \rightarrow q) \wedge (q \rightarrow p).$$

Solution:

p	q	$(p \rightarrow q)$	$\wedge$	$(q \rightarrow p)$
T	T	T	T	T
T	F	F	F	T
F	T	T	F	F
F	F	T	T	T
		(a)	(c)	(b)

p	q	$p \leftrightarrow q$
T	T	T
T	F	F
F	T	F
F	F	T

In Example 3 we constructed a truth table for the statement $(p \rightarrow q) \wedge (q \rightarrow p)$. However, we have previously agreed that this conjunction of statements is equivalent to $p \leftrightarrow q$. This enables us to construct a truth table for $p \leftrightarrow q$ as shown above.

From the truth table we see that $p \leftrightarrow q$ is true when p and q are both true or are both false. Thus each of these statements is true:

$2 \times 2 = 4$ if and only if $7 - 5 = 2$. (Both parts are true.)
$2 \times 2 = 5$ if and only if $7 - 5 = 3$. (Both parts are false.)

Each of the following statements is false because exactly one part of each statement is false:

$$2 \times 2 = 4 \quad \text{if and only if} \quad 7 - 5 = 3.$$
$$2 \times 2 = 5 \quad \text{if and only if} \quad 7 - 5 = 2.$$

As we have previously noted, we use the symbol "$\leftrightarrow$" to show that two statements are equivalent. Consider these statements:

p: I cut the grass this afternoon.
q: The sun is shining.

Then the statement "$p \leftrightarrow q$," that is, p if and only if q, is true in these two cases:

1. I cut the grass and the sun is shining.
2. I do not cut the grass and the sun is not shining.

In all other cases, the statement "$p \leftrightarrow q$" is false. Briefly, two statements "p" and "q" are equivalent if each implies the other; in other words, we may write "$p \leftrightarrow q$" if it is true that $p \rightarrow q$ and also that $q \rightarrow p$.

EXAMPLE 4: Under what conditions is the following statement true?

I will get an A if and only if I work hard.

Solution: The statement is true in each of two cases:
(a) You get an A and you work hard.
(b) You do not get an A and you do not work hard.

EXERCISES FOR SECTION 9-5

Write each statement in if-then form:

1. All ducks are birds.

2. Vertical angles are congruent.

3. Complements of the sàme angle are congruent.

4. Supplements of congruent angles are congruent.

5. Any two parallel lines are coplanar.

6. All triangles are polygons.

7. All circles are round.

8. All mathematics books are dull.

9. All teachers are boring.

10. All p are q.

11. You will like this book only if you like mathematics.

12. A necessary condition for liking this book is that you like mathematics.

13. To like this book it is sufficient that you like mathematics.

14. A sufficient condition for liking this book is that you like mathematics.

15. Liking this book is a necessary condition for liking mathematics.

Write each statement in symbolic form using:

p: The sun shines.
q: I cut the grass.

16. If the sun shines, then I cut the grass.

17. I will cut the grass only if the sun shines.

18. If the sun does not shine, then I do not cut the grass.

19. The sun's shining is a necessary condition for me to cut the grass.

20. I cut the grass if and only if the sun shines.

21. If the sun shines then I do not cut the grass.

22. For me to cut the grass it is sufficient that the sun shine.

23. A necessary and sufficient condition for me to cut the grass is that the sun shine.

Write each statement in symbolic form using:

p: I miss my breakfast.

q: I get up late.

24. I miss my breakfast if and only if I get up late.

25. A necessary condition for me to miss my breakfast is that I get up late.

26. For me to miss my breakfast it is sufficient that I get up late.

27. A necessary and sufficient condition for me to miss my breakfast is that I get up late.

28. For me not to miss my breakfast it is necessary that I do not get up late.

Express each statement in if-then form and classify as true or false:

29. $11 - 3 > 8$ if $9 + 3 < 10$.

30. A necessary condition for 2×2 to be equal to 5 is that $8 - 5 = 3$.

31. For 7×4 to be equal to 25 it is sufficient that $5 + 3 = 8$.

32. $7 \times 6 = 40$ only if $8 \times 5 \neq 40$.

33. $7 \times 6 = 42$ only if $8 \times 5 \neq 40$.

Decide relative to each given assertion whether or not a young man who makes the assertion, receives the money, and fails to marry the young lady can be sued for breach of promise:

34. I will marry your daughter only if you give me $10,000.

35. A sufficient condition for me to marry your daughter is that you give me $10,000.

9-6 THE NATURE OF PROOF

How do you "prove" a statement to a friend? Undoubtedly there are several ways, including these three:

1. Find the statement in an encyclopedia or other reference that he will accept without further proof.
2. Prove to him that the statement is a necessary consequence of some statement that he accepts.
3. Prove to him that the statement cannot be false.

In mathematics there are also several ways of "proving" statements. In essence each proof is based upon:

1. Statements that are accepted as true (assumed).
2. Sequences of statements (arguments) such that each statement is either assumed or is a *logical consequence* of the preceding statements, and the statement to be proved is included in the sequence.
3. Proofs that statements cannot be false.

Thus the "key" to our understanding the nature of proof is our understanding of "logical consequences." We shall find in §9-7 that each logical consequence of a statement depends not only upon the given statement but also upon one or more statements that cannot fail to be true. Any statement such as $p \vee (\sim p)$ that is always true is called a **tautology.**

EXAMPLE: Determine whether or not the statement

$$[(p \to q) \wedge p] \to q$$

is a tautology.

Solution:

p	q	$[(p \longrightarrow q)$	$\wedge$	$p]$	$\longrightarrow$	q
T	T	T	T	T	T	T
T	F	F	F	T	T	F
F	T	T	F	F	T	T
F	F	T	F	F	T	F
		(a)	(c)	(b)	(e)	(d)

The truth value of the given statement is T under all possible situations, as shown in column (e); therefore, the statement is a tautology.

EXERCISES FOR SECTION 9-6

Determine whether or not each statement is a tautology:

1. $p \vee (\sim p)$
2. $\sim[p \wedge (\sim p)]$
3. $[(p \rightarrow q) \wedge (\sim q)] \rightarrow (\sim p)$
4. $[(p \rightarrow q) \wedge q] \rightarrow p$
5. $[(p \rightarrow q) \wedge (\sim p)] \rightarrow (\sim q)$
6. $(p \wedge q) \leftrightarrow (q \wedge p)$
7. $[(p \vee q) \wedge (\sim p)] \rightarrow q$
8. $(p \vee q) \rightarrow (q \vee p)$
9. $[(p \rightarrow q) \wedge (q \rightarrow r)] \rightarrow (p \rightarrow r)$

9-7 VALID ARGUMENTS

We shall consider proofs in terms of the patterns (arguments) formed by the statements used. The assumed statements are identified as **given statements** and called **premises.** The statements to be proved are called **conclusions.**

EXAMPLE 1: Determine whether or not the following argument is valid:

Given: If Mary is a junior, she is taking algebra.
Given: Mary is a junior.
Conclusion: Mary is taking algebra.

Solution: Use

p: Mary is a junior.
q: Mary is taking algebra.

and think of the argument as:

Given: $p \rightarrow q$.
Given: p.
Conclusion: q.

The argument is valid if and only if the statement
$$[(p \rightarrow q) \wedge p] \rightarrow q$$
is a tautology. This statement is a tautology (§9-6, Example 1).
Thus the argument is valid.

The argument used in Example 1 illustrates one of the basic rules
of inference, the **law of detachment,** also called **modus ponens:**

If a statement of the form "If p, then q" is assumed to be true,
and if p is known to be true, then q must be true.

EXAMPLE 2:   Determine whether or not the following argument is valid:

Given: If $3x - 1 = 8$, then $3x = 9$.
Given: $3x - 1 = 8$.
Conclusion: $3x = 9$.

Solution: For
$$p: \quad 3x - 1 = 8$$
$$q: \quad 3x = 9$$
the argument has the form of the tautology
$$[(p \rightarrow q) \wedge p] \rightarrow q$$
and is valid as in Example 1.

EXAMPLE 3:   Determine whether or not the following argument is valid:

Given: If you worked hard, then you passed the course.
Given: You passed the course.
Conclusion: You worked hard.

Solution: For
$$p: \quad \text{You worked hard.}$$
$$q: \quad \text{You passed the course.}$$

the argument has the form

$$[(p \rightarrow q) \wedge q] \rightarrow p.$$

This statement is not a tautology (§9-6, Exercise 4). Thus the argument is not valid.

Notice that anyone who uses the argument in Example 3 to convince his friends that he has worked hard is hoping that his friends will think that the converse of any true conditional statement is also true; that is,

$$\text{If } p \rightarrow q, \quad \text{then} \quad q \rightarrow p.$$

We know from our comparison of truth values of $p \rightarrow q$ and $q \rightarrow p$ that a statement does not necessarily imply its converse. As another example of this type of reasoning consider the advertisement:

If you want to be healthy, eat KORNIES.

The advertiser hopes that the consumer will fallaciously assume the converse statement:

If you eat KORNIES, then you will be healthy.

EXAMPLE 4: Determine whether or not the following argument is valid:

Given: If you worked hard, then you passed the course.
Given: You did not pass the course.
Conclusion: You did not work hard.

Solution: For

p: You worked hard.
q: You passed the course.

the argument has the form

$$[(p \rightarrow q) \wedge (\sim q)] \rightarrow (\sim p).$$

This statement is a tautology (§9-6, Exercise 3), and the argument is valid.

Notice that the argument in Example 4 is based upon the equivalence of any conditional statement $p \rightarrow q$ and its contrapositive statement $(\sim q) \rightarrow (\sim p)$ as we observed in §9-4.

※※

EXAMPLE 5:   Determine whether or not the following argument is valid:

Given: If you worked hard, then you passed the course.
Given: You did not work hard.
Conclusion: You did not pass the course.

Solution: For

> p: You worked hard.
> q: You passed the course.

the argument has the form

$$[(p \rightarrow q) \wedge (\sim p)] \rightarrow (\sim q).$$

This statement is not a tautology (§9-6, Exercise 5), and the argument is not valid.

※※

Notice that anyone who uses the argument in Exercise 5 expects his listeners to assume that the inverse $(\sim p) \rightarrow (\sim q)$ of any true statement $p \rightarrow q$ must be true. As in the case of a conditional statement and its converse, we know that a statement does not necessarily imply its inverse. As another example of this type of reasoning, consider the advertisement:

> If you brush your teeth with SCRUB, then you will have no cavities.

The advertiser would like you to assume fallaciously the inverse statement:

> If you do not brush your teeth with SCRUB, then you will have cavities.

The final form of valid reasoning that we shall consider here is based upon the tautology

$$(p \rightarrow q) \wedge (q \rightarrow r) \rightarrow (p \rightarrow r)$$

(§9-6 Exercise 9). Consider these specific examples:

1. If you like this book, then you like mathematics.
   If you like mathematics, then you are intelligent.
   Therefore, if you like this book, then you are intelligent.
2. If a polygon is a square, then it has 3 sides.
   If a polygon has 3 sides, then it has 4 angles.
   Therefore, if a polygon is a square, then it has 4 angles.
3. If a polygon is a square, then it has 4 sides.
   If a polygon has 4 sides, then it has 3 angles.
   Therefore, if a polygon is a square, then it has 3 angles.

In the second example both premises are false, the conclusion is true, and the argument is valid. In the third example the first premise is true, the second premise is false, the conclusion is false, yet the argument is again valid, since it is based upon a tautology. Thus the truth of the conclusion does not enter in any way into a discussion of the validity of an argument. The *validity* of an argument depends solely upon its form; that is, whether or not it is based upon a tautology. The *truth* of a conclusion of a valid argument depends completely upon the truth of the premises.

It is important to emphasize the fact that validity has nothing to do with the question of whether the conclusion is true or false. The conclusion may be false, yet the argument may be valid if the chain of reasoning is correct. On the other hand, the conclusion may be true, yet the argument may not be valid if the reasoning is incorrect.

EXERCISES FOR SECTION 9-7

Determine whether or not each argument is valid:

1. *Given:* If Elliot is a freshman, then Elliot takes mathematics.
   Given: Elliot is a freshman.
   Conclusion: Elliot takes mathematics.

2. *Given:* If you like dogs, then you will live to be 120 years old.
   Given: You like dogs.
   Conclusion: You will live to be 120 years old.

3. If the Yanks win the game, then they win the pennant.
   They do not win the pennant.
   Therefore, they did not win the game.

4. If you like mathematics, then you like this book.
You do not like mathematics.
Therefore, you do not like this book.

5. If you work hard, then you are a success.
You are not a success.
Therefore, you do not work hard.

6. If you are reading this book, then you like mathematics.
You like mathematics.
Therefore, you are reading this book.

7. If you are reading this book, then you like mathematics.
You are not reading this book.
Therefore, you do not like mathematics.

8. If you work hard, then you will pass the course.
If you pass the course, then your teacher will praise you.
Therefore, if you work hard, then your teacher will praise you.

9. If you like this book, then you like mathematics.
If you like mathematics, then you are intelligent.
Therefore, if you are intelligent, then you like this book.

10. If you are a blonde, then you are lucky.
If you are lucky, then you will be rich.
Therefore, if you do not become rich, then you are not a blonde.

Supply a conclusion so that each of the following arguments will be valid.

11. If you drink milk, then you will be healthy.
You are not healthy.
Therefore, . . .

12. If you eat a lot, then you will gain weight.
You eat a lot.
Therefore, . . .

13. If you like to fish, then you enjoy swimming.
If you enjoy swimming, then you are a mathematician.
Therefore, . . .

14. If you do not work hard, then you will not get an A.
If you do not get an A, then you will have to repeat the course.
Therefore, . . .

15. If you like this book, then you are not lazy.
If you are not lazy, then you will become a mathematician.
Therefore, . . .

9-8 EULER DIAGRAMS

In the eighteenth century the Swiss mathematician Leonhard Euler
used diagrams to present a visual approach to the study of the validity
of arguments. We considered Euler diagrams in §4-5. The diagrams
used in this section are an aid to reasoning but are not essential to the
reasoning process. We use a region, usually a circular region, P to
represent the situations in which a statement p is true. Then p is
false in all situations represented by points of P'. Similarly, we use a
region Q for a statement q, and so forth.

First consider the statement $p \rightarrow q$ (if p, then q). This statement is
equivalent to saying "all p are q," that is, p is a subset of q; if you have
p then you must have q. We show this by drawing circles to represent
p and q with p drawn as a subset of q. Consider the statements:

p: It is a lemon.
q: It is a piece of fruit.

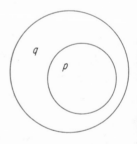

Then the preceding figure may be used as a visualization of the
statement "All lemons are pieces of fruit." Note that statements p and
q are consistent statements.

Next consider the statements:

p: It is a lemon.
s: It is an orange.

Recall that the statements p and s are called contrary statements, since they cannot both be true of the same object. If we wish to draw a diagram to represent the statement "No lemon is an orange," then we may draw two circles whose intersection is the empty set:

Note that this same diagram can be used to represent either of the following equivalent statements:

> If it is a lemon, then it is not an orange.
> If it is an orange, then it is not a lemon.

We may also represent contradictory statements by means of Euler diagrams. Consider the statements:

> p: It is a lemon.
> $\sim p$: It is not a lemon.

If we draw a circle to represent the statement p, then $\sim p$ may be represented by the set of points outside of p; that is, by the complement of p.

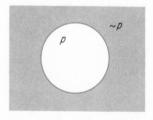

Let us now return to the question of validity and explore a visual approach to the argument

$$[(p \to q) \wedge (q \to r)] \to (p \to r).$$

We have seen that the statement "if p, then q" is equivalent to saying "all p's are q's" and may be drawn with p as a subset of q. Similarly, the statement "if q, then r" can be written in the form "all q's are r's"; that is, q is a subset of r. To represent these two statements we construct circles in such a way that p is contained within q, and q is contained within r, as follows:

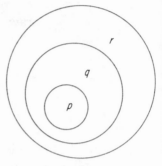

We have followed instructions carefully for our two premises. From the diagram it is clear that p must be a subset of r. That is, we conclude that "all p's are r's" or "if p, then r," which is what we set out to demonstrate as the conclusion of our argument.

From the final diagram it should also be clear that each of the following conclusions would *not* be valid:

$$\text{All } r\text{'s are } q\text{'s}; \qquad r \nrightarrow q.$$
$$\text{All } q\text{'s are } p\text{'s}; \qquad q \nrightarrow p.$$

Can you see that each of the following conclusions follows logically from the diagram drawn?

$$\text{If not } r, \text{ then not } p; \qquad \sim r \rightarrow \sim p.$$
$$\text{If not } q, \text{ then not } p; \qquad \sim q \rightarrow \sim p.$$

Euler diagrams may be used to test the validity of an argument. We draw one or more Euler diagrams, making use of the premises and avoiding the introduction of additional premises. The structure of the diagram indicates whether or not the argument is valid. As in §9-7 we disregard the truth values of the premises and conclusions.

EXAMPLE 1: Test the validity of this argument:

All undergraduates are sophomores.
All sophomores are attractive.
Therefore, all undergraduates are attractive.

Solution: A diagram of this argument follows:

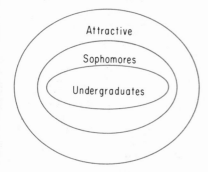

The argument is valid.

᙮᙮

Notice in Example 1 that you may or may not agree with the conclusion or with the premises. The important thing is that you are *forced* to draw the diagram in this manner. The conclusion is an inescapable consequence of the given premises. You should not allow the everyday meaning of words to alter your thinking. Thus the preceding argument can be stated abstractly in this form:

> All *u*'s are *s*'s.
> All *s*'s are *a*'s.
> Therefore, all *u*'s are *a*'s.

Here we rely on logic alone rather than any preconceived notions about the meaning of such words as "undergraduate," "sophomore," and "attractive."

᙮᙮

EXAMPLE 2:   Draw a diagram and test the validity of this argument:

> All freshmen are clever.
> All attractive people are clever.
> Therefore, all freshmen are attractive.

Solution: The first premise tells us that the set of freshmen is a subset of the set of clever individuals. This is drawn as follows:

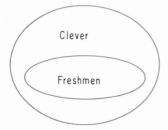

Next we need to draw a circle to represent the set of attractive people as a subset of the set of clever individuals. However, there are several possibilities here:

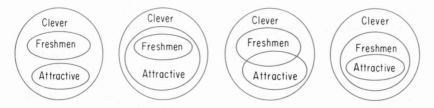

Each of the figures drawn represents a distinct possibility, but only one shows that all freshmen are attractive. Therefore, since we are not *forced* to arrive at this conclusion, the argument is said to be *not valid*. Each of the figures, on the other hand, forces you to arrive at the following valid conclusions:

> Some clever people are attractive.
> Some clever people are freshmen.

Consider next the statement:

> Some freshmen are attractive.

This statement means that there exists *at least one* freshman who is attractive. It does not, however, preclude the possibility that all freshmen are attractive. Now consider the following argument whose validity we wish to check:

> Some freshmen are attractive.
> All girls are attractive.
> Therefore, some freshmen are girls.

To test the validity of this argument we draw Euler circles for the two premises and then see whether we are forced to accept the conclusion. Since some freshmen are attractive, we will draw the following but recognize that the set of freshmen could also be drawn as a proper subset of the set of attractive people.

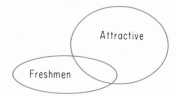

Next we draw a circle to represent the set of girls as a proper subset of the set of attractive people. Here are several possible ways to do this:

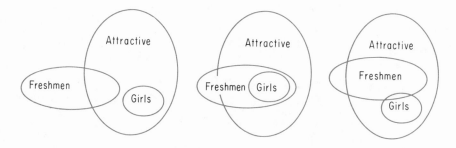

Notice that in two of the figures we find that some freshmen are girls. But we are not forced to adopt this conclusion, as seen in the first of the three figures drawn. Accordingly, we conclude that the argument is not valid.

EXAMPLE 3:   Test the validity of the following argument:

All a's are b's.
Some a's are c's.
Therefore, some c's are b's.

Solution: The argument is valid.

In Example 3 note that since some a's are c's, then there are also some c's that are a's. However, since all a's are b's, it follows that some c's must also be b's as in these diagrams:

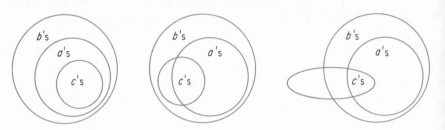

EXERCISES FOR SECTION 9-8

Test the validity of each argument:

1. All students love mathematics.
   Harry is a student.
   Therefore, Harry loves mathematics.

2. All juniors are brilliant.
   All brilliant people love mathematics.
   Therefore, if you are a junior then you are brilliant.

3. All girls are beautiful.
   All beautiful people like this book.
   Therefore, if you like this book then you are a girl.

4. All mathematics teachers are dull.
   Some Ph.D.'s are dull.
   Therefore:
   (a) Some mathematics teachers are Ph.D.'s.
   (b) Some dull people have Ph.D.'s.

5. All juniors are clever.
   Some juniors are males.
   Therefore:
   (a) Some males are clever.
   (b) Some males are juniors.
   (c) Some clever people are males.
   (d) All males are juniors.

6. All boys are handsome.
   Some boys are athletes.
   Therefore, some athletes are handsome.

7. All mathematics teachers are interesting.
   All attractive individuals are interesting.
   Some mathematics teachers are kind.
   Therefore:
   (a) Some interesting people are kind.
   (b) Some mathematics teachers are attractive.
   (c) All mathematics teachers are attractive.
   (d) All mathematics teachers are kind.
   (e) Some kind individuals are attractive.
   (f) No mathematics teachers are attractive.
   (g) No attractive individuals are interesting.

8. All x's are y's.
   Some y's are z's.
   Therefore:
   (a) Some x's are z's.
   (b) Some z's are y's.

9. All a's are b's.
   All b's are c's.
   Some d's are not c's.
   Therefore:
   (a) All a's are c's.
   (b) Some d's are not b's.
   (c) Some d's are not a's.
   (d) Some d's are c's.

10. All booms are mooms.
    Some booms are tooms.
    Some zooms are booms.
    Therefore:
    (a) Some mooms are booms.
    (b) Some zooms are mooms.
    (c) Some mooms are tooms.
    (d) No toom is a zoom.
    (e) Some zooms are moom-tooms.

TEST FOR CHAPTER 9

1. Use an appropriate symbol to identify the quantifier used in each statement for a real variable x:
   (a) For all x, $x + 2 = 2 + x$.

(**b**) There exists at least one x such that $x + 7 = 5$.

(**c**) Some real numbers are rational numbers.

2. State in words the negation of each statement:

(**a**) All cats have tails.

(**b**) Some men are soldiers.

3. Identify the combinations of truth values that may occur for the statements:

$$p: \quad x^2 = 36$$
$$q: \quad x \neq 6$$

4. Write the converse, inverse, and contrapositive of the statement:

$$\text{If } x < 3, \text{ then } x \neq 3.$$

5. Write each statement in if-then form:

(**a**) Right angles are congruent.

(**b**) To like to swim it is necessary that you like water.

6. Write each statement in symbolic form using:

$$p: \quad \text{I wear a coat.}$$
$$q: \quad \text{It is snowing.}$$

(**a**) For me to wear a coat it is necessary that it be snowing.

(**b**) I wear a coat only if it is snowing.

7. Write each statement in symbolic form:

(**a**) p is sufficient for q.

(**b**) p is necessary and sufficient for $(\sim q)$.

8. Identify as true or false:

(**a**) $3 \times 5 = 35$ only if $6 \times 5 = 70$.

(**b**) For $2 \times x = 6$ it is sufficient that $2 \times 5 = 6$.

9. Test the validity of this argument:

(**a**) All dogs love their masters.

   If an animal loves its master, it should be well cared for.

   Therefore, all dogs should be well cared for.

(**b**) If x is a positive integer, then $x^2 > 0$.

   $x^2 \not> 0$.

   Therefore, x is not a positive number.

10. Use a truth table to determine whether or not the statement

$$[(p \rightarrow q) \wedge (\sim q)] \rightarrow (\sim p)$$

is a tautology.

chapter 10

CONCEPTS
OF GEOMETRY

Geometry is a growing body of knowledge with ever widening applications and an inherent beauty in its systematic structure and organization. In this final chapter we shall consider the evolution of geometry from the practical procedures used several thousand years ago to the logical systems that are currently called geometries. We shall briefly examine some of these geometries, but our treatment will be informal and an effort will be made to convey an understanding of, rather than proficiency in, the subject matter discussed.

We have seen that algebra may be used in the study of geometry as, for example, in the use of coordinates. Also geometry may be used in the study of algebra as, for example, in the use of a number line (Chapter 7). The very close relationship between algebra and geometry may be observed by noticing that the algebra of the real numbers and the geometry of points on a Euclidean line are basically the same. Indeed, the early Greeks represented numbers by line segments before more convenient notations were developed. We conclude this final chapter with a consideration of additional properties of coordinate geometry. Coordinate geometry enables us to recognize that algebra and geometry provide two approaches to the same subject—mathematics.

10-1 THE EVOLUTION OF GEOMETRY

Early geometry was a practical science and an empirical science; that is, a science based upon man's experiences and observations. General theories, postulates, and proofs came much later. We do not know the complete history of geometry; however, the following are among the major influences that have contributed to its evolution:

1. The empirical procedures of the early Babylonians and Egyptians.

2. The Greeks' love of knowledge for its own sake and their use of classical constructions.

3. The organization of early geometry by Euclid.

4. The continuation of Euclid's work during the Golden Age of Greece.

5. The contribution of Hindu, Arabian, and Persian mathematicians during the Dark Ages in Europe.

6. The reawakening in Europe with the growth of the universities, the development of the printing press, and the flowering of all branches of knowledge.

7. The introduction of coordinate systems in the seventeenth century.

8. The application of algebra (and also calculus) to geometry in the eighteenth century.

9. The recognition of points and lines as undefined (abstract) elements, giving rise to many different geometries in the nineteenth century.

10. The emphasis upon generalizations, arithmetization, and axiomatic foundations in the twentieth century.

At each stage of the development of geometry we find extensive use and application of geometry to the mathematics of its time. We also find the impact of other mathematical and cultural concepts upon geometry.

The geometry of the early Babylonians and Egyptians was concerned with areas and volumes. The Babylonians of 4000 B.C. used the product of the length and the width of a rectangular field as a measure of the field, probably for taxation purposes. The pyramids of Egypt provide striking evidence of early engineering accomplishments that probably required the use of many geometric concepts. For example, the granite roof members over the chambers of a pyramid built about 3000 B.C. are 200 feet above the ground level, weigh about 50 tons each, and were probably brought from a quarry over 600 miles away. The rules and formulas of the early Babylonians and Egyptians were empirical results. Each was considered solely on its own merits, since there did not exist any underlying body of theoretical geometric knowledge. In general, the Babylonian and Egyptian concepts of geometry appear to have remained at a utilitarian and empirical level until about 600 B.C., when the influence of the Greeks began to have an effect.

The Greeks with their love of reason and knowledge left a profound impression on geometry. They encouraged its study as a science independent of its practical applications and as a part of a liberal education. They enlarged the scope of geometry to include not only empirical formulas for areas and volumes, but also:

1. The use of line segments to represent numbers.
2. The study of properties of polygons and parallel lines.
3. Properties of circles and other conic sections.
4. Classical constructions with straightedge and compasses.
5. Ratios and proportions arising from a study of similar polygons.
6. Proofs of the consequences of a set of postulates.

Most of the intellectual progress of the early Greeks came from schools centered around such outstanding scholars and groups of scholars as Thales, Pythagoras, the Sophists, and Plato.

About 300 B.C. the center of mathematical activity shifted from Greece to Egypt, and especially to the newly established university of Alexandria, where Euclid was a professor of mathematics. Euclid wrote at least ten treatises covering the mathematics of his time. His most famous work is called Euclid's *Elements* and contains thirteen books in which he presents an elegant organization of

> plane geometry (Books I to IV),
> the theory of proportions (Books V and VI),
> the theory of numbers (Books VII to IX),
> the theory of incommensurables (Book X), and
> solid geometry (Books XI to XIII).

These topics were more closely related than we now consider them. Proportions were based upon similar polygons, the theory of numbers upon the lengths of line segments, and incommensurables upon proportions and the construction of line segments. The books on geometry included nearly all of the concepts that are now considered in a high school geometry course. They also included geometric proofs of algebraic identities and geometric solutions of equations (both linear and quadratic). In general, Euclid's *Elements* rendered geometry a tremendous service as an organization of geometry and indeed of all of the mathematical knowledge of that time. We do not know how much of this material was original with Euclid. We do know that the *Elements* represents a logical outgrowth of the geometry of the early Greeks. We shall consider the geometry of Euclid briefly in §10-2.

The prestige of Alexandria lasted for many years after Euclid. Archimedes (about 250 B.C.) studied there and, in addition to discoveries in other fields, made many contributions to geometry. Appolonius (about 225 B.C.) and Pappus (about 300 A.D.) also enhanced the prestige of Alexandria through their work in geometry. However, by 700 A.D. the geometry of measurements of the early Babylonians and Egyptians had been modified in accordance with the Greek love of knowledge and reason and was in need of new influences.

During the Dark Ages in Europe the mathematical achievements of the Greeks were modified by Hindu, Arabian, and Persian mathematicians. Most of these influences were of a practical and utilitarian nature. There were noteworthy advances in number notation, areas, volumes, classical constructions, astronomy, and trigonometry (that is, the measure of triangles). Euclid's parallel postulate (§10-3) was questioned, and Omar Khayyám, the author of the Rubáiyát, wrote a treatise on algebra using a geometric approach.

In mathematics as in trade and art, the first signs of European awakening were in Italy. There were some evidences of mathematical life in England in the eighth century and in France in the tenth century. However, progress was very slow. About the end of the twelfth century Leonardo Fibonacci returned to Italy after traveling extensively, and soon published several treatises making available a vast amount of information regarding previous achievements in number notation, arithmetic, algebra, geometry, and trigonometry. These new ideas were soon picked up in the new European universities, where groups of scholars provided the mutual stimulus that is necessary for great achievements. Then in the fifteenth century the printing press provided a new means of disseminating knowledge, and intellectual activity began to spread rapidly throughout Europe. At first there was an intellectual smoldering while the scholars acquired additional knowledge of past achievements. Soon Alberti and the Italian artists developed some of the principles of descriptive geometry and provided a basis for projective geometry (§10-4). Letters were introduced for numbers in France. Mathematical activity gradually acquired momentum and by the end of the seventeenth century was well under way. During the last three centuries there has burst forth such an avalanche of activity, constantly expanding without any definite signs of spending its force, that we shall be hard pressed to assess or even recognize the evolution of geometric concepts.

Our coordinate systems are called Cartesian coordinate systems in recognition of the work of René Descartes in the seventeenth century. He applied algebraic notation to the study of curves and visualized all algebraic expressions as representing numbers instead of geometric objects. Previously, linear terms such as x or $2y$ had been considered as line segments, quadratic terms such as x^2 or xy had been considered as areas, and cubic terms such as x^3 or x^2y had been considered as volumes. The old interpretations were restrictive in that only like quantities could be added. For example, it was permissible to add x^2 and xy (areas), but it was not permissible to add x^2 and x (that is, an area and a line segment). Descartes' interpretation of all algebraic expressions as numbers and therefore as line segments made it possible to consider sums such as $x^2 + x$. This new point of view provided a basis for the representation of curves by equations. The application of new ideas to geometry typifies the seventeenth century. There was the application of algebra initiated by Descartes and Fermat (§10-6), applications of projections initiated by Desargues and Pascal (§10-4), and application of calculus initiated by Newton and Leibniz.

In the eighteenth and nineteenth centuries we find a broadening of the applications of the new ideas begun in the seventeenth century and the development of the non-Euclidean geometries (§10-3). During the last half of the eighteenth century we find increasing evidence of the forthcoming crescendo of mathematical activity that characterizes the nineteenth and twentieth centuries. Because of the increased specialization of terminology and the detailed and abstract character of many of the contributions, our treatment of the evolution of geometry will, of necessity, become very general.

In the nineteenth century the use of coordinates and the acceptance of points as undefined elements made possible the formal development of the non-Euclidean and other geometries. These have led in the twentieth century to the development of geometries as logical systems and the recognition of the equivalence of algebraic and geometric representations of mathematics. We shall try to illustrate this equivalence of algebraic and geometric representations in our discussions of finite geometry (§10-5) and coordinate geometry (§10-6 through §10-10).

EXERCISES FOR SECTION 10-1

These exercises illustrate the use by the early Greeks of areas of figures to justify statements that we now think of as algebraic. Use the given figure to explain each statement:

1. $(x + 1)^2 = x^2 + 2x + 1$

2. $(a + b)^2 = a^2 + 2ab + b^2$

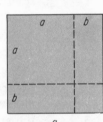

3. $(a - b)^2 = a^2 - 2ab + b^2; a > b$

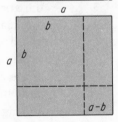

4. $a^2 - b^2 = (a + b)(a - b); a > b$

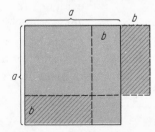

Sketch a figure as in Exercises 1 through 4 and use the figure to explain each statement:

5. $(a + b)a = a^2 + ab$

6. $a(b + c) = ab + ac$

7. $(a + b)(c + d) = ac + ad + bc + bd$

*8. $(a + b)^2 = (a - b)^2 + 4ab$

10-2 EUCLIDEAN GEOMETRY

The geometry that is usually studied in high school is often called Euclidean geometry in recognition of Euclid's *Elements*, which provided an outstanding organization of most of the properties of this geometry. Since Euclid's time mathematicians have found improved sets of postulates and have stated many of the assumptions that Euclid assumed without mentioning them.

Euclid based his work upon five postulates and five common notions that were considered to be applicable to all sciences. His common notions were:

1. Things that are equal to the same thing are equal to each other.
2. If equals are added to equals, the sums are equal.
3. If equals are subtracted from equals, the remainders are equal.
4. Things that coincide are equal.
5. The whole is greater than the part.

Notice that the first three common notions are properties of the relation "equal." The fourth common notion has caused philosophical questions as to whether two distinct things may coincide and has caused logical difficulties from the use of the converse:

Things that are equal may be made to coincide.

The fifth common notion has caused difficulties, since it holds only for finite sets. For example, there are as many positive even integers as there are positive integers.

Euclid's first three postulates were:

1. Any two points may be joined by a line segment.
2. Any line segment may be extended to form a line.
3. A circle may be drawn with any given center and distance.

These three were probably Plato's assumptions for constructions with straightedge and compass. Euclid's remaining two postulates were:

4. Any two right angles are equal.

5. If a line *m* intersects two lines *p* and *q* such that the sum of the interior angles on the same side of *m* is less than two right angles, then the lines *p* and *q* intersect on the side of *m* on which the sum of the interior angles is less than two right angles.

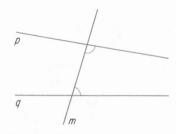

We shall consider Euclid's fifth (or parallel) postulate in more detail in §10-3. The name *parallel postulate* arises from the use of the postulate to prove that lines are parallel and essentially to prove the existence of one and only one line parallel to a given line and through a given point.

The excellence of the logical structure of Euclid's proofs was one of his major contributions to geometry. His proofs included

> a statement of the proposition that was to be proved,
> a statement of the given data (usually with a diagram),
> an indication of the use that was to be made of the data,
> a construction of any needed additional lines or figures,
> a synthetic proof, and
> a conclusion stating what had been done.

Euclid adopted many of the ideas of the Greeks, including Aristotle's distinction between postulates and common notions. With the Greek emphasis upon constructions he often constructed points and lines with straightedge and compass without concerning himself with postulates regarding the existence of points and lines. Accordingly, Euclid tacitly assumed that:

> Points and lines exist.
> Not all points are on the same line.
> Not all points are on the same plane.
> Two distinct lines have at most one point in common.
> A line is a continuous set of points.

He also made tacit assumptions that imply that:

Things that have equal measures may be made to coincide.
All sets of objects are finite.
There are order relations on a line.
A line is infinite in extent.

Euclid often used descriptions of terms as definitions, as illustrated by his first eight definitions:

1. A *point* is that which has no part.
2. A *line* is breadthless length.
3. The extremities of a line are points.
4. A *straight line* is a line that lies evenly with the points on itself.
5. A *surface* is that which has length and breadth only.
6. The extremities of a surface are lines.
7. A *plane surface* is a surface that lies evenly with the straight lines on itself.
8. A *plane angle* is the inclination to one another of two lines in a plane that meet one another and do not lie in a straight line.

We now recognize that it is not possible to define every term that we use. Some terms must be left undefined; for example, we usually leave point and line undefined. Every definition should have the following four properties:

(i) The term to be defined should be placed in its *nearest class*.

For example: A triangle is a geometric figure.

(ii) The necessary *distinguishing properties* should be given.

For example: A triangle consists of three noncollinear points and the line segments determined by them.

(iii) The definition should be *reversible*.

For example: If a geometric figure consists of three noncollinear points and the line segments determined by them, it is a triangle.

(iv) The definition should involve *simpler terms* (that is, undefined or previously defined terms).

As an example consider the definition of a triangle in the example for (ii).

Euclid probably thought of his geometry as describing the physical universe. Modern Euclidean geometry is based upon modifications of Euclid's postulates and appears to provide a good model for the physical universe. However, we actually do not know whether Euclidean geometry is true in the physical universe or not. We suspect that Euclidean geometry does not hold when very large distances are considered, as in astronomy.

Euclidean geometry is the geometry of **isometries;** that is, the geometry in which distances are unchanged (invariant). Many people think of isometries as rigid motions and thus think of Euclidean geometry as the geometry in which figures may be moved without changing their size and shape. Triangles are often introduced as rigid figures; that is, figures whose size and shape cannot be changed without changing the length of at least one of the sides. If we assume that triangles have this property, how many diagonals are required to make plane polygons of 3, 4, 5, . . . , n sides into rigid figures? The pattern is shown in the following array:

Numbers of sides	3	4	5	6	7	8	9	10	12	n
Number of diagonals needed to make rigid	0	1	2	3	4	5	6	7	9	$n-3$

When you have satisfied yourself that this is the correct pattern, consider the number of ways in which the necessary diagonals can be picked for a quadrilateral and for a pentagon. In the case of the quadrilateral, one diagonal is needed and either one may be used. Thus, the diagonal may be selected in two ways. In the case of the pentagon, the two diagonals may have a common vertex (any one of the five), or they may use four of the vertices (thus avoiding any one of the five) and, hence, may be chosen in ten ways. There are at least forty ways for a hexagon. A complete discussion of the number of ways to make a hexagon a rigid figure is beyond the scope of this book.

Throughout the study of Euclidean geometry, and indeed any geometry, it is helpful to make conjectures and to test them in the postulational system under discussion. When a theorem is proved on a plane, consider it also in space. Consider the converse of the theorem on a plane and in space. The treatment in space can be either deductive or informal; usually the informal, or intuitive, approach provides sufficient insight. As an example of the extension of concepts on a plane to concepts in space, consider perpendicularity (that is, intersections at right angles). Under what conditions do perpendicular figures exist on a plane? Under what conditions are the perpendiculars *unique* (that is, determined so that one and only one exists which satisfies the given conditions)? Now extend each of these considerations to space figures. Parallels may be treated in the same way. These ideas are developed in Exercises 7 through 18.

EXERCISES FOR SECTION 10-2

In Exercises 1 through 6, does each definition have the four properties listed in this section? Explain.

1. A point is that which has no part.

2. A line is length without breadth.

3. A duck is a bird.

4. A circle is the locus of points at a given distance from a given point.

5. A triangle is a three-sided polygon.

6. A polygon is convex if the entire figure is on the same half-plane or on its edge when each of the sides of the polygon is taken as the common edge of two half-planes.

7. Is it always possible on a plane to have:
   (**a**) A line *t* perpendicular to a given line *m*?
   (**b**) A line *t* perpendicular to a given line *m* and containing a given point *A* of *m*?
   (**c**) A line *t* perpendicular to a given line *m* and containing a given point *B* that is not a point of *m*?
   (**d**) A line *t* perpendicular to a given line *m* and containing both a given point *A* of *m* and a given point *B* that is not a point of *m*?
   (**e**) A line *t* perpendicular to each of two given lines *m* and *n*?

8. Repeat Exercise 7 for points and lines in space.

9. In Exercise 7, which of the lines *t* that always exist are uniquely determined?

10. In Exercise 8, which of the lines *t* that always exist are uniquely determined?

11. Is it always possible in space to have:
   (**a**) A line *t* perpendicular to a given plane *α*?

(**b**) A line t perpendicular to a given plane α and containing a given point A of α?

(**c**) A line t perpendicular to a given plane α and containing a given point B that is not a point of α?

(**d**) A line t perpendicular to a given plane α and containing both a given point A of α and a given point B that is not a point of α?

(**e**) A line t perpendicular to each of two given planes α and β?

12. Is it always possible in space to have:

(**a**) A plane β perpendicular to a given plane α?

(**b**) A plane β perpendicular to a given plane α and containing a given point A of α?

(**c**) A plane β perpendicular to a given plane α and containing a given line m on α?

(**d**) A plane β perpendicular to a given plane α and containing a given point B that is not a point of α?

(**e**) A plane β perpendicular to a given plane α and containing a given line n that is not on α?

(**f**) A plane β perpendicular to a given plane α and containing both a given point A of α and a given point B that is not a point of α?

13. In Exercise 11 which of the lines t that always exist are uniquely determined?

14. In Exercise 12 which of the planes β that always exist are uniquely determined?

Replace "perpendicular" by "parallel" and repeat:

15. Exercises 7 and 9.

16. Exercises 8 and 10.

17. Exercises 11 and 13.

18. Exercises 12 and 14.

10-3 NON-EUCLIDEAN GEOMETRIES

The fifth postulate of Euclid appears to have been a "child of necessity." Euclid postponed his use of it as long as possible but could not complete his proofs without it. For over two thousand years mathematicians tried to avoid using the fifth postulate. However, each time they either made a mistake or (often unknowingly) made an equivalent assumption. Here are a few of the equivalent assumptions that were used:

1. If a (straight) line intersects one of two parallel lines, it will intersect the other also (Proclus, fifth century).

2. Given any line m and any point P that is not on m, there is one and only one line through P and parallel to m (Playfair's axiom).

3. There exists a pair of coplanar (straight) lines that are everywhere equidistant from one another.

4. There exists at least one triangle having the sum of its three angles equal to 180°.

5. There exists a pair of similar triangles that are not congruent.

6. A circle can be drawn through any three points that are not on the same (straight) line.

Each assumption could be proved as a theorem in Euclidean geometry. However, at some stage in the proof the fifth postulate or a statement whose proof requires the use of the fifth postulate would be needed as a reason.

There are two non-Euclidean geometries, called *elliptic geometry* and *hyperbolic geometry* respectively. They are based upon modifications of Euclid's fifth postulate, his other postulates being kept. For example, consider the fifth postulate in the form of Playfair's axiom and notice these two other possibilities:

> Given any line m and any point P that is not on m, there is no line through P and parallel to m. (Elliptic geometry.)

> Given any line m and any point P that is not on m, there are at least two lines through P and parallel to m. (Hyperbolic geometry.)

These are the postulates that distinguish elliptic and hyperbolic geometries from Euclidean geometry. Euclid's other postulates are satisfied in all three geometries.

There are many geometries that are different from Euclidean; that is, that are *not* Euclidean. However, only the elliptic and hyperbolic geometries are called *non*-Euclidean. This distinction between "not Euclidean" and "non-Euclidean" reflects the growth of man's concept of geometry.

We often think of the physical universe as a model of Euclidean geometry. Accordingly, we now consider the points and lines on a plane as a model of Euclidean two-dimensional geometry and seek models of the non-Euclidean two-dimensional geometries.

A model for two-dimensional elliptic geometry may be obtained by thinking of the diametral lines (lines through the center) and the diametral planes (planes through the center) of a sphere. The diametral lines represent points of elliptic geometry; the diametral planes represent lines of elliptic geometry. Then, since in Euclidean geometry any two lines with a point in common determine a plane, we have in elliptic geometry:

> Any two points (diametral lines) determine a line (diametral plane).

The absence of parallel lines is evidenced by the fact that in elliptic geometry we also have:

> Any two lines (diametral planes) determine a point (diametral line).

There are also other models for elliptic geometry. Different models are used for different purposes. Elliptic geometry is sometimes called Riemannian geometry in recognition of the work on it by Bernard Riemann (1826–1866).

A model for two-dimensional hyperbolic geometry may be obtained by thinking of the circles that intersect a given (fixed) circle at right angles and considering only the interior points of the fixed circle. This model is based upon the work of Henri Poincaré (1854–1912). He visualized the physical universe as the interior of a sphere of radius R such that the absolute temperature t at any point at a distance r from the center of the sphere is given by the formula

$$t = c(R^2 - r^2),$$

where c is a constant of proportionality. He made an assumption (which is not accepted at present) that physical bodies decrease in volume with decreasing temperature and vanish altogether at the bounding surface of the above-mentioned sphere where the temperature is absolute zero. Under this assumption the shortest path between two given points may be shown to be along an arc of a circle that intersects the sphere at right angles.

We now obtain a model for two-dimensional hyperbolic geometry by considering the interior points of the circle in which a plane through the center of Poincaré's sphere intersects the sphere. The arcs of circles that intersect this fixed circle at right angles represent lines. Two lines intersect if they have an interior point of the fixed circle in common, are parallel if they have a point of the fixed circle in common, and are nonintersecting if they are neither intersecting nor parallel. In this model the diameters of the fixed circle are treated as arcs of circles of infinite radius.

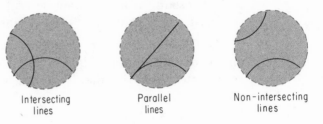

| Intersecting lines | Parallel lines | Non-intersecting lines |

Euclidean, elliptic, and hyperbolic geometries have many different properties. However, in the neighborhood of any point the three geometries approximately coincide. Notice also that the geometry on a sphere in the neighborhood of a point P is essentially the same as the geometry in the neighborhood of that point P on the plane that is tangent to the sphere at P. Relative to the physical universe we know that the geometry in the neighborhood of any point appears to be Euclidean. We do not know whether the neighborhood of the point that we are able to observe is relatively so small that what we are in fact observing is the geometry in the neighborhood of a point in elliptic or hyperbolic space. The three geometries are equally consistent and in a sense equally likely as the geometries of the physical universe.

We know that Euclidean geometry is at least a good approximation to the geometry of the portion of physical space in which man is able to make measurements. It is a relatively simple geometry with numerous theorems and applications, and accordingly, until there is overwhelming evidence that the physical universe has a different geometry, we shall undoubtedly continue to study Euclidean geometry.

EXERCISES FOR SECTION 10-3

1. There is a geometry of points of a sphere and great circles (sections by a plane through the center) of the sphere. This geometry in which points of the sphere are **spherical points** and great circles of the sphere are **spherical lines** is called **spherical geometry.** Sketch a sphere with two spherical lines m and n.

2. Sketch a sphere with spherical points A and B and a spherical line containing A and B.

3. Think of the surface of the earth as a sphere. Sketch this sphere with the equator as a spherical line. Label the north pole N and the south pole S. Draw several spherical lines through the spherical points N and S. (Think of the meridians.)

*4. Use latitudes and longitudes to explain how the position of any point on Earth (and thus on any sphere) can be identified by two coordinates; that is, that spherical geometry is a *two-dimensional geometry.*

Identify the two-dimensional geometry or geometries (Euclidean, elliptic, hyperbolic, spherical) in which each statement appears to hold:

5. Any two distinct lines intersect in at most one point.

6. Any two distinct lines intersect in at least one point.

7. Parallel lines are equidistant. (In hyperbolic geometry two lines are parallel if they have a point of the fixed circle in common.)

8. Parallel lines exist.

9. Parallel lines exist and any two distinct lines that are parallel to the same line are parallel to each other.

10. Two lines perpendicular to the same line are parallel.

11. Two lines perpendicular to the same line do not intersect.

10-4 PROJECTIVE GEOMETRY

The early Greeks knew that straight lines often did not appear to be straight. For example, they knew that if the edges of the steps of a large temple, such as the Parthenon, were to appear straight, then the edges of the steps had to be curved. We observe the same phenomenon when we stand near a long, straight, level road and notice that the edges of the road appear to come together at a point P on the horizon.

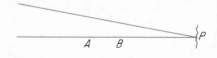

Perhaps you have also seen roads that were straight but not level. Then, assuming that the part between A and B is behind a hill and the rest of the road is in sight, the edges of the road appear as in the next figure. The change in the apparent width of the road from AC to BD helps a person at R driving along the road to estimate the distance from A to B.

(a)

(b)

Dürer: The Designer of the Sitting.Man

The Renaissance artists thought of the horizon points as vanishing points and developed a system of *focused perspective* to make their paintings appear realistic; that is, to enable them to paint pictures of our three-dimensional world on a two-dimensional canvas. The extent of their use of mathematics is indicated by the opening statement in Leonardo da Vinci's *Trattato della Pittura*: "Let no one who is not a mathematician read my works." The artists of the late fifteenth century realized that perspective must be studied scientifically and that this could only be done by using geometry.

Alberti, Leonardo da Vinci, Dürer (1471–1528), and others thought of the artist's canvas as a glass screen through which he looked at the object or scene to be painted. As shown in the woodcut at the bottom of page 333, the artist held the position of one eye fixed, looked only through that eye, and thought of the lines of light from his eye to each point of the scene. He marked a point on the glass screen where each line pierced it. These points make the same impression on the eye as the scene itself. We call the set of lines from the eye to the object the *projection;* we call the set of points on the glass screen a *section* of the projection.

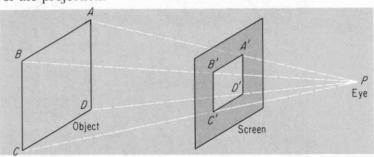

Notice that each point *A, B, C, D* of the object or scene being painted is on the same line (collinear) with the point *P* at the eye and a corresponding point *A', B', C', D'* of the screen. We describe this situation by saying that the two figures *ABCD* and *A'B'C'D'* are *perspective* from the point *P*.

Perspective figures are also used in many ways today. If we use a pin-hole camera to avoid the necessity of considering a lens, the picture on the film is perspective with the object or scene being photographed. Thus the object and its image on the film are perspective with respect to the pin-hole.

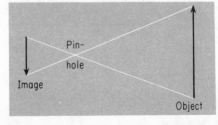

Projections may also be illustrated by the projection of a camera slide or movie. Think of a point source of light and notice that the image on the film and the image on the screen are perspective with respect to the source of light.

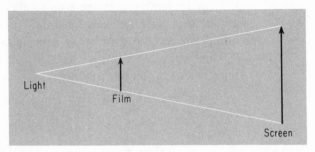

The Renaissance artists could think of their canvases as transparent, but actually the canvases were not transparent. Also, the artists often wished to paint scenes that existed only in their imagination. Accordingly, it was necessary to develop the principles of their system of focused perspectivity. These principles provided the basis for a geometry based upon projections, which we call *projective geometry*. The postulates (rules) for projective geometry are relatively simple, and the theorems are useful to artists, mechanical draftsmen, mapmakers, photographers, mathematicians, and many others. We shall not attempt to develop the theory of projective geometry; rather, we shall conclude this section by pointing out a few of its properties. Projective geometry is a very general geometry that can be restricted by adding appropriate postulates to obtain Euclidean geometry or either of the non-Euclidean geometries.

We have seen that the artists represent parallel lines by lines that intersect at vanishing points on the horizon. The horizon line is an ideal line or a line at infinity in the sense that it is not a line of our physical universe and is not a line of a Euclidean plane. Thus in projective geometry a new line has been added to the Euclidean plane so that any two coplanar lines intersect; in other words, since the lines that were considered to be parallel in Euclidean geometry now intersect on this new line, there are no parallel lines in projective geometry. This means that the usual statement,

> Any two points on a plane determine a line.

now has a corresponding statement,

> Any two lines on a plane determine a point.

In general, any valid statement about points and lines on a plane in projective geometry may be used to obtain a valid statement about lines and points simply by interchanging the words "point" and "line." This property of projective plane geometry is known as the **principle of planar duality.**

There is a corresponding **principle of space duality** which states that in projective geometry any valid statement about points, lines, and planes may be used to obtain a valid statement about planes, lines, and points simply by interchanging the words "point" and "plane" and leaving the word "line" unchanged. Since there are no parallels in projective geometry,

> Any two points are on a line.
> Any two planes are on a line.

Also:

> Any three points are on at least one plane.
> Any three planes are on at least one point.

As described ·by the Renaissance artists, two figures are **perspective from a point** P if the lines through corresponding vertices of the figures all pass through the point P. For example, triangle ABC is perspective from P with triangle $A'B'C'$, since the lines AA', BB', and CC' all pass through P.

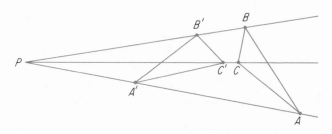

Let us now use the principle of planar duality and the definition of figures perspective from a point to define figures perspective from a line. Two figures are **perspective from a line** m if the points of intersection of corresponding sides of the figure are all on m. For example, triangle ABC is perspective from m with triangle $A'B'C'$ since the points $\overleftrightarrow{AB} \cap \overleftrightarrow{A'B'}$, $\overleftrightarrow{BC} \cap \overleftrightarrow{B'C'}$, and $\overleftrightarrow{AC} \cap \overleftrightarrow{A'C'}$ are all on m.

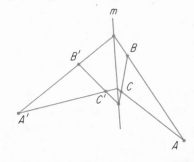

In a detailed study of projective geometry we could prove the **Theorem of Desargues:** If two triangles are perspective from a point, they are perspective from a line, and conversely. (See Exercises 8 and 9.)

We conclude this section with a brief description of two other theorems from projective geometry. Notice that the theorems of projective geometry involve lines and intersections of lines but do not involve measures of distances.

We define a **hexagon** as a plane figure consisting of six lines a, b, c, d, e, f, no three of which are on the same point, and the six points (vertices) $a \cap b$, $b \cap c$, $c \cap d$, $d \cap e$, $e \cap f$, $f \cap a$ obtained by taking the intersections of the lines in cyclic order. Notice that a hexagon may appear in many ways:

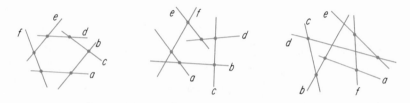

Our final two theorems involve the diagonal points of hexagons that are inscribed in intersecting lines or in a conic (that is, in a circle, parabola, ellipse, or hyperbola). The sides a and d, b and e, c and f of any hexagon $abcdef$ are called **opposite sides.** The three points of intersection of the pairs of opposite sides of a hexagon are its **diagonal points.** (Remember that in projective geometry any two lines on a plane must intersect.) A hexagon is said to be **inscribed** in a figure if the vertices of the hexagon are points of the figure.

Each of the following theorems may be proved in projective geometry. We shall consider only figures illustrating the theorems.

Theorem of Pappus: If a hexagon is inscribed in two lines that are not lines of the hexagon, then the diagonal points of the hexagon are collinear. (In the figure the hexagon $ABCDEF$ is inscribed in the intersecting lines m and m'; the line through the diagonal points is dashed.)

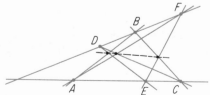

Theorem of Pascal: If a hexagon is inscribed in a conic, then the diagonal points of the hexagon are collinear. (In the figure the hexagon *ABCDEF* is inscribed in a circle; the line through the diagonal points is dashed.)

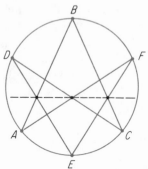

EXERCISES FOR SECTION 10-4

1. Write the plane dual of the statement: Any two distinct lines on the same plane determine a unique point.

2. Write the space dual of the statement given in Exercise 1.

3. Write the plane dual of the statement that was obtained as an answer for Exercise 1.

4. Write the space dual of the statement that was obtained as an answer for Exercise 1.

5. The figure consisting of four coplanar points (vertices), no three of which are on the same line, and the six lines (sides) determined by them is called a complete quadrangle on the plane. Sketch a complete quadrangle and label the given points *A*, *B*, *C*, *D*.

6. The plane dual of a complete quadrangle is a complete quadrilateral. Use the plane dual of the definition given in Exercise 5 to obtain a definition for a complete quadrilateral.

7. Sketch a complete quadrilateral and label the given lines *a*, *b*, *c*, *d*.

8. (a) Draw triangle *RST* and triangle *R'S'T'* perspective from a point *M*. (b) In your drawing show that there exists a line *m* such that these triangles are also perspective from *m*.

9. (a) Draw triangle XYZ and triangle $X'Y'Z'$ perspective from a line t. (b) In your drawing show that there exists a point T such that these triangles are also perspective from T.

10. Draw a figure for the Theorem of Pappus.

11. Draw a figure for the Theorem of Pascal.

10-5 A FINITE GEOMETRY

We now consider a finite projective geometry; that is, a projective geometry with only a finite number of elements. In our geometry there are two types of undefined elements and one undefined relation among those elements. We call the elements of the first type of undefined elements students in a certain class; we call the elements of the second type of undefined elements committees. We describe the undefined relation by saying that a student is on (or is a member of) a committee. As a matter of convenience we shall use capital letters A, B, C, . . . to represent students and columns of letters to represent committees. Here are the postulates for our geometry of students and committees:

    I. There exists at least one committee.
    II. Each committee has at least three members.
    III. No committee has more than three members.
    IV. Any two students serve together on at least one committee.
    V. Any two distinct students serve together on at most one committee.
    VI. Not all students are members of the same committee.
    VII. Any two committees have at least one member in common.

We may use Postulates I through VII to determine the number of students in the class and the committee structure of the class. By Postulates I and II there exists at least one committee with at least three members A, B, C and which we may designate as committee

$$A$$
$$B$$
$$C$$

By Postulate III this committee does not have any other members. By Postulate VI there must be a student D who does not serve on this committee. By Postulate IV and V student D must serve on exactly one committee with each of the students A, B, and C. The committee on which A and D serve together must have a third member (Postulate II) and (by Postulate V) this third member cannot be B or C. Thus the third member must be a fifth student E.

The preceding discussion may be continued to determine the complete committee structure of the class. (See Exercises 1 through 44 for the determination of this structure in terms of points and lines.) We conclude the present discussion with a sequence of figures in which students are represented as points and committees as collinear sets of points, where the lines are not necessarily straight. The figures are given to illustrate the sequence of steps used in the exercises to prove that there are exactly seven points and seven lines in the geometry obtained when Postulates I through VII are restated for points and lines:

     I. There exists at least one line.

    II. Each line has at least three points.

   III. No line has more than three points.

   IV. Any two points are both on at least one line.

    V. Any two distinct points are both on at most one line.

   VI. Not all points are on the same line.

  VII. Any two lines have at least one point in common.

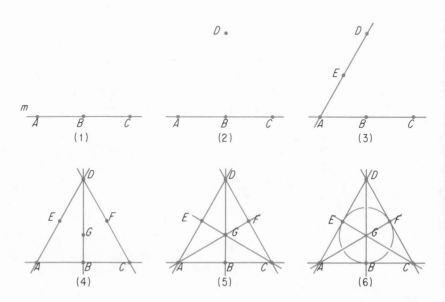

Notice that each of the seven postulates is a correct statement for the seven points and seven lines in Figure 6, where one of the lines appears as an oval. In more advanced courses this two-dimensional finite geometry of seven points and seven lines may be extended to obtain a three-dimensional finite geometry of 15 points, 35 lines, and 15 planes.

EXERCISES FOR SECTION 10-5

Use Postulates I through VII as restated for points and lines and prove each statement in the order given:

1. There exists a line m. (See Figure 1.)

2. The line m has at least three points, which we shall call A, B, C.

3. The line m has no points other than A, B, and C.

4. The line m has exactly three points.

5. There is a point D that is not on AB; that is, which is not on the line through A and B.. (See Figure 2.)

6. There is a line AD. (See Figure 3.)

7. There is a third point E on the line AD.

8. $E \neq B$; that is, the point E is distinct from the point B.

9. $E \neq C$ and thus E is a fifth point of the set.

10. There are lines DB and DC. (See Figure 4.)

11. There is a third point G on the line DB and a third point F on the line DC.

12. $F \neq A$

13. $F \neq B$

14. $F \neq E$, and thus F is a sixth point of the set.

15. $G \neq A$

16. $G \neq C$

17. $G \neq E$

18. $G \neq F$, and thus G is a seventh point of the set.

19. There is a line AF. (See Figure 5.)

20. The lines AF and DB must have a point P in common.

21. $P \neq B$.

22. $P \neq D$

23. P must coincide with one of the points B, D, G and therefore P coincides with G; that is, AF and DB are both on G.

24. There is a line CE.

25. The lines CE and AF must have a point S in common.

26. $S \neq A$

27. $S \neq F$

28. $S = G$; that is, CE and AF are both on G.

29. There is a line EF. (See Figure 6.)

30. The lines EF and AC must have a point R in common.

31. $R \neq A$

32. $R \neq C$

33. $R = B$; that is, the lines AC and EF are both on B.

34. If there were an eighth point H, there would be a line AH.

35. The line AH would intersect the line BD in a point O.

36. $O \neq B$

37. $O \neq D$

38. $O \neq G$

39. AH cannot intersect BD.

40. There cannot exist a line AH.

41. There cannot exist an eighth point H and thus the set consists of exactly seven points which we call A, B, C, D, E, F, and G.

42. There exist at least seven lines as shown by these columns:

$$
\begin{array}{ccccccc}
A & A & B & C & A & C & E \\
B & D & D & D & F & E & F \\
C & E & G & F & G & G & B
\end{array}
$$

43. There exist exactly seven points and seven lines.

44. When Postulates I through VII are stated for students and committees there are seven students in the class and seven committees.

10-6 COORDINATE GEOMETRY

Each point on a line in Euclidean geometry has a real number as its coordinate; each real number has a point on a Euclidean line as its graph (§5-6). We used a number line in Chapter 5 to help us understand the properties of sets of numbers. In Chapter 7 we used a number line to graph statements in one variable; then we used a Cartesian coordinate plane to graph statements in two variables and to help us understand relations, functions, and inverse relations. We now use a coordinate plane to help us understand the properties of geometric figures.

In the study of geometry the location of any point (x, y) on a coordinate plane may be determined after parallel lines have been introduced and a unit of measure has been given. For example, the points that are one unit from the x-axis are on the lines $y = 1$ and $y = -1$ parallel to the x-axis. The points that are two units from the y-axis are on the lines $x = 2$ and $x = -2$ parallel to the y-axis. The point $(2, 1)$ is at the intersection of the lines $x = 2$ and $y = 1$.

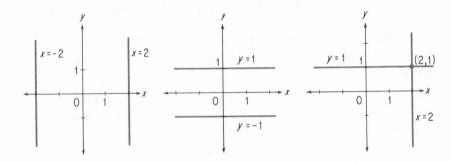

Any two points with the same first coordinate are on the same line parallel to the y-axis; any two points with the same second coordinate are on the same line parallel to the x-axis. Lines parallel to the y-axis have equations of the form $x = k$; lines parallel to the x-axis have equations of the form $y = n$. Each line is a locus; that is, a set of points satisfying a given condition. We locate points (k, n) as the intersection of these loci. The x-coordinate is sometimes called the **abscissa** of the point and the y-coordinate is sometimes called the **ordinate** of the point.

The distance from the origin of a point $(x, 0)$ on the x-axis may be expressed as $|x|$, or as $|x - 0|$. Also, on the x-axis the length of any line segment with endpoints $(x_1, 0)$ and $(x_2, 0)$ may be expressed as $|x_2 - x_1|$. On the coordinate plane, the length of any line segment with endpoints (x_1, y_1) and (x_2, y_1) may be expressed as $|x_2 - x_1|$; the length of any line segment with endpoints (x_1, y_1) and (x_1, y_2) may be expressed as $|y_2 - y_1|$.

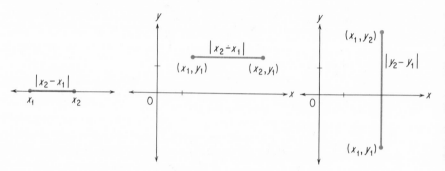

EXAMPLE: Find the equation of the line through, and the length of the line segment determined by, the points $(4, -1)$ and $(7, -1)$.

Solution: Each point has y-coordinate -1. Thus the equation of the line is $y = -1$. The length of the line segment is $|7 - 4|$; that is, 3.

The exercises that follow illustrate the development of the desired concepts. Notice that this material is very susceptible to explorations, conjectures, and discoveries; also, that additional relations among points may be developed by determining whether or not three points having given coordinates lie on a straight line. For example, consider three points A, B, and C on a line. The point B is said to be **between** A and C if the lengths of the line segments satisfy the equation $AB + BC = AC$.

The concept of betweenness has been essentially undefined until recent times. It may be defined for points using lengths of line segments as just noted. It may also be defined using the intersection of two rays. As in §6-1, two points A and B determine a line $\overleftrightarrow{AB}$. They also determine a ray $\overrightarrow{AB}$ and a ray $\overrightarrow{BA}$. The intersection of these two rays is the line segment $\overline{AB}$. This line segment consists of the two endpoints A and B and the points *between* A and B.

EXERCISES FOR SECTION 10-6

Plot on the same coordinate plane:

    1. $(2, 5)$ **2.** $(-2, 5)$

    3. $(-3, -4)$ **4.** $(3, -4)$

    5. $(0, -2)$ **6.** $(-3, 0)$

    7. $(5, -2)$ **8.** $(-2, -3)$

Draw coordinate axes, sketch each locus, and give its equation:

    9. The points 2 units above the x-axis.

    10. The points 3 units to the left of the y-axis.

    11. The points 2 units from the origin and on the x-axis.

    12. The points with coordinates that are equal.

Graph each equation or inequality on a coordinate plane and give the coordinates of any three points of the graph:

    13. $y = 2$ **14.** $x = -3$

    15. $x = y$ **16.** $x + y = 1$

    17. $y = 2x - 1$ **18.** $x > 3$

    19. $x > 3$ and $y < 4$ ***20.** $|x| + |y| = 1$

    *21. $|x - y| < 1$ ***22.** $|x - 2y| \leq 1$

Find the equation of the line through and the lengths of the line segment determined by each pair of points:

    23. $(-3, 2)$ and $(-3, 7)$.   **24.** $(2, 1)$ and $(2, 5)$.

    25. $(-3, 2)$ and $(-7, 2)$.   **26.** $(2, 1)$ and $(5, 1)$.

    27. $(-1, -3)$ and $(5, -3)$.   **28.** $(5, -2)$ and $(5, 7)$.

10-7 THE MIDPOINT FORMULA

The midpoint formula for the line segment determined by any two given points (x_1, y_1) and (x_2, y_2) is derived by using the fact that if three parallel lines cut off congruent segments on one transversal, they cut off congruent segments on every transversal. To do this, we need to be able to find the midpoint of a line segment on a coordinate axis; that is, on a number line.

Consider the points with coordinates 5 and 11 on a number line; the length of the line segment determined by them is $11 - 5$; that is, 6. The midpoint of the line segment has coordinate $5 + \frac{1}{2}(6)$; that is, 8. Notice that $8 = \frac{1}{2}(5 + 11)$. The points with coordinates 3 and -5 on a number line determine a line segment of length $3 - (-5)$, that is, 8; the midpoint has coordinate $-5 + \frac{1}{2}(8)$; that is, -1. Notice that $-1 = \frac{1}{2}(-5 + 3)$.

Suppose that R and S are points on a number line with coordinates r and s. Then the line segment $\overline{RS}$ has length $|r - s|$. When $r < s$, as in the figure, the length is $s - r$; then the midpoint has coordinate $r + \frac{1}{2}(s - r)$; that is, $\frac{1}{2}(r + s)$, since

$$r + \frac{1}{2}s - \frac{1}{2}r = \frac{1}{2}r + \frac{1}{2}s.$$

This formula holds for any two points R and S on a number line.

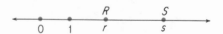

Now consider any two points A: (x_1, y_1) and B: (x_2, y_2) on a coordinate plane. The line that passes through A and is parallel to the y-axis has the equation $x = x_1$ and crosses the x-axis at $(x_1, 0)$; the line that passes through B and is parallel to the y-axis has the equation $x = x_2$ and crosses the x-axis at $(x_2, 0)$. These points with coordinates x_1 and x_2 on the x-axis determine a line segment; the midpoint D of this line segment has x-coordinate $\frac{1}{2}(x_1 + x_2)$. The line that passes through D and is parallel to the y-axis has equation $x = \frac{1}{2}(x_1 + x_2)$.

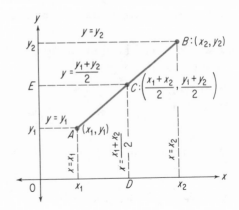

Notice that the three parallel lines

$$x = x_1, \qquad x = \tfrac{1}{2}(x_1 + x_2), \quad \text{and} \quad x = x_2$$

cut off congruent segments on the x-axis; therefore, they cut off congruent segments on the line AB. In other words, the line $x = \tfrac{1}{2}(x_1 + x_2)$ passes through the midpoint C of the line segment $\overline{AB}$, and C has x-coordinate $\tfrac{1}{2}(x_1 + x_2)$.

Similarly, the lines that pass through A and B and are parallel to the x-axis have equations $y = y_1$ and $y = y_2$. These lines intersect the y-axis in points $(0, y_1)$ and $(0, y_2)$; they determine a line segment with midpoint $\left(0, \dfrac{y_1 + y_2}{2}\right)$. The three parallel lines

$$y = y_1, \qquad y = \tfrac{1}{2}(y_1 + y_2), \quad \text{and} \quad y = y_2$$

cut off congruent segments on the y-axis and therefore cut off congruent segments on the line AB. In other words, the line $y = \tfrac{1}{2}(y_1 + y_2)$ passes through the midpoint C of the line segment $\overline{AB}$, and C has y-coordinate $\tfrac{1}{2}(y_1 + y_2)$.

We have now completed the derivation of the **midpoint formula:** Any line segment with endpoints (x_1, y_1) and (x_2, y_2) has midpoint

$$\left(\frac{x_1 + x_2}{2}, \frac{y_1 + y_2}{2}\right).$$

Notice that after the coordinate plane has been introduced, the midpoint formula can be derived without any additional assumptions. This development is based upon the theorem: If three parallel lines cut off congruent segments on one transversal, then they cut off congruent segments on any transversal. Applications of the midpoint formula will be considered in the following examples and the exercises.

EXAMPLE 1:   Find the midpoint of the line segment with end-points $(2, 7)$ and $(8, -3)$.

Solution:

$$\frac{2 + 8}{2} = 5; \quad \frac{7 + (-3)}{2} = \frac{4}{2} = 2.$$

The midpoint is $(5, 2)$.

EXAMPLE 2:   Represent the figure on a coordinate plane and prove that the diagonals of a rectangle bisect each other.

Solution: Any rectangle may be represented on a coordinate plane with vertices at $R: (0, 0)$, $S: (a, 0)$, $T: (a, b)$, and $U: (0, b)$.

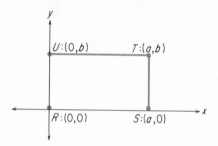

Then the midpoint of $\overline{RT}$ is $\left(\frac{a + 0}{2}, \frac{b + 0}{2}\right)$; that is, $\left(\frac{a}{2}, \frac{b}{2}\right)$.

Similarly, the midpoint of $\overline{US}$ is $\left(\frac{a}{2}, \frac{b}{2}\right)$. Thus the two diagonals have the same point as midpoint. Then each diagonal contains the midpoint of the other, and the diagonals are said to bisect each other.

EXERCISES FOR SECTION 10-7

In Exercises 1 through 4 find the midpoint of the line segment with the given endpoints:

1. $(1, 2)$ and $(3, 8)$.   **2.** $(2, -3)$ and $(4, 7)$.

3. $(-5, 4)$ and $(3, -2)$.   **4.** $(-3, -7)$ and $(5, 9)$.

5. Each set of coordinates represents the vertices of a right triangle, an isosceles triangle, or a triangle that is neither an isosceles triangle nor a right triangle. Identify each figure:

    (**a**) $(0, 0)$, $(3, 0)$, $(0, 5)$.

    (**b**) $(-1, 0)$, $(1, 0)$, $(0, 2)$.

    (**c**) $(0, 0)$, $(a, 0)$, $(0, b)$.

    (**d**) $(-a, 0)$, $(a, 0)$, $(0, b)$.

    (**e**) $(0, -3)$, $(2, 4)$, $(-2, 4)$.

6. Each set of coordinates represents the vertices of a square, a rectangle that is not a square, or a parallelogram that is not a rectangle. Identify each figure:

    (**a**) $(0, 0)$, $(5, 0)$, $(5, 5)$, $(0, 5)$.

    (**b**) $(-1, 0)$, $(3, 0)$, $(3, 2)$, $(-1, 2)$.

    (**c**) $(0, 0)$, $(a, 0)$, (a, a), $(0, a)$.

    (**d**) $(0, 0)$, $(a, 0)$, (a, b), $(0, b)$, $b \neq a$.

    (**e**) $(0, 0)$, $(6, 0)$, $(8, 3)$, $(2, 3)$.

    (**f**) $(2, -1)$, $(2, 3)$, $(-1, 3)$, $(-1, -1)$.

    (**g**) $(0, 0)$, $(a, 0)$, $(a + b, c)$, (b, c).

7. A line segment $\overline{RS}$ has endpoint R: $(1, 3)$ and midpoint M: $(2, 7)$. Find the coordinates of S.

8. Repeat Exercise 7 for R: $(2, -5)$ and M: $(5, -8)$.

9. The points A: $(0, 0)$ and B: $(5, 0)$ are vertices of a rectangle. Give the coordinates of the other vertices of two rectangles with side $\overline{AB}$.

10. Repeat Exercise 9 for A: $(0, 0)$ and B: $(a, 0)$, $a \neq 0$.

11. The points A: $(0, 0)$ and B: $(2, 0)$ are vertices of a square. Give the coordinates of the other vertices of (**a**) a square with side $\overline{AB}$; (**b**) a second square with side $\overline{AB}$; (**c**) a square with diagonal $\overline{AB}$.

12. Repeat Exercise 11 for A: $(0, 0)$ and B: $(-6, 0)$.

13. Repeat Exercise 11 for A: $(0, 0)$ and B: $(2a, 0)$, $a \neq 0$.

Represent each figure on a coordinate plane and prove:

14. The line segment joining the midpoints of two sides of a triangle is parallel to the third side and its length is equal to one-half of the length of the third side.

15. The median of a trapezoid is parallel to the bases and its length is equal to one-half the sum of the lengths of the bases.

16. The diagonals of a parallelogram bisect each other.

17. The lines joining the midpoints of the opposite sides of a quadrilateral bisect each other.

10-8 THE SLOPE OF A LINE

Given any two points A: (x_1, y_1) and B: (x_2, y_2), either the line AB is parallel to a coordinate axis or a right triangle ACB with legs parallel to the coordinate axes may be formed by using C: (x_2, y_1) as the third vertex. Then the sides $\overline{AC}$ and $\overline{BC}$ have lengths $|x_2 - x_1|$ and $|y_2 - y_1|$.

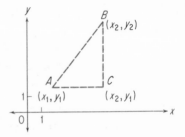

The ratio $\dfrac{y_2 - y_1}{x_2 - x_1}$ of the directed segments $\overline{CB}$ and $\overline{AC}$ is defined to be the slope of the line segment $\overline{AB}$.

Slope is important primarily as a property of lines rather than of line segments. Any two points A: (x_1, y_1) and B: (x_2, y_2) determine a line AB. This line is parallel to the y-axis if and only if $x_2 = x_1$. If $x_2 = x_1$, the ratio $\dfrac{y_2 - y_1}{x_2 - x_1}$ is undefined, since we cannot divide by zero.

If $x_2 \neq x_1$, the ratio $\dfrac{y_2 - y_1}{x_2 - x_1}$ is defined for any points A and B on the line. Properties of similar figures are needed to prove that the ratio $\dfrac{y_2 - y_1}{x_2 - x_1}$ has the same value whatever points A and B are selected on the line. This value is called the **slope** m of the line; we write

$$m = \frac{y_2 - y_1}{x_2 - x_1}.$$

EXAMPLE 1: Find the slope of the line through $(2, 3)$ and $(5, -2)$.

Solution:

$$\frac{-2 - 3}{5 - 2} = -\frac{5}{3}$$

The slope is $-\dfrac{5}{3}$.

Notice that the slope is defined for any line that is not parallel to the y-axis; the slope of any line parallel to the x-axis is zero. Slope is usually introduced for lines through the origin; then defined in general, as we have done; then it is proved that, for lines that are not parallel to the y-axis, two lines are parallel if and only if they have the same slope.

The equation of any line that is "determined" may now be found. We shall consider these cases:

1. A line through two arbitrary points.
2. A line through two points on the coordinate axes.
3. A line through any given point and parallel to a given line.
4. A line through a point on the y-axis and parallel to a given line.

Let $A: (x_1, y_1)$ and $B: (x_2, y_2)$ be any two given points. If $x_1 = x_2$, the line AB has equation $x = x_1$. If $x_1 \neq x_2$, a point $P: (x, y)$ is on the line AB if and only if the slope $\dfrac{y - y_1}{x - x_1}$ of the line segment $\overline{AP}$ is equal to the slope $\dfrac{y_2 - y_1}{x_2 - x_1}$ of the line segment $\overline{AB}$. We write

$$\frac{y - y_1}{x - x_1} = \frac{y_2 - y_1}{x_2 - x_1}.$$

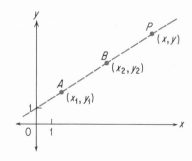

as the equation of a line through any two points $A: (x_1, y_1)$ and $B: (x_2, y_2)$, where $x_1 \neq x_2$. This equation is called the **two-point form** of the equation of the line.

EXAMPLE 2: Find an equation for the line through $(2, 3)$ and $(5, -2)$.

Solution:

$$\frac{y - 3}{x - 2} = \frac{-2 - 3}{5 - 2}; \qquad \frac{y - 3}{x - 2} = -\frac{5}{3}.$$

The equation obtained in Example 2 may also be expressed as

$$3(y - 3) = -5(x - 2);$$
$$5x + 3y - 19 = 0.$$

Any equation of the form

$$ax + by + c = 0,$$
$$a \text{ and } b \text{ not both zero}$$

is the **general form** of the linear equation.

Let $A: (a, 0)$ and $B: (0, b)$ be two given points on the coordinate axes. If $a = 0$, both A and B are on the y-axis and the line AB has equation $x = 0$. If $a \neq 0$, the line AB consists of points (x, y) such that

$$\frac{y - 0}{x - a} = \frac{b - 0}{0 - a};$$

that is, of points with coordinates satisfying the two-point form of the equation of the line. We may rewrite this equation in the forms

$$(-a)y = b(x) + (-a)b;$$

$$\frac{y}{b} = -\frac{x}{a} + 1;$$

$$\frac{x}{a} + \frac{y}{b} = 1.$$

The last equation is called the **intercept form** of the equation of the line. The number a is the x-coordinate of the point at which the line cuts the x-axis and is called the *x-intercept* of the line. The number b is the y-coordinate of the point at which the line cuts the y-axis and is called the *y-intercept* of the line. Notice that a line parallel to a coordinate axis fails to have two intercepts and cannot be written in intercept form.

EXAMPLE 3:   Find an equation for the line with x-intercept 3 and y-intercept 7.

Solution:

$$\frac{x}{3} + \frac{y}{7} = 1$$

Let $A: (x_1, y_1)$ be any given point, and let m be the slope of a given line. The coordinates of each point $P: (x, y)$ on the line through A with slope m satisfy the equation

$$\frac{y - y_1}{x - x_1} = m.$$

When written in the form

$$y - y_1 = m(x - x_1),$$

this equation is called the **point-slope form** of the equation of the line.

Let $A: (0, b)$ be any point on the y-axis, and let m be the slope of any given line. Then the point-slope form of the equation is

$$y - b = m(x - 0)$$

and may be written in the form

$$y = mx + b.$$

This equation is called the **slope-intercept form** of the equation of the line. Notice that it is the y-intercept (that is, the y-coordinate of the point at which the line cuts the y-axis) that is used.

EXAMPLE 4: Find an equation for the line through $(2, 3)$ and $(5, -2)$ in (a) point-slope form; (b) in slope-intercept form.

Solution: As in Example 2,

$$\frac{y - 3}{x - 2} = -\frac{5}{3}.$$

Thus we have

(a) $y - 3 = -\frac{5}{3}(x - 2)$;

(b) $y = -\frac{5}{3}x + \frac{10}{3} + 3$; that is, $y = -\frac{5}{3}x + 6\frac{1}{3}$.

Practice in using these four forms of the equations of a line is provided in the exercises. Notice that, if an equation of a line is given in one form, it may be rewritten in each of the other forms. For example, this equation in two-point form,

$$\frac{y - 1}{x - 1} = \frac{3 - 1}{2 - 1},$$

may be written in point-slope form as

$$y - 1 = 2(x - 1),$$

in slope-intercept form as

$$y = 2x - 1,$$

and in intercept form as

$$\frac{x}{\frac{1}{2}} + \frac{y}{-1} = 1.$$

Notice also that, for any given equation, it is possible to find as many points as desired on the line. For example, if the equation is $y = 2x + 3$, then each point has coordinates of the form $(x, 2x + 3)$. If $x = 1, y = 5$; if $x = -1, y = 1$; if $x = 5, y = 13$, and so forth. Each of the points $(1, 5)$, $(-1, 1)$, and $(5, 13)$ is on the line whose equation is $y = 2x + 3$. Any two of these points may be used to write an equation for the line in two-point form. For example,

$$\frac{y - 5}{x - 1} = \frac{13 - 5}{5 - 1}.$$

EXERCISES FOR SECTION 10-8

1. Find the slope of the line through the given points:

(**a**) (1, 4) and (5, 6).   (**b**)(2, −3) and (6, 5).
(**c**) (−2, −3) and (4, 5).   (**d**) (3, 5) and (−6, 11).

For each line in Exercise 1 find:

2. An equation in point-slope form.

3. An equation in slope-intercept form.

4. The *y*-intercept.

5. The *x*-intercept.

6. An equation in intercept form.

Find an equation for the line:

7. Through (7, −11) and (3, 1).

8. Through (−5, −7) and (−10, 3).

9. Through (0, −2) with slope $\frac{3}{2}$.

10. Through (1, 3) with slope −2.

11. With *x*-intercept 5 and *y*-intercept 4.

12. With *x*-intercept 4 and *y*-intercept −2.

13. Through the origin and parallel to the line $y = 2x + 5$.

14. Through the point (1, 2) and parallel to the line $y = -x + 7$.

*Assume (**a**) that the coordinate axes have been selected so that none of the lines under discussion is parallel to the y-axis, and (**b**) that two lines on a coordinate plane are parallel if and only if they have the same slope. Then prove each of these statements for lines on a coordinate plane:*

15. If two lines are parallel to the same line, they are parallel to each other.

16. If a line intersects one of two parallel lines, then it intersects the other also.

17. If a line is parallel to one of two intersecting lines, then it intersects the other.

18. Lines parallel to intersecting lines intersect.

19. Quadrilateral *ABCD* is a parallelogram when its vertices are *A*: (0, 0), *B*: (5, 7), *C*: (7, 13), and *D*: (2, 6).

10-9 THE DISTANCE FORMULA

We assume that the Pythagorean theorem is known to the reader and use it to obtain a general formula for the length of any line segment on a coordinate plane. Let the endpoints of the line segment have coordinates (x_1, y_1) and (x_2, y_2). As in §10-8, either the line segment is parallel to a coordinate axis, or a right triangle may be formed with the vertex of the right angle at (x_2, y_1). The lengths of the legs of the right triangle are $|x_2 - x_1|$ and $|y_2 - y_1|$; by the Pythagorean theorem, the length of the hypotenuse is

$$d = \sqrt{(x_2 - x_1)^2 + (y_2 - y_1)^2}.$$

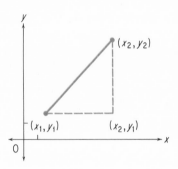

This is the **distance formula** on a plane. It holds also when the line segment is parallel to a coordinate axis, since

$$|x_2 - x_1| = \sqrt{(x_2 - x_1)^2} \quad \text{and} \quad |y_2 - y_1| = \sqrt{(y_2 - y_1)^2}.$$

EXAMPLE: Find the length of the line segment with endpoints (2, 5) and (7, 3).

Solution:

$$\sqrt{(7 - 2)^2 + (3 - 5)^2} = \sqrt{5^2 + 2^2} = \sqrt{29}$$

The treatment of circles can now be considered from both a synthetic and a coordinate point of view.

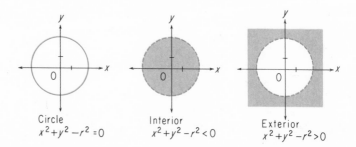

Circle
$x^2 + y^2 - r^2 = 0$

Interior
$x^2 + y^2 - r^2 < 0$

Exterior
$x^2 + y^2 - r^2 > 0$

The distance formula can be used to obtain proofs of many common theorems in coordinate geometry. Several of these are considered in exercises. The proof of the following theorem provides an opportunity to use inequalities as well as equations.

If two chords of a circle are of unequal length, the longer chord is nearer the center.

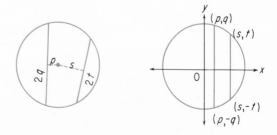

Consider the lengths of the chords as $2q$ and $2t$, where $2q > 2t$. Call their distances from the center of the circle p and s, respectively. The radius of the circle with equation $x^2 + y^2 = r^2$ is r. Consider the chord with endpoints (p, q) and $(p, -q)$ and the chord with endpoints (s, t) and $(s, -t)$. These chords are congruent to the given chords, since in the same circle or congruent circles chords equally distant from the center are congruent. The statement that the endpoints of the chords are on the circle is $p^2 + q^2 = r^2$ and $s^2 + t^2 = r^2$. Thus, $p^2 + q^2 = s^2 + t^2$. Given that $2q > 2t$, and that p, q, s, and t are distances (that is, nonnegative), then $q > t$, $q^2 > t^2$, and, subtracting the inequality from the equality, we have

$$p^2 + q^2 = s^2 + t^2$$
$$\underline{ q^2 > t^2}$$
$$p^2 < s^2$$

whence $p < s$, as was to be proved. Obviously, the statements require previous consideration of inequalities.

The distance formula enables us to classify triangles when the coordinates of their vertices are given. A triangle is isosceles if at least two of its sides are congruent, equilateral if all three sides are congruent, and right if the sum of the squares of two sides is equal to the square of the third side.

EXERCISES FOR SECTION 10-9

Find the length of the line segment with endpoints:

1. $(1, 3)$ and $(4, 3)$.
2. $(2, -1)$ and $(2, 5)$.
3. $(1, 3)$ and $(4, 7)$.
4. $(2, -3)$ and $(7, 9)$.
5. $(-1, 5)$ and $(2, -3)$.
6. $(-3, -4)$ and $(-7, -15)$.
7. $(7, 11)$ and $(1, 3)$.
8. $(-2, -3)$ and $(6, 12)$.

Find an equation for the circle with:

9. Center $(1, 2)$ and radius 3.
10. Center $(2, -3)$ and radius 5.

Find the lengths of the sides and tell whether the triangle with the given vertices is (a) *an isosceles triangle,* (b) *an equilateral triangle,* (c) *a right triangle:*

11. $(4, 5)$, $(3, 7)$, and $(6, 6)$.
12. $(-1, 15)$, $(7, -12)$, and $(-3, -5)$.

In Exercises 13 through 16 prove on a coordinate plane:

13. A line $x = p$ is tangent to circle $x^2 + y^2 = r^2$ if $p^2 = r^2$; is a secant if $p^2 < r^2$; does not intersect the circle if $p^2 > r^2$.

14. The diagonals of a rectangle are congruent.

15. An isosceles triangle has two congruent medians.

16. The sum of the squares of the distances from any point P on the plane of a rectangle to the endpoints of one diagonal of the rectangle is equal to the sum of the squares of the distances from P to the endpoints of the other diagonal.

*17. In coordinate space each point is identified by three coordinates (x, y, z). The distance formula in space is

$$d = \sqrt{(x_1 - x_2)^2 + (y_1 - y_2)^2 + (z_1 - z_2)^2}.$$

Find the length of the line segment with endpoints:
  (a) $(1, 0, 2)$ and $(1, 4, 5)$;
  (b) $(2, 7, -3)$ and $(1, 5, 0)$.

*18. Find the length of the line segment with endpoints:
  (a) $(2, -1, 0)$ and $(3, 1, 2)$;
  (b) $(1, 5, -6)$ and $(-2, 3, 1)$.

*19. Find an equation for the sphere with
  (a) center $(1, -2, 5)$ and radius 2;
  (b) center $(2, 3, -4)$ and radius 5.

*20. Describe the set of points in space such that
  (a) $(x - 1)^2 + (y - 2)^2 + (z - 3)^2 = 4$;
  (b) $x^2 + y^2 + z^2 = 5$.

10-10 PERPENDICULAR LINES

Two lines on a coordinate plane are parallel if and only if they are both parallel to the y-axis or if they have the same slope (§10-8). We now use the Pythagorean theorem and prove that if neither of two lines is parallel to the x-axis and if the lines are perpendicular, then the product of their slopes is -1.

Consider two lines p and q on a coordinate plane. If at least one of the lines is parallel to the x-axis, then the lines are perpendicular if and only if the other line is parallel to the y-axis. If neither line is parallel to the x-axis, then each line intersects the x-axis. Suppose that one line intersects the x-axis at $A: (a, 0)$ and that the other line intersects the x-axis at $B: (b, 0)$, where $b > a$. This assumption implies that the lines do not intersect on the x-axis. When the lines intersect on the x-axis, either a new coordinate system may be used with a different choice of the x-axis or a new proof may be given with A and B selected on a line $y = k, k \neq 0$.

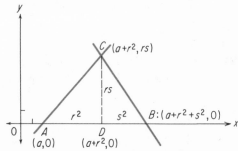

If $p \perp q$, call their point of intersection C and draw the altitude $\overline{CD}$ of triangle ABC. Since $b > a$, we may choose $r > 0$ such that $\overline{AD} = r^2$, and thus D has coordinates $(a + r^2, 0)$. In any right triangle ABC with right angle at C and altitude $\overline{CD}$, we know that $\overline{CD}^2 = (\overline{AD})(\overline{DB})$, since the altitude to the hypotenuse is the mean proportional between the segments of the hypotenuse. Therefore, we may choose s such that $\overline{CD} = rs$ and $\overline{DB} = s^2$. Then we have

$$C: (a + r^2, rs) \quad \text{and} \quad B: (a + r^2 + s^2, 0),$$

as in the figure. The slope of $\overset{\leftrightarrow}{AC}$ is

$$\frac{rs - 0}{(a + r^2) - a};$$

that is, $\dfrac{s}{r}$. The slope of $\overset{\leftrightarrow}{BC}$ is

$$\frac{rs - 0}{(a + r^2) - (a + r^2 + s^2)};$$

that is, $-\dfrac{r}{s}$. The product of the slopes of the two lines is

$$\frac{s}{r}\left(-\frac{r}{s}\right);$$

that is, -1. We have proved that the product of the slopes of the perpendicular lines p and q is -1. As a matter of convenience, in this text we shall assume the converse statement without proof: If the product of the slopes of two lines is -1, the lines are perpendicular.

EXAMPLE 1:   Find the slope of any line that is perpendicular to the line through $(2, 5)$ and $(-1, 7)$.

Solution: The line m through $(2, 5)$ and $(-1, 7)$ has slope $\dfrac{7 - 5}{-1 - 2}$; that is, $-\dfrac{2}{3}$. Therefore, any line perpendicular to m has slope $\dfrac{3}{2}$.

EXAMPLE 2:   Find an equation for the line that is perpendicular to the line $y = 2x + 3$ at the point $(1, 5)$.

Solution: The given line has slope 2. Therefore, the desired line has slope $-\frac{1}{2}$. The line through $(1, 5)$ with slope $-\frac{1}{2}$ has equation

$$y - 5 = -\frac{1}{2}(x - 1).$$

EXERCISES FOR SECTION 10-10

Find the slope of any line that is perpendicular to the line:

1. $y = 2x$ **2.** $y = \frac{3}{4}x + 5$

3. Through $(1, 5)$ and $(6, 7)$.

4. Through $(-1, -3)$ and $(3, 5)$.

Find an equation for the line that is perpendicular to the line:

5. $y = 3x$ at the origin.

6. $y = -5x$ at the origin.

7. $y = \frac{1}{2}x - 3$ at $(0, -3)$.

8. $y = -\frac{2}{5}x + 4$ at $(0, 4)$.

9. $y = 3x + 5$ at $(-1, 2)$.

10. $x + y - 2 = 0$ at $(1, 1)$.

11. $x + y - 6 = 0$ at $(2, 4)$.

12. $2x - y + 5 = 0$ at $(3, 1)$.

Assume that the lines are not parallel to coordinate axes and prove:

13. A line perpendicular to one of two parallel lines is perpendicular to the other.

14. Two lines perpendicular to the same line are parallel.

15. Two lines perpendicular, respectively, to two intersecting lines intersect.

Represent each figure on a coordinate plane and prove:

16. The diagonals of a square are mutually perpendicular.

*17. The altitudes of a triangle are on concurrent lines.

TEST FOR CHAPTER 10

1. Copy the given figure, label each region with its area, and use the figure to obtain a formula for $(x + 2)^2$.

2. Is it always possible in space to have:
(**a**) A line perpendicular to each of two given planes?
(**b**) A line perpendicular to each of two lines that are on a plane?

3. In each of the two non-Euclidean geometries describe the appearance of two lines that are perpendicular to the same line.

4. Write the plane dual of the statement: Any two distinct points on the same plane determine a unique line.

5. For the line through $(-2, 3)$ and $(4, 9)$ find an equation in (**a**) point-slope form; (**b**) slope-intercept form.

6. Find the length of the line segment with endpoints: (**a**) $(2, 5)$ and $(6, 5)$; (**b**) $(2, 5)$ and $(6, 8)$.

7. Find the midpoint of the line segment with endpoints: (**a**) $(1, 7)$ and $(5, 3)$; (**b**) $(-1, 4)$ and $(6, 4)$.

8. Find the slope of any line that is perpendicular to the line (**a**) $y = 3x$; (**b**) $y = \frac{2}{3}x - 4$.

9. Find the slope of any line that is parallel to the line (**a**) $y = -\frac{1}{3}x + 6$; (**b**) through $(1, 2)$ and $(5, -2)$.

10. Find an equation for the circle with center $(3, 5)$ and radius 2.

EPILOGUE

Twenty-five hundred years ago arithmetic (the theory of numbers), geometry, music, and spherics (astronomy) were the basic subjects in the liberal arts program of study of the Pythagoreans. Grammar, logic, and rhetoric were added in the Middle Ages and these seven liberal arts were considered essential for an educated person. Mathematics is still an important part of the background of any educated person.

Mathematics today includes many topics such as arithmetic, number theory, algebra, geometry, logic, probability, and linear programming that we have considered in this introduction to mathematical concepts. The concepts of sets provided a unifying theme for all of these topics.

The study of separate courses in arithmetic, algebra, and geometry is misleading since it makes them appear as separate subjects rather than as parts of the same subject, mathematics. We have seen that algebra may be used in the study of geometry as, for example, in the use of coordinates. Also geometry may be used in the study of algebra as, for example, in the use of the number line. The very close relationship between algebra and geometry may be observed by noticing that the algebra of the real numbers and the geometry of the points on a Euclidean line are essentially the same. Indeed, the early Greeks represented numbers by line segments before more convenient notations were developed. Thus algebra provides one approach or point of view for the study of mathematics and geometry provides another approach or point of view.

Mathematics is a living and rapidly growing subject. More new mathematics has been developed during the last fifty years than in all previous time of recorded history. Also mathematics is permeating the scientific advances of our time so that we must either understand the basic mathematical concepts or live in fear of the scientific advances. In this book we have tried to help you remove your fears of mathematics and develop an understanding that will enable you to proceed with confidence in your chosen careers.

ANSWERS TO ODD-NUMBERED EXERCISES

CHAPTER 1: FUN WITH MATHEMATICS

1-1 MATHEMATICAL PATTERNS

1. The text shows the diagrams for 3×9, 7×9, and 4×9 respectively. Here are the others:

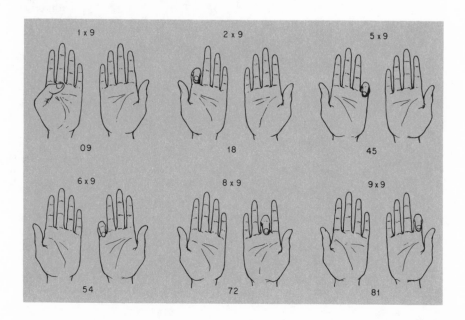

3. $6^2 = 1 + 2 + 3 + 4 + 5 + 6 + 5$
$+ 4 + 3 + 2 + 1$
$7^2 = 1 + 2 + 3 + 4 + 5 + 6 + 7$
$+ 6 + 5 + 4 + 3 + 2 + 1$
$8^2 = 1 + 2 + 3 + 4 + 5 + 6 + 7$
$+ 8 + 7 + 6 + 5 + 4 + 3$
$+ 2 + 1$
$9^2 = 1 + 2 + 3 + 4 + 5 + 6 + 7$
$+ 8 + 9 + 8 + 7 + 6 + 5$
$+ 4 + 3 + 2 + 1$

7. (a) $9 \times 47 = 423$

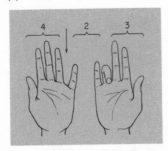

(b) $9 \times 39 = 351$

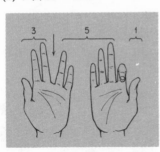

(c) $9 \times 18 = 162$

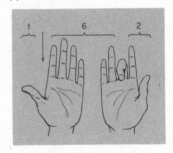

(d) $9 \times 27 = 243$

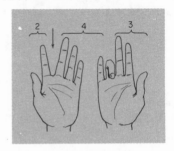

9. (a) 40×81, that is, 3240;
(b) 100×201, that is, 20,100;
(c) $\frac{25}{2} \times 50$, that is, 625;
(d) 50×200, that is, 10,000;
(e) 100×402, that is, 40,200.

11. (a) $\frac{3}{4}$;
(b) $\frac{7}{8}$;
(c) $\frac{15}{16}$. In general: $\dfrac{2^n - 1}{2^n}$.

1-2 MATHEMATICAL RECREATIONS

1. (a) 12.
(b) Only one, if it's long enough.
(c) Only halfway; then you start walking out.
(d) *One* of them is not a nickel, but the other one is.
(e) There is no dirt in a hole.
(f) Brother-sister.

3. There are eleven trips needed. First one Indian and one missionary go over; the missionary returns. Then two Indians go over and one returns. Next two missionaries go over; one missionary and one Indian return. Two missionaries go over next and one Indian returns. Then two Indians go over and one of them returns. Finally, the last two Indians go over.

5. After 27 days the cat still has 3 feet to

go. It does this the next day and is at the top after 28 days.

7.

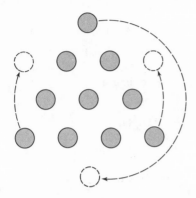

9. Use the matchsticks to form a triangular pyramid.

11. Both A's and B's will say that they are B's. Therefore, when the second man said that the first man said he was a B, the second man was telling the truth. Thus the first two men told the truth and the third man lied.

13. If the penny is in the left hand and the dime in the right hand, the computation will give $3 + 60 = 63$, an odd number. If the coins are reversed, we have $30 + 6 = 36$, an even number.

15. There really is no missing dollar. The computation may be done in one of two ways: $(30 - 3) - 2 = 25$, or $25 + 2 + 3 = 30$. In the problem the arithmetic was done in a manner that is not legitimate; that is, $(30 - 3) + 2$.

17. Eight moves are needed. The coins are identified in the following diagram as well as the squares which may be used. The moves are as follows, where the first numeral indicates the position of the coin and the second one tells you where to move it: D_1: $4 - 3$; P_2: $2 - 4$; P_1: $1 - 2$; D_1: $3 - 1$; D_2: $5 - 3$; P_2: $4 - 5$; P_1: $2 - 4$; D_2: $3 - 2$.

1	2	3	4	5
P_1	P_2		D_1	D_2

1-3 BEYOND THE GOOGOL

1. It would take one billion seconds; that is, about 11,574 days.

3. (a) 7, that is, $2^3 - 1$;
  (b) 15, that is, $2^4 - 1$;
  (c) 31, that is, $2^5 - 1$;
  (d) 63, that is, $2^6 - 1$. For 30 days: $2^{30} - 1$, that is, \$10,737,418.23.

5. (a) Approximately three billion;

  (b) 3,156,000,000.

7. $\{ 5, 10, 15, 20, 25, \ldots, 5n, \ldots \}$
  $\updownarrow \ \updownarrow \ \updownarrow \ \updownarrow \ \updownarrow \qquad \updownarrow$
  $\{ 1, 2, 3, 4, 5, \ldots, n, \ldots \}$

*9. 200; $10^{100} \times 10^{100} = 10^{200}$. This number is much smaller than a googolplex, which is 10 raised to the googol power; that is, 10 with 10^{100} zeros.

1-4 IMPOSSIBLE AND UNSOLVED PROBLEMS

1. (a) 5;
  (b) 9;
  (c) $D = \dfrac{n(n - 3)}{2}$.

3. (a) Multiply the tens digit by the next consecutive integer and then by 100; add 25.

(b) Let the number be written as $10n + 5$. Then

$$(10n + 5)^2 = 100n^2 + 100n$$
$$+ 25 = 100n(n + 1) + 25.$$

We may then rearrange factors to write this last expression as $n(n + 1)(100) + 25$, which is the pattern given for (a).

5. (a) One possible tracing:

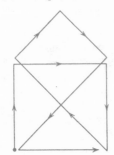

(b) Impossible.

7. As in Exercise 11 of §1-1, the sum of n terms is $\dfrac{2^n - 1}{2^n}$; that is, $1 - \dfrac{1}{2^n}$.

As n becomes very large, $\dfrac{1}{2^n}$ becomes very small and the sum approaches closer and closer to 1. Thus, the limit is 1.

9. 6

*11. (a) 3;
   (b) 6;
   (c) 10;
   (d) $\dfrac{n(n - 1)}{2}$.

*13. $28 = 1 + 2 + 4 + 7 + 14$
(The next perfect number is 496.)

CHAPTER 2: SYSTEMS OF NUMERATION

2-1 EGYPTIAN NUMERATION

1. ∩∩ ⏐ ⏐ ⏐ ⏐ ⏐

3. 𝓇𝟫𝟫𝟫𝟫∩∩ ⏐ ⏐ ⏐ ⏐ ⏐ ⏐

5. ⌐ 𝓇 𝓇 𝟫𝟫𝟫𝟫 ⏐ ⏐ ⏐ ⏐ ⏐ ⏐ ⏐

7. 22

9. 1102

11. 1324

13.   ∩∩∩∩ ⏐ ⏐
   +   ∩∩ ⏐
   _____
   ∩∩∩∩∩∩ ⏐ ⏐ ⏐

15.   𝟫𝟫∩∩∩ ⏐ ⏐ ⏐ ⏐ ⏐ ⏐ ⏐ ⏐
   +   𝟫∩∩∩ ⏐ ⏐ ⏐ ⏐ ⏐
   _____
   𝟫𝟫𝟫∩∩∩∩∩∩∩ ⏐ ⏐ ⏐

17.   𝓇𝟫𝟫∩∩∩∩∩ ⏐ ⏐ ⏐
   −   𝟫∩∩∩   ⏐ ⏐ ⏐ ⏐ ⏐ ⏐ ⏐
   _____

                      ⏐ ⏐ ⏐ ⏐ ⏐ ⏐ ⏐ ⏐ ⏐ ⏐
      𝓇𝟫𝟫∩∩∩ ⏐ ⏐ ⏐
   −   𝟫∩∩∩ ⏐ ⏐ ⏐ ⏐ ⏐ ⏐
   _____
      𝓇 𝟫   ⏐ ⏐ ⏐ ⏐ ⏐ ⏐

19. ①× 45 = ㊺
   2 × 45 = 90
   4 × 45 = 180
   8 × 45 = 360
   ⑯× 45 = ⑦⑳
   17 = 1 + 16
   17 × 45 = (1 + 16) × 45
      = 45 + 720 = 765

21. ①× 31 = ㉛
   ②× 31 = ㊂
   4 × 31 = 124

8 × 31 = 248
16 × 31 = 496
27 = 1 + 2 + 8 + 16
27 × 31 = (1 + 2 + 8 + 16) × 31
= 31 + 62 + 248 + 496
= 837

23. 19 → 33
9 → 66
4 132
2 264
1 → 528

19 × 33 = 33 + 66 + 528 = 627

25. 21 → 52
10 104
5 → 208
2 416
1 → 832
21 × 52 = 52 + 208 + 832 = 1092

27. We need a symbol for zero because the value of a numeral in our decimal system depends upon both the value and the position of the digits in the numeral. For example, 405 and 450 represent two entirely different numbers, yet the same digits are used in the two numerals. The ancient Egyptians were not dependent upon the position of a symbol in determining its value, so zero as a "placeholder" was not needed.

2-2 OTHER METHODS OF COMPUTATION

1.

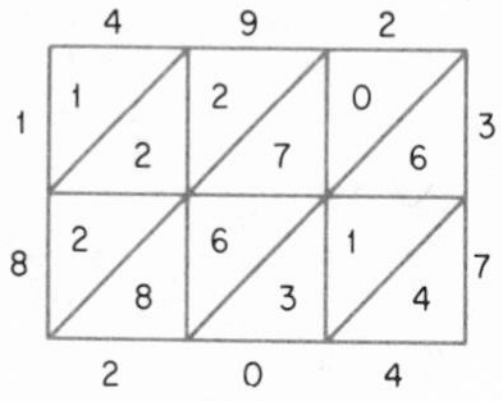

Answer: 18,204

3.

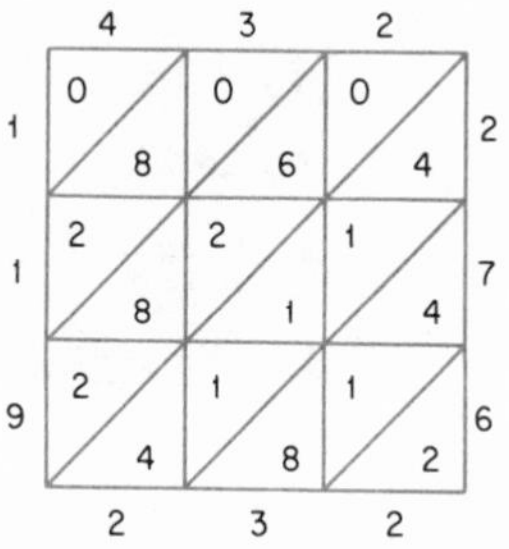

Answer: 119,232

5.

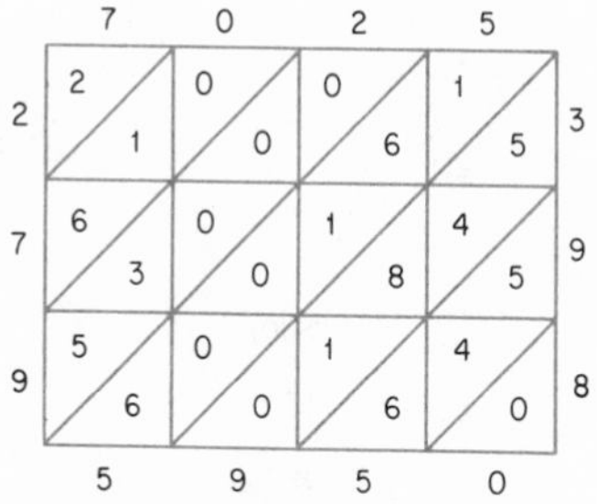

Answer: 2,795,950

7.

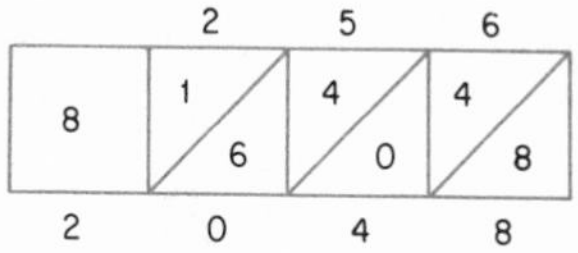

Answer: 2048

9.

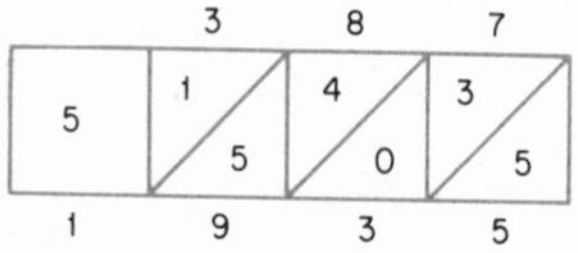

Answer: 1935

11.

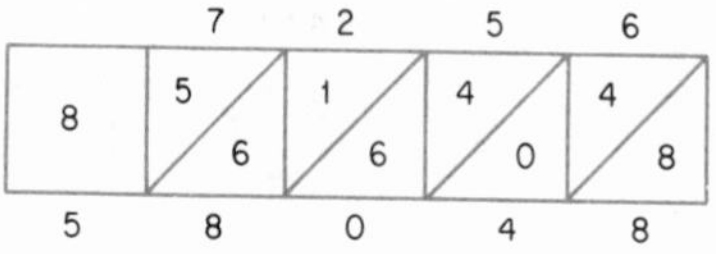

Answer: 58,048

2-3 DECIMAL NOTATION

1. 125

3. 0.001

5. 1

7. 0.04

9. 2000

*11. 0.0002

13. $(4 \times 10^2) + (3 \times 10^1) + (2 \times 10^0)$

15. $(4 \times 10^0) + (2 \times 10^{-1})$
$+ (3 \times 10^{-2})$

17. $(2 \times 10^3) + (3 \times 10^2) + (4 \times 10^1)$
$+ (5 \times 10^0)$

19. $(4 \times 10^2) + (2 \times 10^1) + (3 \times 10^0)$
$+ (8 \times 10^{-1}) + (3 \times 10^{-2})$

21. (7×10^{-3})

23. (1×10^{-4})

25. 3253

27. 52.173

29. 0.0251

2-4 OTHER SYSTEMS OF NOTATION

1. 22_{five}

3. 30_{four}

5.

7.

9.

11. 23

13. 26

15. 19

17. 32_{five}

19. 32_{six}

2-5 BASE FIVE NUMERATION

1. 113

3. 124

5. 86

7. 141

9. 41.8

11. 3012_5

13. 11112_5

15. 10000_5

17. 1022_5

19. 4012_5

*21. 287

*23. 11

*25. 462

*27. 469

2-6 OTHER NUMBER BASES

1. 314

3. 1076

5. 50

7. 662

9. 2590

11. 3598_{12}

13. $87e0_{12}$

15. 11010_4

17. 1551_6

19. 11143_5

21. 655_9

23. 187_{12}

*25. $1e7_{12}$

*27. 101111_2

2-7 COMPUTATION IN BASE FIVE NOTATION

1. 111_5

3. 432_5

5. 11312_5

7. 112_5

9. 134_5

11. 413_5

13. 222_5

15. 3023_5

17. 3401_5

19. 1423_5

21. 21022_5

23. 22_5

25. $224_5\,R\,2$

27. 13_5

29. 41_5

31.

X	0	1	2	3	4
0	0	0	0	0	0
1	0	1	2	3	4
2	0	2	4	11_5	13_5
3	0	3	11_5	14_5	22_5
4	0	4	13_5	22_5	31_5

*33.

+	0	1	2	3	4	5	6	7
0	0	1	2	3	4	5	6	7
1	1	2	3	4	5	6	7	10_8
2	2	3	4	5	6	7	10_8	11_8
3	3	4	5	6	7	10_8	11_8	12_8
4	4	5	6	7	10_8	11_8	12_8	13_8
5	5	6	7	10_8	11_8	12_8	13_8	14_8
6	6	7	10_8	11_8	12_8	13_8	14_8	15_8
7	7	10_8	11_8	12_8	13_8	14_8	15_8	16_8

X	0	1	2	3	4	5	6	7
0	0	0	0	0	0	0	0	0
1	0	1	2	3	4	5	6	7
2	0	2	4	6	10_8	12_8	14_8	16_8
3	0	3	6	11_8	14_8	17_8	22_8	25_8
4	0	4	10_8	14_8	20_8	24_8	30_8	34_8
5	0	5	12_8	17_8	24_8	31_8	36_8	43_8
6	0	6	14_8	22_8	30_8	36_8	44_8	52_8
7	0	7	16_8	25_8	34_8	43_8	52_8	61_8

*35. 10322_6

*37. 226_8

*39. 14446_8

*41. $210_4\,R\,1$

2-8 BINARY NOTATION

1. 11100_2

3. 10011_2

5. 10011000_2

7. 15

9. 55

11. 38

13. 11000_2

15. 101_2

17. 100111_2

19. (a) 1000010_2;

    (b) 1000100_2;

    (c) 1000111_2

*21. $214 = 326_8 = 11010110_2$. When placed in groups of three, starting from the units digit, the binary representation can be translated into the octal system, and conversely. Thus

$$\underbrace{011}_{3}\ \ \underbrace{010}_{2}\ \ \underbrace{110_2}_{6} = 326_8.$$

2-9 JUST FOR FUN

1. The numerals at the top of each column represent powers of 2: $2^0 = 1$; $2^1 = 2$; $2^2 = 4$; $2^3 = 8$. Every number less than 15 can be represented in binary notation in exactly one way. Each such number will or will not contain one of these powers of 2. For each such power of 2 that it contains, it will appear in the corresponding column A, B, C, or D.

3. First write the numbers 0 through 15 in binary notation, with place values identified by columns A, B, C, and D.

The four questions to be asked are "Does the number have a 1 in position A?" "Does the number have a 1 in position B?" "Does the number have a 1 in position C?" "Does the number have a 1 in position D?" Suppose the answers are "Yes, No, Yes, Yes." Then the number is identified as 1101_2; that is, 13.

*5. There are many references. One is: Burton W. Jones, *Elementary Concepts of Mathematics*, 2nd ed. (New York: Macmillan, 1963).

	D	C	B	A
0	0	0	0	0
1	0	0	0	1
2	0	0	1	0
3	0	0	1	1
4	0	1	0	0
5	0	1	0	1
6	0	1	1	0
7	0	1	1	1
8	1	0	0	0
9	1	0	0	1
10	1	0	1	0
11	1	0	1	1
12	1	1	0	0
13	1	1	0	1
14	1	1	1	0
15	1	1	1	1

CHAPTER 3: MATHEMATICAL SYSTEMS

3-1 AN ABSTRACT SYSTEM

1. #

3. Σ

5. Commutative property for multition.

7. Identity element (∗).

9. Associative property for multition.

11. Inverse element.

13. $\triangle$

15. Yes.

17. Yes.

19. No; it must hold for all possible choices of three elements.

21. Yes; the inverse of $\triangle$ is Q, the inverse of $\square$ is $\square$, the inverse of Q is $\triangle$.

23. No; the entries within the table contain elements ∘ and ∼, which are not members of the original set of elements.

25. Yes; •.

SUPPLEMENTARY EXERCISES FOR SECTION 3-1

1. Take the sum of the two numbers.

3. Add 1 to the sum of the two numbers.

*5. Subtract the second number from twice the first number.

7. One counterexample is sufficient; for example, $8 \div 3$ is not a counting number.

9. 1. $8 \times 1 = 8$; $13 \times 1 = 13$.

11. Yes. Yes.

*13. Regardless of the answer to $(b \# c)$, the result of $a \$ (b \# c)$ is always a, since $\$$ means to select the first number. Also $a \$ b = a$, $a \$ c = a$, and thus $a \# a = a$.

3-2 THE DISTRIBUTIVE PROPERTY

1. 8, 8, 3, 7.

3. 7, 7.

5. 3, 3.

7. No.

9. $7 \times 79 = 7 \times (80 - 1) = 560 - 7$
$= 553.$

11. 3.

13. 5.

15. 7.

17. 7.

19. True for all replacements of n.

3-3 CLOCK ARITHMETIC

1. (a) Yes;
(b) yes.

3. The identity with respect to addition is 12; the identity with respect to multiplication is 1.

5. 3

7. 9

9. 3

11. 5

13. 8

15. 6

17. 1, 5, or 9.

19. 4

*21. An impossible equation; that is, there is no value of t for which this equation is true.

*23. An identity; that is, this equation is true for all possible replacements of t.

25. (a) 6;
(b) 16_{12}.

27. (a) 9;
(b) 39_{12}.

29. (a) 12;
(b) 30_{12}.

3-4 MODULAR ARITHMETIC

1.

X	0	1	2	3	4
0	0	0	0	0	0
1	0	1	2	3	4
2	0	2	4	1	3
3	0	3	1	4	2
4	0	4	3	2	1

3. Two specific cases are $(3 \cdot 2) \cdot 4 = 3 \cdot (2 \cdot 4) = 4$ and $(4 \cdot 3) \cdot 4 = 4 \cdot (3 \cdot 4) = 3$. There many others.

5. The inverse of 1 is 1, of 2 is 3, of 3 is 2, and of 4 is 4. Note that 0 does not have an inverse with respect to multiplication.

7. 4

9. 4

11. 3

13. 3

15. 4

17. 4

19. 3

21. 4

23. An impossible equation; that is, there is no value of x for which this equation is true.

SUPPLEMENTARY EXERCISES FOR SECTION 3-4

1.

+	0	1	2	3
0	0	1	2	3
1	1	2	3	0
2	2	3	0	1
3	3	0	1	2

X	0	1	2	3
0	0	0	0	0
1	0	1	2	3
2	0	2	0	2
3	0	3	2	1

This system is closed, commutative, and associative with respect to both addition and multiplication. It satisfies the distributive property for multiplication with respect to addition. There are identity elements for both addition (0) and multiplication (1). Each element has an inverse with respect to addition; not every element has an inverse with respect to multiplication.

3. 2

5. 5

7. 3

9. 3

11. 4

13. An impossible equation; that is, there is no value of x for which this equation is true.

15. 0

17. $2 \cdot 6 = 0$; $3 \cdot 8 = 0$; $4 \cdot 6 = 0$; $4 \cdot 9 = 0$; $6 \cdot 6 = 0$; $6 \cdot 8 = 0$; $6 \cdot 10 = 0$; $8 \cdot 9 = 0$. Thus the zero divisors in arithmetic modulo 12 are 2 and 6, 3 and 4, 3 and 8, 4 and 9, 6 and 6, 6 and 8, 6 and 10, and 8 and 9.

19.

~	I	R	H	V
I	I	R	H	V
R	R	I	V	H
H	H	V	I	R
V	V	H	R	I

The system is closed, commutative, and associative with respect to the given operation. There is an identity element I, and each element is its own inverse with respect to ~.

CHAPTER 4: SETS AND STATEMENTS

4-1 SET NOTATION

1. $\in$

3. $\notin$

5. Well-defined.

7. Not well-defined.

9. Equal.

11. Equal.

13. {January, February, March, ..., December}.

15. $\{2, 3, 4, \ldots, 9\}$.

17. The set of counting numbers 1 through 6.

19. The set of counting numbers greater than 50.

21. The set of multiples of 10 from 10 through 150.

*23. The set of numbers that can be expressed in the form $n(n - 1)$, where n ranges from 1 through 10.

4-2 SUBSETS

1. Among the many correct answers are: the set of odd integers divisible by 2; the set of integers between 4 and 5; the set of even integers between 6 and 8; the human beings who traveled to Venus prior to 1968; the hens that lay glass eggs; the people born with ten left feet.

3. (a) $\{p, r, o, f, e, s\}$;
   (b) $\{f, s\}$;
   (c) $\{p, f\}$;
   (d) $\{f\}$.

5. (a) $\{2, 4, 6, 8\}$;
   (b) $\{1, 2, 4, 5, 7, 8\}$.

7.

Number of elements	0	1	2	3	4	5	6
Number of subsets	1	2	4	8	16	32	64

9. $N = 2^n$

4-3 EQUIVALENT SETS

1. $\{1, 2\} \leftrightarrow \{p, q\}$ $\{1, 2\} \leftrightarrow \{q, p\}$

3.
$\{1, 2, 3, 4\} \leftrightarrow \{r, e, s, t\}$ $\{1, 2, 3, 4\} \leftrightarrow \{r, e, t, s\}$

$\{1, 2, 3, 4\} \leftrightarrow \{r, s, e, t\}$ $\{1, 2, 3, 4\} \leftrightarrow \{r, s, t, e\}$

$\{1, 2, 3, 4\} \leftrightarrow \{r, t, e, s\}$ $\{1, 2, 3, 4\} \leftrightarrow \{r, t, s, e\}$

$\{1, 2, 3, 4\} \leftrightarrow \{e, r, s, t\}$ $\{1, 2, 3, 4\} \leftrightarrow \{e, r, t, s\}$

$\{1, 2, 3, 4\} \leftrightarrow \{e, s, r, t\}$ $\{1, 2, 3, 4\} \leftrightarrow \{e, s, t, r\}$

$\{1, 2, 3, 4\} \leftrightarrow \{e, t, r, s\}$ $\{1, 2, 3, 4\} \leftrightarrow \{e, t, s, r\}$

$\{1, 2, 3, 4\} \leftrightarrow \{s, r, e, t\}$ $\{1, 2, 3, 4\} \leftrightarrow \{s, r, t, e\}$

$\{1, 2, 3, 4\} \leftrightarrow \{s, e, r, t\}$ $\{1, 2, 3, 4\} \leftrightarrow \{s, e, t, r\}$

$\{1, 2, 3, 4\} \leftrightarrow \{s, t, r, e\}$ $\{1, 2, 3, 4\} \leftrightarrow \{s, t, e, r\}$

$\{1, 2, 3, 4\} \leftrightarrow \{t, r, e, s\}$ $\{1, 2, 3, 4\} \leftrightarrow \{t, r, s, e\}$

$\{1, 2, 3, 4\} \leftrightarrow \{t, e, r, s\}$ $\{1, 2, 3, 4\} \leftrightarrow \{t, e, s, r\}$

$\{1, 2, 3, 4\} \leftrightarrow \{t, s, r, e\}$ $\{1, 2, 3, 4\} \leftrightarrow \{t, s, e, r\}$

5. Among the many correct answers is: the set $\{n, u, m, b, e, r\}$ of letters in "number."

7. Among the many correct answers is: the empty set.

9. 3

11. 8

13. 0

15. Among the many correct answers is: the set of counting numbers.

17. (a) Yes. Any two sets that consist of the same elements have the same number of elements.
   (b) No. Two sets may have the same number of elements without having the same elements.

19. Among the many correct answers is:

$\{a, e, i, o, u\} \leftrightarrow \{2, 4, 6, 8, 10\}$

*21. $\{1, 3, 5, 7, 9, \ldots, 2n - 1, \ldots\} \leftrightarrow \{5, 10, 15, 20, 25, \ldots, 5n, \ldots\}$

4-4 RELATIONSHIPS BETWEEN SETS

1. (a) $\{1, 2, 3, 5, 7\}$;
   (b) $\{1, 3\}$.

3. (a) $\{1, 3, 5, 7, 9\}$;
   (b) $\{7\}$.

5. (a) $\{1, 3, 5, 7, 8, 10\}$;
   (b) $\varnothing$.

7. (a) $\{1, 2, 3, \ldots\}$;
   (b) $\varnothing$.

9. (a) $\{3, 4, 5\}$;
   (b) $\{2, 4\}$;
   (c) $\{2, 3, 4, 5\}$;
   (d) $\{4\}$.

11. (a) $\{2, 4, 6, \ldots\}$;
   (b) $\{1, 3, 5, \ldots\}$;

   (c) $\{1, 2, 3, \ldots\}$;
   (d) $\varnothing$.

13. (a) $\{2, 3\}$;
   (b) $\{1, 2\}$;
   (c) $\{1, 2, 3\}$;
   (d) $\{2\}$.

15. $\{6, 8\}$

17. $\{2, 4, 5, 6, 8, 9, 10\}$

19. $\{4, 5, 9\}$

21. (a) A;
   (b) B;
   (c) $\varnothing$;
   (d) U.

4-5 SETS OF POINTS

1. (a) 2;
   (b) 9;
   (c) 4;
   (d) 13.

3.

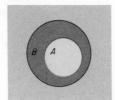

5.

7.

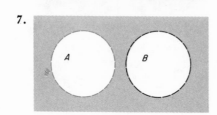

9. A' is shaded with horizontal lines; B is shaded with vertical lines. The union of these two sets is the subset of U that is shaded with lines in either or both directions.

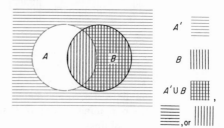

11. A is shaded with vertical lines; B' is shaded with horizontal lines. The intersection of these two sets is the subset of U that is shaded with lines in both directions.

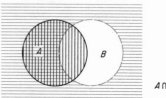

13.

$A \cup B = B \cup A$

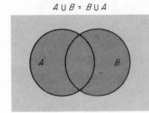

15.

$A \cap B \subseteq A$

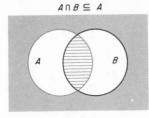

17. In the following pair of diagrams, the final result is the same, showing the equivalence of the statements given.

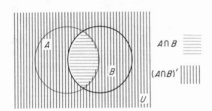

The set $(A \cap B)$ is shaded with horizontal lines. Its complement, $(A \cap B)'$, is the remaining portion of U shaded with vertical lines.

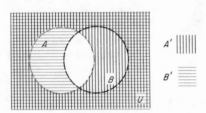

The set A' is shaded with vertical lines; the set B' is shaded with horizontal lines. Their union, $A' \cup B'$, is the portion of U shaded with lines in either or both directions.

19. (a) 1;
   (b) 5;
   (c) 4;
   (d) 12;
   (e) 21;
   (f) 25.

21. (a) 25;
   (b) 7;
   (c) 7;
   (d) 29;
   (e) 37;
   (f) 6.

23. There are 11 students who are not taking any of the three subjects, 10 taking only chemistry, and 2 taking physics and chemistry but not biology. The given data are shown in the following Venn diagram:

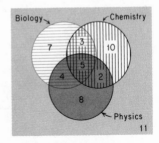

25. (a)

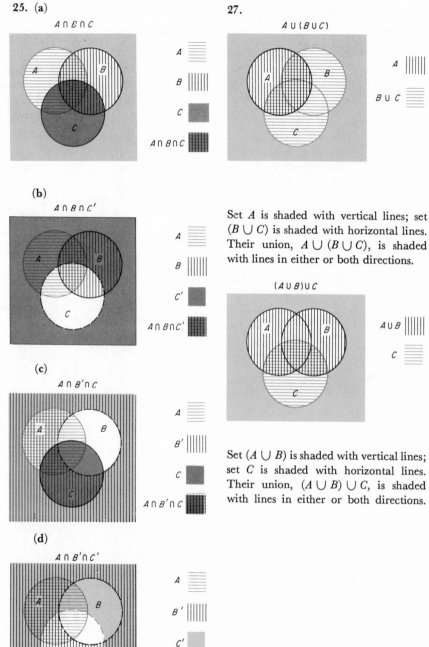

27.

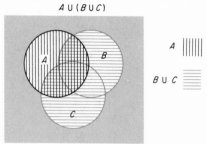

Set A is shaded with vertical lines; set $(B \cup C)$ is shaded with horizontal lines. Their union, $A \cup (B \cup C)$, is shaded with lines in either or both directions.

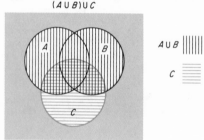

Set $(A \cup B)$ is shaded with vertical lines; set C is shaded with horizontal lines. Their union, $(A \cup B) \cup C$, is shaded with lines in either or both directions.

4-6 SETS OF STATEMENTS

1. (a) $(\sim p) \wedge (\sim q)$;
    (b) $(\sim p) \wedge q$;
    (c) $(\sim p) \wedge q$;
    (d) $\sim[p \wedge (\sim q)]$;
    (e) $p \vee (\sim q)$.

3. (a) $p \wedge (\sim q)$;
    (b) $p \vee (\sim q)$;
    (c) $(\sim p) \wedge q$;
    (d) $\sim[(\sim p) \wedge q]$;
    (e) $\sim[(\sim p) \wedge q]$.

5. (a) I like this book and I like mathematics.
    (b) I do not like mathematics.
    (c) I do not like this book.
    (d) I do not like this book and I do not like mathematics.

7. 5(a), 6(b), and 6(d).

*9. (a) True;
    (b) true;
    (c) true;
    (d) true.

4-7 TRUTH VALUES OF STATEMENTS

1.

p	q	$(\sim p) \wedge q$
T	T	F
T	F	F
F	T	T
F	F	F

3.

p	q	$(\sim p) \vee (\sim q)$
T	T	F
T	F	T
F	T	T
F	F	T

5.

p	q	$\sim(p \wedge q)$
T	T	F
T	F	T
F	T	T
F	F	T

7.

p	q	$\sim$	$[p$	$\vee$	$(\sim q)]$
T	T	F	T	T	F
T	F	F	T	T	T
F	T	T	F	F	F
F	F	F	F	T	T
		(d)	(a)	(c)	(b)

9.

p	q	$\sim$	$[(\sim p)$	$\wedge$	$(\sim q)]$
T	T	T	F	F	F
T	F	T	F	F	T
F	T	T	T	F	F
F	F	F	T	T	T
		(d)	(a)	(c)	(b)

11.

p	q	$p \underline{\vee} q$
T	T	F
T	F	T
F	T	T
F	F	F

13. $\sim(p \wedge q)$

4-8 CONDITIONAL STATEMENTS

1. If you will study hard, then you will get an A.

3. If you do not study hard, then you will not get an A.

5. (a) If a triangle is equilateral, then the triangle is isosceles.
(b) If a triangle is isosceles, then the triangle is equilateral.
(c) If a triangle is not equilateral, then the triangle is not isosceles.
(d) If a triangle is not isosceles, then the triangle is not equilateral.

7. (a) T;
(b) T;
(c) T.

9.

p	q	p⟶q	(~p)	V	q
T	T	T	F	T	T
T	F	F	F	F	F
F	T	T	T	T	T
F	F	T	T	T	F
		(a)	(b)	(d)	(c)

Note that the truth values in columns (a) and (d) are the same.

11.

p	q	(p⟶q)	∧	(q⟶p)
T	T	T	T	T
T	F	F	F	T
F	T	T	F	F
F	F	T	T	T
		(a)	(c)	(b)

13.

p	q	[(~p)	∧	q]	⟶	(p V q)
T	T	F	F	T	T	T
T	F	F	F	F	T	T
F	T	T	T	T	T	T
F	F	T	F	F	T	F
		(a)	(c)	(b)	(e)	(d)

15. {7}

*17. The set of all real numbers.

*19. The set of all real numbers different from 2.

CHAPTER 5: SETS OF NUMBERS

5-1 USES OF NUMBERS

1. Ordinal.

3. Ordinal.

5. Ordinal.

7. Identification.

9. Ordinal.

11. $\{1, 2, 3, 4, 5, \ldots, \quad n, \quad \ldots\}$
$\{1, 3, 5, 7, 9, \ldots, 2n - 1, \ldots\}$

13. $\{2, 4, 6, 8, 10, \ldots, \quad 2n, \quad \ldots\}$
$\{1, 3, 5, 7, 9, \ldots, 2n - 1, \ldots\}$

15.
$\{101, 103, 105, 107, 109, \ldots, \quad n, \quad \ldots\}$
$\{102, 104, 106, 108, 110, \ldots, n+1, \ldots\}$

17. Infinite.

19. Finite.

21. Finite.

23. Infinite.

25. The set $\{1, 2, 3, \ldots, n, \ldots\}$ has the transfinite cardinal number $\aleph_0$; the set $\{\triangle, \square, 1, 2, 3, \ldots, n, \ldots\}$ has cardinal number $\aleph_0 + 2$, which is the same as $\aleph_0$. The equivalence of the two sets may be shown as follows:

$$\{1, \quad 2, \quad 3, 4, 5, \ldots, \quad n \ldots\},$$
$$\updownarrow \quad \updownarrow \quad \updownarrow \updownarrow \updownarrow \qquad \updownarrow$$
$$\{\triangle, \quad \square, \quad 1, 2, 3, \ldots, n - 2, \ldots\}$$

27. The set $\{1, 2, 3, \ldots, n, \ldots\}$ has the transfinite cardinal number $\aleph_0$; the set with the number 1 removed has cardinal number $\aleph_0 - 1$, which is the same as $\aleph_0$. The equivalence of the two sets may be shown as follows:

$$\{1, \quad 2, \quad 3, \quad \ldots, \qquad n, \qquad \ldots\}$$
$$\updownarrow \quad \updownarrow \quad \updownarrow \qquad \qquad \updownarrow$$
$$\{2, \quad 3, \quad 4, \quad \ldots, \quad n + 1, \quad \ldots\}$$

5-2 PRIME NUMBERS

1. Any number that is divisible by 15 is also divisible by 3.

3. The set of numbers divisible by 3 and 5 is the set of numbers divisible by 15.

5. Any number that is divisible by 12 is also divisible by 3.

7. $\{21, 22, 24, 25, 26, 27, 28, 30, 32, 33, 34, 35, 36, 38, 39\}$

9. No. No.

11. There are other possible answers in many cases. $4 = 2 + 2$, and

$$6 = 3 + 3; \qquad 8 = 3 + 5;$$
$$10 = 3 + 7; \qquad 12 = 5 + 7;$$
$$14 = 7 + 7; \qquad 16 = 3 + 13;$$
$$18 = 5 + 13; \qquad 20 = 7 + 13;$$
$$22 = 5 + 17; \qquad 24 = 7 + 17;$$
$$26 = 3 + 23; \qquad 28 = 5 + 23;$$
$$30 = 7 + 23; \qquad 32 = 3 + 29;$$
$$34 = 5 + 29; \qquad 36 = 7 + 29;$$
$$38 = 7 + 31; \qquad 40 = 3 + 37.$$

13. Any three consecutive odd numbers includes 3 or a multiple of 3. Each multiple of 3 is composite, and 1 is by definition not a prime. Therefore 3, 5, 7 is a set of three consecutive odd numbers that are all prime numbers and, since any other such set contains a composite number that is a multiple of 3, this is the only prime triplet.

*15. (a) 13;
     (b) 19;
     (c) 31.

17. 1×15; 3×5.

19. 1×20; 2×10; 4×5.

21. 1×29.

23. $2^2 \times 17$.

25. 3×41.

27. $3 \times 5^2 \times 19$.

29. 2×409.

5-3 APPLICATIONS OF PRIME FACTORIZATIONS

1. $\{1, 2, 4, 5, 10, 20\}$

3. $\{1, 3, 9\}$

5. $\{1, 2, 4, 7, 14, 28\}$

7.
$\{1, 2, 3, 4, 5, 6, 10, 12, 15, 20, 30, 60\}$

9. $68 = 2^2 \times 17; 76 = 2^2 \times 19;$
G. C. F. $= 4.$

11. $76 = 2^2 \times 19;$
$1425 = 3 \times 5^2 \times 19; \text{G.C.F.} = 19.$

13. $215 = 5 \times 43;$
$1425 = 3 \times 5^2 \times 19; \text{ G.C.F.} = 5.$

15. $12 = 2^2 \times 3; 15 = 3 \times 5;$
$20 = 2^2 \times 5; \text{G.C.F.} = 1.$

17. $12 = 2^2 \times 3; 18 = 2 \times 3^2;$
$30 = 2 \times 3 \times 5;$
$\text{G.C.F.} = 2 \times 3 = 6.$

19. $\{7, 14, 21, 28, 35\}$

21. $\{15, 30, 45, 60, 75\}$

23. See Exercise 9; L.C.M.
$= 2^2 \times 17 \times 19 = 1292.$

25. See Exercise 11; L.C.M.
$= 2^2 \times 3 \times 5^2 \times 19 = 5700.$

27. See Exercise 13; L.C.M.
$= 3 \times 5^2 \times 19 \times 43 = 61{,}275.$

29. See Exercise 15; L.C.M.
$= 2^2 \times 3 \times 5 = 60.$

31. See Exercise 17; L.C.M.
$= 2^2 \times 3^2 \times 5 = 180.$

33. $\frac{123}{215}$

35. $\frac{5}{12}$

37. $\dfrac{1{,}259}{26{,}445}$

*39. 1

5-4 THE SET OF INTEGERS

1. -3

3. -3

5. -21

7. -4

9. -15

11. 24

13. -4

15. The set of integers is not associative with respect to division. For example, $8 \div (4 \div 2) = 8 \div 2 = 4$ and also $(8 \div 4) \div 2 = 2 \div 2 = 1.$

17. The empty set.

19. (a)

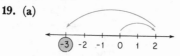

(b)

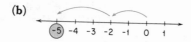

21. True.

23. True.

25. True.

27. Let $2k$ and $2m$ represent two even integers. Then

$$2k \times 2m = 2 \times 2 \times k \times m = 2(2km),$$

where $2km$ is an integer. Thus $2(2km)$ is an even integer.

*29. Any integer is either even or odd. If an integer is even, then its square is even (as in Example 5). If an integer is odd, then its square is odd (as in Exercise 28). If the square of an integer is odd, the integer cannot be even and thus must be odd. If the square of an integer is even, the integer cannot be odd and thus must be even.

5-5 THE SET OF RATIONAL NUMBERS

1. $\frac{7}{6}$

3. $\frac{10}{21}$

5. $\frac{5}{6}$

7. $\frac{3}{4}$

9. $\frac{1}{2}$

11. $\frac{9}{8}$

13. $\frac{2}{3} + \frac{4}{3} = 2$

15. $\frac{3}{4} \div \frac{3}{4} = 1$

17. False.

19. False.

21. 23. 25.

Set	3	0	$-\frac{2}{3}$
Counting numbers	✓	X	X
Whole numbers	✓	✓	X
Integers	✓	✓	X
Rational numbers	✓	✓	✓

	Sentence	Counting numbers	Whole numbers	Integers	Rational numbers
27.	$n+2=2$	none	0	0	0
29.	$2n=3$	none	none	none	$\frac{3}{2}$

5-6 THE SET OF REAL NUMBERS

	(a)	(b)	(c)	(d)
1.	Yes.	Yes.	No.	Yes.
3.	Yes.	Yes.	No.	Yes.
5.	No.	No.	Yes.	Yes.
7.	No.	Yes.	No.	Yes.
9.	No.	No.	Yes.	Yes.

11. Terminating.

13. Repeating.

15. Terminating.

17. 0.6

19. 1.8

21. $\frac{5}{11}$

23. $\frac{58}{111}$

25. $\frac{19}{9}$

27. $\frac{212}{99}$

29. $\frac{41}{333}$

31. True.

33. True.

35. True.

37. (a) 7;
(b) 8.

5-7 ORDER RELATIONS

1. $3 < 6$

3. $7 < 11$

5. $3 + 4 > 5$

7. $3 - 2 < 5 - 3$

9. $5 \times 6 = 6 \times 5$

11. $\frac{720}{180} < \frac{720}{120}$

13. (1) $3 \neq 6$;   (2) $11 \neq 17$;

(3) $7 \neq 11$;   (4) $7 \neq 3$;
(5) $3 + 4 \neq 5$; (6) $3 + 4 = 7$;
(7) $3 - 2 \neq 5 - 3$;
(8) $7 + 5 = 5 + 7$;
(9) $5 \times 6 = 6 \times 5$;
(10) $\frac{120}{30} \neq \frac{120}{40}$;
(11) $\frac{720}{180} \neq \frac{720}{120}$;
(12) $17 \times 31 \neq 17 \times 29$.

15. (1) $3 \leq 6$;   (2) $11 \leq 17$;
(3) $7 \leq 11$;   (4) $7 > 3$;
(5) $3 + 4 > 5$; (6) $3 + 4 \leq 7$;
(7) $3 - 2 \leq 5 - 3$;
(8) $7 + 5 \leq 5 + 7$;
(9) $5 \times 6 \leq 6 \times 5$;
(10) $\frac{120}{30} > \frac{120}{40}$;
(11) $\frac{720}{180} \leq \frac{720}{120}$;
(12) $17 \times 31 > 17 \times 29$.

17. 1.4; 1.414; 1.4141; $1.414114111\ldots$; $1.\overline{41}$.

19. (a), (b), and (d).

21. 0.5235; $0.\overline{523}$; many other answers are possible.

23. $0.787887888\ldots$; $0.788788578855\ldots$; many other answers are possible.

CHAPTER 6: AN INTRODUCTION TO GEOMETRY

6-1 POINTS, LINES, AND PLANES

1.

(a) 10;
(e) 15;
*(f) 45;
*(g) $n(n - 1)/2$.

7. True.

9. False.

11. False.

13. False.

15. False.

17. True.

3. *ABC, ABD, ACD, BCD.*

5. (a) 1;
(b) 3;
(c) 6;

6-2 RAYS, LINE SEGMENTS, AND ANGLES

1. $\overline{AD}$

3. $\overline{BC}$

5. $\overline{BC}$

7. $\overline{BC}$

9. $\overrightarrow{BC}$ (or $\overrightarrow{BD}$).

11. B

13. Empty set.

15. Interior of $\angle ABD$.

17. $\overset{\circ}{\underset{}{\to}}BA$

19. $\overset{\circ}{\underset{}{\to}}PA$

21. $\angle BPC$

23. $\overleftrightarrow{AC} \cup \overset{\circ}{\underset{}{\to}}PB$

SUPPLEMENTARY EXERCISES FOR SECTION 6-2

1. $\overline{BD}$

3. $\overline{BC}$

5. $\overline{DA}$

7. $\overline{BD}$

9. $\overset{\leftrightarrow}{AB}$

11. $\overline{DB}$

13. $\overset{\rightarrow}{DB}$

15. Empty set.

17. $\overline{BD}$

19. (Interior $\angle ADC$) $\cup D$.

21. Exterior $\angle ADB$.

6-3 PLANE FIGURES

1.
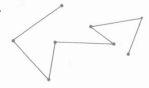

3.

7.

9. Empty set.

11. M

13. P

15. $\overset{\circ\!-\!\circ}{MN}$

17. $\triangle RMN$

19. $\overset{\rightarrow}{MP} \cup \overset{\circ\rightarrow}{NV}$

21. $\overline{MN}$

23. Interior $\triangle MRN$.

25. Interior of quadrilateral $STNM$.

27. Interior $\triangle RST$.

SUPPLEMENTARY EXERCISES FOR SECTION 6-3

There are many correct answers for Exercises 1 and 3.

1.
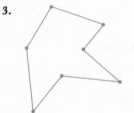

3.

5. Empty set.

7. $\{B, D\}$

9. $\overline{BF}$

11. Interior $\triangle CBD$.

13. $\overset{\circ\rightarrow}{FG}$

15. $\overset{\circ\!-\!\circ}{BD}$

6-4 SPACE FIGURES

1. (a) M, N, O, P;
   (b) $\overline{MN}, \overline{MO}, \overline{MP}, \overline{ON}, \overline{NP}, \overline{PO}$;
   (c) the triangular regions MNO, PMN, PNO, PMO.

3. (a) A, B, C, D, E, F, G, H;
   (b) $\overline{AB}, \overline{BC}, \overline{CD}, \overline{AD}, \overline{AE}, \overline{BF}, \overline{CG}$, $\overline{DH}, \overline{EF}, \overline{FG}, \overline{GH}, \overline{HE}$;
   (c) the square regions $ABCD, ABFE$, $BCGF, CDHG, DAEH, EFGH$.

5. (a) J, K, L, M, N, O;
   (b) $\overline{JK}, \overline{KL}, \overline{JL}, \overline{JM}, \overline{KN}, \overline{LO}, \overline{MN}$, $\overline{NO}, \overline{OM}$;

(c) the triangular regions JKL, MNO and the rectangular regions $JKNM, KLON, LJMO$.

	V	E	F
7. Pentagonal pyramid.	6	10	6
9. Hexagonal prism.	12	18	8
11. (Given figure.)	5	9	6
13. (Given figure.)	9	16	9

15. (a) 6;
    (b) 1, 6, 12, 8, 0

6-5 PLANE CURVES

Exercises 1, 3, 5, and 7 may be done in many ways.

1.

3.

5.

7.

		V	A	R
9.	(a)	4	4	2
	(b)	4	5	3
11.	(a)	2	2	2
	(b)	2	3	3
13.	(a)	5	4	1
	(b)	16	24	10

15. $A = V + R - 2$

6-6 NETWORKS

1. (a) 4;
   (b) 0;
   (c) traversable, A, B, C, D.

3. (a) 2;
   (b) 2;
   (c) traversable, K, M.

5. (a) 4;
   (b) 0;
   (c) traversable, U, V, W, X.

7. (a) 0;
   (b) 4;
   (c) not traversable.

9. The inspector can use a map for the highways involved as a network, determine the number of odd vertices, and know that each section can be traversed exactly once in a single trip if there are at most two odd vertices.

***13.** Add one more bridge joining any two of the points A, B, C, D.

11. Think of the six regions as labeled and note the line segments that are needed as represented by arcs in the network. Since the network has four odd vertices (B, D, E, and F), the network is not traversable and the suggested broken line cannot be drawn.

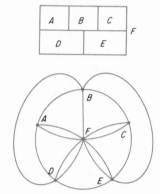

6-7 TOPOLOGY

5. Any two points of the surface may be joined by an arc that does not cross an edge.

CHAPTER 7: AN INTRODUCTION TO ALGEBRA

7-1 SENTENCES AND GRAPHS

1. (a) Equality;
(b) false.

3. (a) Inequality;
(b) true.

5. (a) Inequality;
(b) true.

7. (a) Inequality;
(b) true.

9. (a) Equality;
(b) true.

11. (a) Equality;
(b) false.

13. (a) Inequality;
(b) false.

15. (a) Inequality;
(b) false.

17. Point.

19. The empty set.

21. Half-line.

23. Line segment.

25. Line.

27.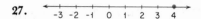

29.

31.

33.

35.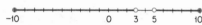

37.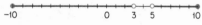

***39.**

SUPPLEMENTARY EXERCISES FOR SECTION 7-1

1. {1, 2, 3, 4, 5}

3. {3, 4, 5}

5. {3, 4, 5, 6}

7. [−2, 5]

9. [0, 5]

11. [3, 5]′

13. [−7, 2] and [3, 5] are disjoint sets; their intersection is the empty set. The complement of the empty set is the universal set, namely, [−10, 10].

15. [−2, 5] ∪ [3,8] = [−2, 8];
[−5, 7] ∩ [−3, 3] = [−3, 3];
[−2, 8] ∩ [−3, 3] = [−2, 3].

7-2 COMPOUND SENTENCES

1. {−1, 0, 1, 2}

3. All integers.

5.

7.

9.

11.

13.

15.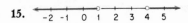

17.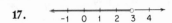

19.

21.

23.

*25.

27. 5

29. 10

31. $x = 3$ or $x = -3$.

33. $x \leq 3$ and $x \geq -3$.

35. $x - 2 = 3$ or $x - 2 = -3$; that is, $x = 5$ or $x = -1$.

*37. $x - 1 \leq 3$ and $x - 1 \geq -3$; that is, $x \leq 4$ and $x \geq -2$.

*39. $-2 < x < 1$ or $x = 3$ or $x = -3$.

7-3 LINEAR SENTENCES IN TWO VARIABLES

1. $\{(1, 1), (1, 2), (2, 1), (2, 2)\}$

3. $\{(0, 3), (1, 2), (2, 1), (3, 0)\}$

5. $\{(0, 0), (0, 1), (0, 2), (1, 0), (1, 1), (2, 0)\}$

7. $\{(1, 2), (2, 3)\}$

9. $\{(2, 1), (3, 1), (3, 2)\}$

11.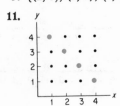

13.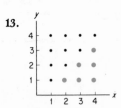

15.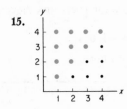

17.

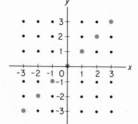

21.

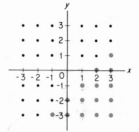

19.

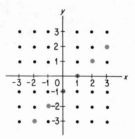

23. The solution set is the empty set.

7-4 GRAPHS ON A PLANE

1. (a) 4;
  (b) 4.

3. (a) −2;
  (b) 4.

5. (a) 6;
  (b) 4.

7. (a) 4;
  (b) 2.

9.

x	-3	-2	-1	0	1	2	3
y	-1	0	1	2	3	4	5

11.

x	-3	-2	-1	0	1	2	3
y	4	3	2	1	2	3	4

13.

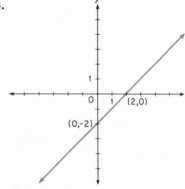

15.

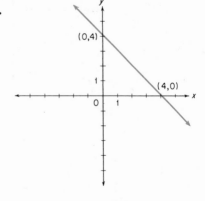

17.

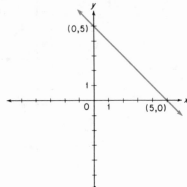

23.

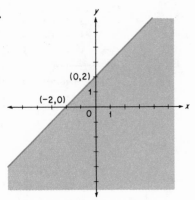

19.

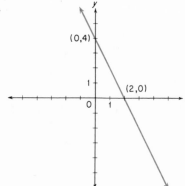

25.

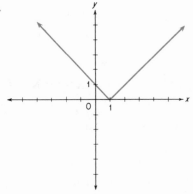

21.

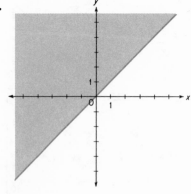

27.

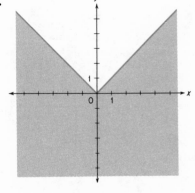

29.

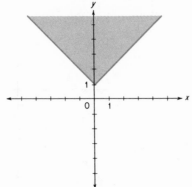

31.

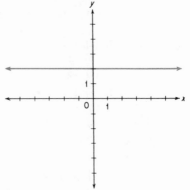

SUPPLEMENTARY EXERCISES FOR SECTION 7-4

1.

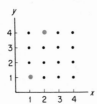

3.

5.

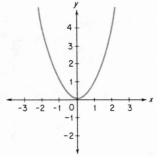

7.

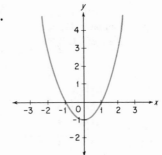

9.

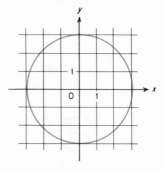

*11.

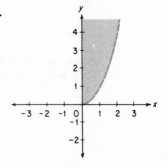

7-5 RELATIONS AND FUNCTIONS

1. (a) −1;
   (b) 0;
   (c) 15.

3. (a) 1;
   (b) −8;
   (c) −15.

5.

A function.
Domain: {1, 2, 3}
Range: {1, 2, 3}

7.

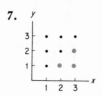

Not a function.

9.

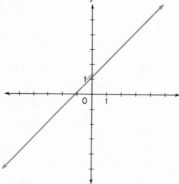

A function. Both the domain and the range are the set of real numbers.

11.

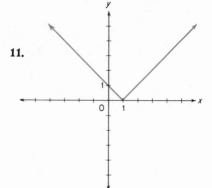

A function. The domain is the set of real numbers; the range is the set of nonnegative real numbers.

13.

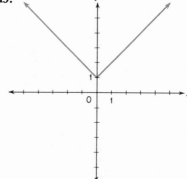

A function. The domain is the set of real numbers; the range is the set of real numbers greater than or equal to 1.

15.

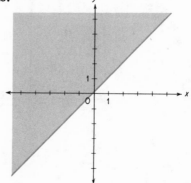

Not a function.

*17.

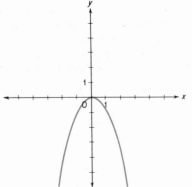

27.

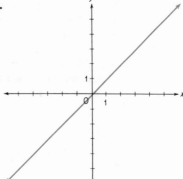

A function. The domain is the set of real numbers; the range is the set of real numbers less than or equal to 0.

19. $\{(1, 1), (2, 2), (3, 3)\}$: a function.

21. $\{(3, 1), (4, 2), (4, 3)\}$: not a function.

23. $x = y + 1$: a function.

25.

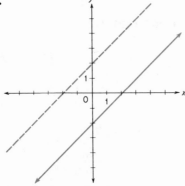

A function.

A function. (Note that the inverse is the same as the given function.)

*29.

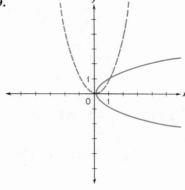

Not a function.

7-6 LINEAR PROGRAMMING

1.

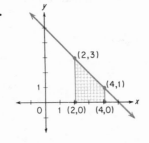

(2,3)

(4,1)

(2,0)   (4,0)

3. (a) Maximum value of 8 at $(2, 3)$;
   (b) Minimum value of 2 at $(2, 0)$.

5. (a) Maximum value of 5 at $(3, 2)$;
   (b) Minimum value of 0 at $(0, 0)$.

7. The conditions are $0 \leq x$, $0 \leq y$, $x + y \leq 180$, and $5x + 3y \leq 750$. The maximum of $3x + 2y$ occurs at $(105, 75)$; thus under the assumptions of this exercise, 105 minutes of regular teaching and 75 minutes of television instruction would be best for the students.

9. The maximum of $x + 2y$ occurs at $(30, 150)$; thus under the assumptions of this exercise, 30 minutes of regular teaching and 150 minutes of television instruction would be best for the students.

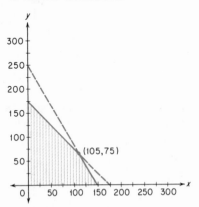

CHAPTER 8: AN INTRODUCTION TO PROBABILITY

8-1 COUNTING PROBLEMS

1. (a) 60;
(b) 125.

3. 12

5. 24

7. 25; 20.

9. 1320

11. 90,000

13. (a) 12;
(b) 3.

*15. (a) 450;
(b) 180;
(c) 648;
(d) 200.

*17. $26 \times 25 \times 9 \times 9 \times 8$; that is, 421,200.

8-2 PERMUTATIONS

1. 120

3. 56

5. 42

7. 10

9. 12!; that is, 479,001,600.

11. 30

13. 720

15. 6

17. 5

19. (a) 20;
   (b) 120.

21. 210

23. 9!; that is, 362,880.

25. $_nP_0 = 1$

8-3 COMBINATIONS

1. (a) 15;
   (b) 56.

3. (a) 21;
   (b) 35.

5. (a) 55;
   (b) 455.

7. $pqr, prq, qpr, qrp, rpq, rqp$;
$pqs, psq, qps, qsp, spq, sqp$;
$prs, psr, rps, rsp, spr, srp$;
$qrs, qsr, rqs, rsq, sqr, srq$.
Thus $_4C_3 = 4$.

9. $_nC_n = 1$

11. $_3C_0 + _3C_1 + _3C_2 + _3C_3 = 1 + 3 + 3 + 1 = 8 = 2^3$

13. $_nC_0 + _nC_1 + \cdots + _nC_{n-1} + _nC_n = 2^n$

15. $_5C_2$; that is, 10.

17. $_{52}C_{13}$; that is, 635,013,559,600.

19. Order is important.

21. $_{10}C_4$; that is, 210; $_7C_3 \times _3C_1$; that is, 105.

*23. $_nC_r = \dfrac{n!}{r!(n-r)!}$;

$_nC_{n-r} = \dfrac{n!}{(n-r)!\,r!} = _nC_r$

since $n - (n - r) = n - n + r = r$.

SUPPLEMENTARY EXERCISES FOR SECTION 8-3

1. $_{20}C_2$; that is, 190.

3. $_8C_4$; that is, 70.

5. $_{10}C_2$; that is, 45.

7. (a) $_{52}C_4$; that is, 270,725.
   (b) $_{52}C_7$; that is, 133,784,560.

9. $_4P_4$; that is, 24.

11. $\frac{1}{2} \times _8C_4$; that is, 35.

8-4 DEFINITION OF PROBABILITY

1. $\frac{1}{2}$

3. $\frac{1}{2}$

5. $\frac{5}{6}$

7. 0

9. $\frac{5}{6}$

11. $\frac{1}{2}$

13. $\frac{5}{6}$

15. $\frac{1}{13}$

17. $\frac{1}{4}$

19. $\frac{7}{8}$

8-5 SAMPLE SPACES

1. $\frac{1}{10}$

3. $\frac{2}{5}$

5. $\frac{3}{5}$

7. $\frac{1}{2}$

9.

First coin	Second coin	Third coin	Fourth coin
H	H	H	H
H	H	H	T
H	H	T	H
H	H	T	T
H	T	H	H
H	T	H	T
H	T	T	H
H	T	T	T
T	H	H	H
T	H	H	T
T	H	T	H
T	H	T	T
T	T	H	H
T	T	H	T
T	T	T	H
T	T	T	T

11. $\frac{5}{16}$

13.

$(1, 1), (1, 2), (1, 3), (1, 4), (1, 5), (1, 6),$
$(2, 1), (2, 2), (2, 3), (2, 4), (2, 5), (2, 6),$
$(3, 1), (3, 2), (3, 3), (3, 4), (3, 5), (3, 6),$
$(4, 1), (4, 2), (4, 3), (4, 4), (4, 5), (4, 6),$
$(5, 1), (5, 2), (5, 3), (5, 4), (5, 5), (5, 6),$
$(6, 1), (6, 2), (6, 3), (6, 4), (6, 5), (6, 6).$

15. $\frac{1}{36}$

17. $\frac{1}{18}$

19. $\frac{1}{6}$

21. $\frac{1}{6}$

23.

$R_1R_2, \ R_2R_1, \ W_1R_1, \ W_2R_1,$
$R_1W_1, \ R_2W_1, \ W_1R_2, \ W_2R_2,$
$R_1W_2, \ R_2W_2, \ W_1W_2, \ W_2W_1; \frac{1}{6}.$

25.

$R_1R_2, \ R_2R_1, \ R_3R_1, \ W_1R_1, \ W_2R_1,$
$R_1R_3, \ R_2R_3, \ R_3R_2, \ W_1R_2, \ W_2R_2,$
$R_1W_1, \ R_2W_1, \ R_3W_1, \ W_1R_3, \ W_2R_3,$
$R_1W_2, \ R_2W_2, \ R_3W_2, \ W_1W_2, \ W_2W_1; \frac{3}{10}.$

27. To distinguish the various sides, denote the sides of the first card by R_1 and R_2, the sides of the second card by W_1 and W_2, and the sides of the third card by R_3 and W_3. The sample space for the problem is:

Side showing	Other side
R_1	$R_2.$
R_2	R_1
R_3	W_3

In two of the three cases we see that if the side showing is red, then the opposite side is also red. Therefore, the probability is $\frac{2}{3}$.

8-6 COMPUTATION OF PROBABILITIES

1. $\frac{2}{13}$

3. $\frac{4}{13}$

5. $\frac{1}{52}$

7. $\frac{19}{52}$

9. (a) $\frac{1}{16}$

     (b) $\frac{1}{2704}$;

     (c) $\frac{1}{16}$;

     (d) $\frac{1}{676}$;

     (e) $\frac{1}{4}$.

11. $\frac{31}{32}$

13. (a) $\frac{7}{10}$;
  (b) $\frac{7}{15}$.

15. (a) $\frac{1}{220}$;
  (b) $\frac{1}{22}$;
  (c) $\frac{7}{44}$;
  *(d) $\frac{3}{44}$.

17. (a) $\frac{1}{6}$;
  (b) $\frac{1}{36}$;
  (c) $\frac{1}{216}$;
  (d) $\frac{25}{216}$.

*19. (a) $\frac{91}{216}$;
  (b) $\frac{75}{216}$.

8-7 ODDS AND MATHEMATICAL EXPECTATION

1. 1 to 3.

3. 1 to 3.

5. 3 to 1.

7. 11 to 2.

9. 2 to 7.

11. $4

13. $1.67

15. $2.00

17. The probability that both of the bills drawn will be tens is $\frac{2}{5} \times \frac{1}{4} = \frac{1}{10}$. The probability that both will be fives is $\frac{3}{5} \times \frac{2}{4} = \frac{3}{10}$. The probability that one will be a five and one a ten is found as $(\frac{3}{5} \times \frac{2}{4}) + (\frac{2}{5} \times \frac{3}{4}) = \frac{3}{5}$. The mathematical expectation is then found to be $(\$20)(\frac{1}{10}) + (\$10)(\frac{3}{10}) + (\$15)(\frac{3}{5}) = \$14$.

19. $\frac{1}{3}(1) + \frac{1}{6}(5) + \frac{1}{6}(10) + \frac{1}{6}(25) + \frac{1}{6}(50)$; that is, $15\frac{1}{3}$ cents.

8-8 PASCAL'S TRIANGLE

1. $\frac{1}{32}$

3. $\frac{5}{16}$

5. $\frac{5}{32}$

7. $\frac{5}{32}$

9. $\frac{13}{16}$

11.

```
              1   1
           1   2   1
         1   3   3   1
       1   4   6   4   1
     1   5  10  10   5   1
   1   6  15  20  15   6   1
 1   7  21  35  35  21   7   1
1  8  28  56  70  56  28   8   1
1  9  36  84 126 126  84  36   9   1
1 10 45 120 210 252 210 120 45  10  1
```

13. $\binom{12}{0}, \binom{12}{1}, \binom{12}{2}, \binom{12}{3}, \binom{12}{4},$
$\binom{12}{5}, \binom{12}{6}, \binom{12}{7}, \binom{12}{8}, \binom{12}{9},$
$\binom{12}{10}, \binom{12}{11}, \binom{12}{12}.$

15. (a) $\frac{11}{32}$;
  (b) $\frac{1}{2}$.

17. (a) $\frac{11}{32}$;
  (b) $\frac{163}{256}$.

*19. $1a^7 + 7a^6b + 21a^5b^2 + 35a^4b^3 + 35a^3b^4 + 21a^2b^5 + 7ab^6 + 1b^7$

CHAPTER 9: CONCEPTS OF LOGIC

9-1 UNIVERSAL QUANTIFIERS

1. $\forall_x$: x a real number.

3. $\forall_t$: t an integer.

5. $\forall_x$: x a real number.

7. $\forall_x$: x a triangle.

9. $\forall_x$: x a house.

11. $\forall_x$: x an integer.

13. (a) 9;

    (b) 7, or any value different from 9.

15. (a) -6;

    (b) 0, or any value different from -6.

17. $\forall_x\forall_y$: $x + 2y = 2x + y$

19. $\forall_x\forall_y\forall_z$: $x + yz = (x + y)z$

21. True.

23. False: consider $x = 1$.

25. False: undefined when $x = 0$.

9-2 EXISTENTIAL QUANTIFIERS

1. $\exists_x$: x a nonnegative number.

3. $\exists_x$: x an integer.

5. $\exists_x$: x a real number.

7. $\exists_x$: x a real number.

9. $\exists_x$: $2x - 5 = 11$

11. $\exists_x$: $x^2 - x - 6 = 0$

13. Not all apples are pieces of fruit; that is, there exists at least one apple that is not a piece of fruit.

15. Not all whole numbers are positive; that is, there exists at least one whole number that is not positive.

17. All rational numbers are integers.

19. No complex numbers are real numbers; that is, all complex numbers are not real numbers.

21. $\exists_x$: $x \neq 2$

23. $\forall_x$: $x^2 > 0$

25. (a) False: consider $x = 3$ and $x = -3$;

    (b) true;

    (c) false: consider $x = -1$, $x = 0$, and $x = 1$;

    (d) false: consider $x \geq 0$.

9-3 DEPENDENT STATEMENTS

	TT	TF	FT	FF	Case
17.	✕	✓	✓	✓	9
19.	✕	✓	✓	✓	9
21.	✓	✓	✕	✕	4

23. All pairs are dependent.

25. The statements in Exercises 17, 18, and 19 are contrary.

9-4 EQUIVALENT STATEMENTS

1.

p	q	$\sim$	$(p \wedge q)$	$\longleftrightarrow$	$(\sim p)$	$\vee$	$(\sim q)$
T	T	F	T	T	F	F	F
T	F	T	F	T	F	T	T
F	T	T	F	T	T	T	F
F	F	T	F	T	T	T	T
		(b)	(a)	(f)	(c)	(e)	(d)

$$[\sim (p \wedge q)] \longleftrightarrow [(\sim p) \vee (\sim q)]$$

3.

p	q	$(p \to q)$	$\longleftrightarrow$	q	$\vee$	$(\sim p)$
T	T	T	T	T	T	F
T	F	F	T	F	F	F
F	T	T	T	T	T	T
F	F	T	T	F	T	T
		(a)	(e)	(b)	(d)	(c)

$$(p \to q) \longleftrightarrow [q \vee (\sim p)]$$

5. *Converse:* If we buy a new car, then we can afford it.

Inverse: If we cannot afford it, then we do not buy a new car.

Contrapositive: If we do not buy a new car, then we cannot afford it.

7. *Converse:* If the triangles are congruent, then two sides and the included angle of one are congruent to two sides and the included angle of the other.

Inverse: If two sides and the included angle of one triangle are not congruent to two sides and the included angle of another triangle, then the triangles are not congruent.

Contrapositive: If two triangles are not congruent, then two sides and the included angle of one are not congruent to two sides and the included angle of the other.

9. *Converse:* If $x = 1$, then
$$x(x - 1) = 0.$$
Inverse: If $x(x - 1) \neq 0$, then $x \neq 1$.
Contrapositive: If $x \neq 1$, then
$$x(x - 1) \neq 0.$$

11. The statement is always true in Exercises 7 and 8.

13. The inverse is always true in Exercises 7 and 9.

9-5 FORMS OF STATEMENTS

1. If it is a duck, then it is a bird.

3. If two angles are complements of the same angle, then they are congruent.

5. If two lines are parallel, then they are coplanar.

7. If a geometric figure is a circle, then it is round.

9. If a person is a teacher, then he is boring.

11. If you like this book, then you like mathematics.

13. If you like mathematics, then you like this book.

15. If you like mathematics, then you will like this book.

17. $q \to p$

19. $q \to \mathrm{p}$

21. $p \to (\sim q)$

23. $p \leftrightarrow q$

25. $p \to q$

27. $p \leftrightarrow q$

29. If $9 + 3 < 10$, then $11 - 3 > 8$; true.

31. If $5 + 3 = 8$, then $7 \times 4 = 25$; false.

33. If $7 \times 6 = 42$, then $8 \times 5 \neq 40$; false.

35. The assertion is equivalent to the statement: "If you give me \$10,000, then I will marry your daughter." If he received the money, then he should have married the girl. Thus he should be sued for breach of promise.

9-6 THE NATURE OF PROOF

1. A tautology.

p	p	$\lor$	$(\sim p)$
T	T	T	F
F	F	T	T
	(a)	(c)	(b)

3. A tautology.

p	q	$[(p \longrightarrow q)$	$\land$	$(\sim q)]$	$\longrightarrow$	$(\sim p)$
T	T	T	F	F	T	F
T	F	F	F	T	T	F
F	T	T	F	F	T	T
F	F	T	T	T	T	T
		(a)	(c)	(b)	(e)	(d)

5. Not a tautology.

p	q	$[(p \longrightarrow q)$	$\land$	$(\sim p)]$	$\longrightarrow$	$(\sim q)$
T	T	T	F	F	T	F
T	F	F	F	F	T	T
F	T	T	T	T	F	F
F	F	T	T	T	T	T
		(a)	(c)	(b)	(e)	(d)

7. A tautology.

p	q	$[(p \lor q)$	$\land$	$(\sim p)]$	$\longrightarrow$	q
T	T	T	F	F	T	T
T	F	T	F	F	T	F
F	T	T	T	T	T	T
F	F	F	F	F	T	F
		(a)	(c)	(b)	(e)	(d)

9. A tautology.

p	q	r	$[(p \rightarrow q)$	$\land$	$(q \rightarrow r)]$	$\longrightarrow$	$(p \rightarrow r)$
T	T	T	T	T	T	T	T
T	T	F	T	F	F	T	F
T	F	T	F	F	T	T	T
T	F	F	F	F	T	T	F
F	T	T	T	T	T	T	T
F	T	F	T	F	F	T	T
F	F	T	T	T	T	T	T
F	F	F	T	T	T	T	T
			(a)	(c)	(b)	(e)	(d)

9-7 VALID ARGUMENTS

1. For

     p: Elliot is a freshman.
     q: Elliot takes mathematics.

the argument has the form

$$[(p \rightarrow q) \land p] \rightarrow q.$$

This statement is a tautology (§9-6, Example), and the argument is valid.

3. For

    p: The Yanks win the game.

    q: The Yanks win the pennant.

the argument has the form

$$[(p \to q) \wedge (\sim q)] \to (\sim p).$$

This statement is a tautology (§9-6, Exercise 3), and the argument is valid.

  5. For

       p: You work hard.

       q: You are a success.

the argument has the form

$$[(p \to q) \wedge (\sim q)] \to (\sim p).$$

This statement is a tautology (§9-6, Exercise 3), and the argument is valid.

7. For

    p: You are reading this book.

    q: You like mathematics.

the argument has the form

$$[(p \to q) \wedge (\sim p)] \to (\sim q).$$

This statement is not a tautology (§9-6, Exercise 5), and the argument is not valid.

9. This argument is of the form $[(p \to q) \wedge (q \to r)] \to (r \to p)$ and is not valid.

11. You do not drink milk.

13. If you like to fish, then you are a mathematician.

15. If you like this book, then you will become a mathematician.

9-8 EULER DIAGRAMS

1. Valid.

3. Not valid.

5. (a) Valid;
    (b) valid;
    (c) valid;
    (d) not valid.

7. (a) Valid;
    (b) not valid;

    (c) not valid;
    (d) not valid;
    (e) not valid;
    (f) not valid;
    (g) not valid.

9. (a) Valid;
    (b) valid;
    (c) valid;
    (d) not valid.

CHAPTER 10: CONCEPTS OF GEOMETRY

10-1 THE EVOLUTION OF GEOMETRY

1. The area of the entire figure is equal to the sum of the areas of its parts. The early Greeks thought of the area $(x + 1)^2$ of the square with side $(x + 1)$ as the square on $(x + 1)$; they thought of the area $x \times 1$ of the rectangle with sides x and 1 as the rectangle contained by x and 1. Then the square on $(x + 1)$ is equal to the sum of the square on x and the square on 1 together with twice the rectangle contained by x and 1.

3. As in Exercise 1 the square on $(a - b)$ together with twice the rectangle contained by a and b is equal to the sum of the squares on a and b; that is,

$$(a - b)^2 + 2ab = a^2 + b^2$$

and thus

$$(a - b)^2 = a^2 - 2ab + b^2.$$

5. As in Exercise 1 the rectangle contained by $(a + b)$ and a is equal to the sum of the square on a and the rectangle contained by a and b.

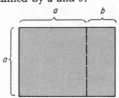

7. As in Exercise 1 the rectangle contained by $(a + b)$ and $(c + d)$ is equal to the sum of:

the rectangle contained by a and c,
the rectangle contained by a and d,
the rectangle contained by b and c,
the rectangle contained by b and d.

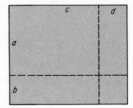

10-2 EUCLIDEAN GEOMETRY

1. No; "point" is not classified, and the definition is not reversible.

3. No; the definition is not reversible.

5. No; for most people, a general polygon is not a simpler figure than a triangle.

7. (a) yes;
   (b) yes;
   (c) yes;
   (d) no;
   (e) no.

9. (b), (c).

11. (a) yes;
    (b) yes;
    (c) yes;
    (d) no;
    (e) no.

13. (b), (c).

15. Under the definition that a line is not parallel to itself, we have:
For Exercise 7:
   (a) yes;
   (b) no;
   (c) yes;
   (d) no;
   (e) no.
For Exercise 9: (c).

17. Under the definition that a line on a plane is not parallel to that plane, we have:
For Exercise 11:
   (a) yes;
   (b) no;
   (c) yes;
   (d) no;
   (e) yes.
For Exercise 13: none.

10-3 NON-EUCLIDEAN GEOMETRIES

1.

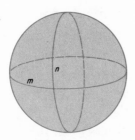

	Euclidean	*Elliptic*	*Hyperbolic*	*Spherical*
5.	yes	yes	yes	no
7.	yes	——	no	——
9.	yes	no	no	no
11.	yes	no	yes	no

3.

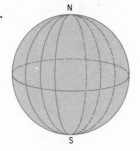

10-4 PROJECTIVE GEOMETRY

1. Any two distinct points on the same plane determine a unique line.

3. Any two distinct lines on the same plane determine a unique point.

5.

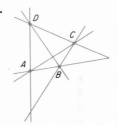

7.

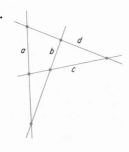

9.

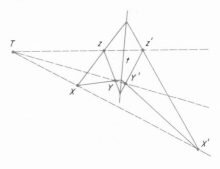

11. See the figure immediately preceding these exercises.

10-5 A FINITE GEOMETRY

1. Postulate I.

3. Postulate III.

5. Postulate VI.

7. Postulate II.

9. Postulate V.

11. Postulate II.

13. Postulate V.

15. Postulate V.

17. Postulate V.

19. Postulate IV.

21. Postulate V.

23. Postulates III and VII and Exercises 21 and 22.

25. Postulate VII.

27. Postulate V.

29. Postulate IV.

31. Postulate V.

33. Postulates III and VII and Exercises 31 and 32.

35. Postulate VII.

37. Postulate V.

39. Postulate III and Exercises 36, 37, and 38.

41. Exercises 34 and 40.

43. Exercises 1 through 41.

10-6 COORDINATE GEOMETRY

1, 3, 5, and **7.**

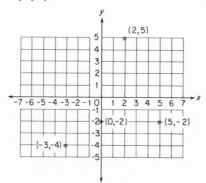

9.

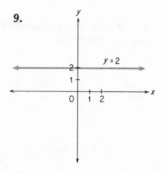

11.

$|x| = 2$ and $y = 0$

13.

In Exercises 13 through 21, there are many possible correct selections of points satisfying the conditions.

15.

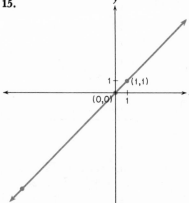

19.

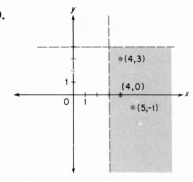

17.

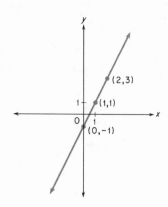

21.

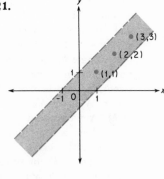

23. $x = -3; 5.$

25. $y = 2; 4.$

27. $y = -3; 6.$

10-7 THE MIDPOINT FORMULA

1. $(2, 5)$

3. $(-1, 1)$

5. (a) Right triangle;
   (b) isosceles triangle;
   (c) right triangle;
   (d) isosceles triangle;
   (e) isosceles triangle.

7. $(3, 11)$

9. $(0, k)$ and $(5, k)$ for any $k \neq 0$.

11. (a) $(2, 2)$ and $(0, 2)$;
   (b) $(2, -2)$ and $(0, -2)$;
   (c) $(1, 1)$ and $(1, -1)$.

13. (a) $(2a, 2a)$ and $(0, 2a)$;
   (b) $(2a, -2a)$ and $(0, -2a)$;
   (c) (a, a) and $(a, -a)$.

15. A quadrilateral *PQRS* is a trapezoid if *PQ∥RS*. We may represent the trape-

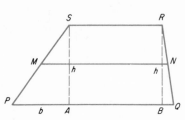

zoid on a coordinate plane with $P'Q'$ on the x-axis, P' at $(0, 0)$, Q' at $(a, 0)$ where $m(\overline{PQ}) = a$, and R' with a positive y-coordinate. Since $SR∥PQ$, the altitudes $\overline{SA}$ and $\overline{RB}$ onto PQ are congruent; suppose $m(\overline{SA}) = h$. Then S' and R' each have y-coordinate h; they may have any distinct numbers b and d, respectively, as x-coordinates, where $b < d$ for a convex figure. We take S' at (b, h) and R' at (d, h). Any trapezoid *PQRS* may be represented on a coordinate plane in this manner with vertices at $(0, 0)$, $(a, 0)$, (d, h), and (b, h) for suitable choices of values for a, b, d, and h. Let M' be the midpoint of $\overline{P'S'}$ and N' be the midpoint of $\overline{R'Q'}$. Then we have

$$M': \left(\frac{b}{2}, \frac{h}{2}\right) \quad \text{and} \quad N': \left(\frac{a+d}{2}, \frac{h}{2}\right).$$

The line $M'N'$ is parallel to the x-axis and, thus, to $\overleftrightarrow{P'Q'}$, since the y-coordinates of M' and N' are equal. The length of $\overline{M'N'}$ is $\left|\frac{a+d}{2} - \frac{b}{2}\right|$; that is, $\frac{1}{2}[a + (d - b)]$. The length of $\overline{P'Q'}$ is

a; the length of $\overline{S'R'}$ is $(d - b)$. Thus, the length of $\overline{M'N'}$ is one-half the sum of the lengths of the bases of the trapezoid.

17. Any given quadrilateral *PQRS* may be represented on a coordinate plane by $P'Q'R'S'$ with P': $(0, 0)$, Q': $(a, 0)$, R': (b, c), and S': (d, e). The sides $\overline{P'Q'}$ and $\overline{R'S'}$ are opposite sides and have midpoints $\left(\frac{a}{2}, 0\right)$ and $\left(\frac{b+d}{2}, \frac{c+e}{2}\right)$, respectively. The line segment joining these midpoints itself has midpoint $\left(\frac{a+b+d}{4}, \frac{c+e}{4}\right)$. Similarly, the sides $\overline{P'S'}$ and $\overline{Q'R'}$ are opposite sides and have midpoints $\left(\frac{d}{2}, \frac{e}{2}\right)$ and $\left(\frac{a+b}{2}, \frac{c}{2}\right)$, respectively. The line segment joining these midpoints itself has midpoint $\left(\frac{a+b+d}{4}, \frac{c+e}{4}\right)$. Since the line segments joining the midpoints of the opposite sides of the quadrilateral have the same midpoint, they bisect each other.

10-8 THE SLOPE OF A LINE

1. (a) $\frac{1}{2}$;
   (b) 2;
   (c) $\frac{4}{3}$;
   (d) $-\frac{2}{3}$.

3. (a) $y = \frac{1}{2}x + 3\frac{1}{2}$;

(b) $y = 2x - 7$;
(c) $y = \frac{4}{3}x - \frac{1}{3}$;
(d) $y = -\frac{2}{3}x + 7$.

5. (a) -7;
   (b) $3\frac{1}{2}$;

(c) $\frac{1}{4}$;

(d) $10\frac{1}{2}$.

7. $y + 11 = -3(x - 7)$

9. $y + 2 = \frac{3}{2}x$

11. $\frac{x}{5} + \frac{y}{4} = 1$

13. $y = 2x$

15. *Given:* Lines a, b, c, such that $a\|b$ and $c\|b$.

To prove: $a\|c$.

Proof: The line b is taken not parallel to the y-axis, so that it has a slope m. Then the line a has slope m, since $a\|b$;

also, the line c has slope m, since $c\|b$. Finally, $a\|c$, since each has slope m.

17. *Given:* Lines a, b, and c such that $a\|b$ and b intersects c.

To prove: a intersects c.

Proof: As in Exercise 16, let m be the slope of the line b; the slope of a is also m; the slope of c is not equal to m; a and c have different slopes and thus intersect.

19. AB and CD each have slope $\frac{7}{5}$; AD and BC each have slope 3; $AB\|CD$ and $AD\|BC$; thus, by definition, $ABCD$ is a parallelogram.

10-9 THE DISTANCE FORMULA

1. 3

3. 5

5. $\sqrt{73}$

7. 10

9. $(x - 1)^2 + (y - 2)^2 = 9$

11. $\sqrt{5}$, $\sqrt{5}$, $\sqrt{10}$;

(a) yes;

(b) no;

(c) yes.

13. *Given:* Circle $x^2 + y^2 = r^2$, $x = p_1$ where $p_1 > r$, $x = p_2$ where $p_2 = r$, $x = p_3$ where $p_3 < r$.

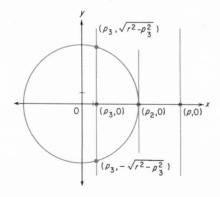

To prove: the line $x = p_1$ does not intersect the circle; $x = p_2$ is tangent to the circle; $x = p_3$ is a secant of the circle.

Proof: If we solve the equation $x^2 + y^2 = r^2$ of the circle simultaneously with the equation $x = p_1$ of the line, $p_1^2 + y^2 = r^2$; that is, $y^2 = r^2 - p_1^2$. But $p_1^2 > r^2$; therefore, $(r^2 - p_1^2)$ is negative and y is imaginary; in other words, this line does not intersect the circle. If we use the line $x = p_2$, $y^2 = r^2 - p_2^2$. But $r^2 = p_2^2$ because $r = p_2$; therefore, $y = 0$ and the only point common to $x^2 + y^2 = r^2$ and $x = p_2$ is the point $(p_2, 0)$; hence, $x = p_2$ is tangent to the circle. If we use the line $x = p_3$, $y^2 = r^2 - p_3^2$. But $r^2 > p_3^2$ because $r > p_3$; therefore, $(r^2 - p_3^2)$ is positive and y has two distinct real roots. Hence, $x = p_3$ cuts $x^2 + y^2 = r^2$ at $(p_3, \sqrt{r^2 - p_3^2})$ and $(p_3, -\sqrt{r^2 - p_3^2})$, and $x = p_3$ is a secant of the circle.

15. *Given:* Isosceles triangle ABC, $\overline{AB} \cong \overline{BC}$ with $\overline{AE}$ and $\overline{CD}$ as medians, $A: (0, 0)$, $B: (a, b)$, $C: (2a, 0)$.

To prove: $\overline{AE} \cong \overline{CD}$.

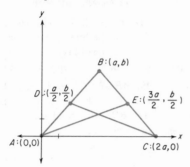

Proof: By the midpoint formula, we have $E: \left(\dfrac{3a}{2}, \dfrac{b}{2}\right)$ and $D: \left(\dfrac{a}{2}, \dfrac{b}{2}\right)$. By the distance formula,

$$m(\overline{AE}) = \sqrt{\left(\frac{3a}{2}\right)^2 + \frac{b^2}{4}} = \frac{\sqrt{9a^2 + b^2}}{2}$$

and

$$m(\overline{CD}) = \sqrt{\left(2a - \frac{a}{2}\right)^2 + \left(-\frac{b}{2}\right)^2}$$

$$= \sqrt{\left(\frac{3a}{2}\right)^2 + \left(\frac{b}{2}\right)^2}$$

$$= \frac{\sqrt{9a^2 + b^2}}{2};$$

hence,

$$\overline{AE} \cong \overline{CD},$$

since each has measure $\dfrac{\sqrt{9a^2 + b^2}}{2}$.

*17. (a)

$\sqrt{(1 - 1)^2 + (4 - 0)^2 + (5 - 2)^2}$; that is, 5;

(b)

$\sqrt{(1 - 2)^2 + (5 - 7)^2 + [0 - (-3)]^2}$; that is, $\sqrt{14}$.

*19. (a) $(x - 1)^2 + (y + 2)^2 + (z - 5)^2 = 4$;

(b) $(x - 2)^2 + (y - 3)^2 + (z + 4)^2 = 25$.

10-10 PERPENDICULAR LINES

1. $-\frac{1}{2}$

3. $-\frac{5}{2}$

5. $y = -\frac{1}{3}x$

7. $y + 3 = -2x$

9. $y - 2 = -\frac{1}{3}(x + 1)$

11. $y - 4 = x - 2$

13. *Given:* $a||b$, $r \perp a$, slope of a is m.
To prove: $r \perp b$.

Proof: Slope of b is m, since $a||b$ and parallel lines have the same slope. Slope of r is $-\dfrac{1}{m}$, because $r \perp a$; hence, their slopes must be negative reciprocals. The slope of b and the slope of r are negative reciprocals; hence, $r \perp b$, because two lines whose slopes are negative reciprocals are perpendicular.

15. *Given:* Intersecting lines a with slope m and b with slope n, lines $r \perp a$ and $s \perp b$.
To prove: r intersects s.

Proof: The slopes m and n are not equal, since the lines a and b intersect. Thus,

$$\frac{1}{m} \neq \frac{1}{n} \quad \text{and} \quad -\frac{1}{m} \neq -\frac{1}{n}.$$

The slope of r is $-\dfrac{1}{m}$; the slope of s is $-\dfrac{1}{n}$; r and s intersect.

*17. *Given:* $\triangle ABC$ with altitudes $\overline{CD}$, $\overline{AE}$, and $\overline{BF}$, $A: (0, 0)$, $B: (b, 0)$, $C: (a, c)$.
To prove: $\overleftrightarrow{AE}$, $\overleftrightarrow{BF}$, and $\overleftrightarrow{DC}$ are concurrent.

Proof: Since $\overleftrightarrow{CD} \perp \overleftrightarrow{AB}$, $\overleftrightarrow{CD}||y$-axis and the equation of $\overleftrightarrow{CD}$ is $x = a$. The slope of $\overleftrightarrow{AC}$ is $\dfrac{c}{a}$ and the slope of $\overline{BF}$, the altitude to $\overleftrightarrow{AC}$, is $-\dfrac{a}{c}$; in the same manner, the slope of $\overleftrightarrow{BC}$ is $\dfrac{c}{a - b}$ and the slope of $\overline{AE}$, the altitude to $\overleftrightarrow{BC}$, is $-\dfrac{a - b}{c}$ or $\dfrac{b - a}{c}$ because an altitude is perpendicular to the side to which it is drawn, and the slopes of perpendicular lines are negative reciprocals. By the point-slope formula, the equation of $\overleftrightarrow{AE}$ is $y = \dfrac{b - a}{c} x$ and the equation of $\overleftrightarrow{BF}$ is $y = -\dfrac{a}{c}(x - b)$. Solving these two equations simultaneously, we have

$$\frac{b - a}{c} x = -\frac{a}{c}(x - b);$$

that is, $x = a$ and $y = \dfrac{ab - a^2}{c}$. Thus, the coordinates of the point of intersection of $\overleftrightarrow{AE}$ and $\overleftrightarrow{BF}$ are $\left(a, \dfrac{ab - a^2}{c}\right)$, which is also a point on $x = a$; therefore, $\overleftrightarrow{AE}$, $\overleftrightarrow{BF}$, and $\overleftrightarrow{DC}$ are concurrent

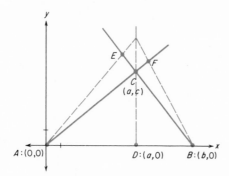

INDEX

A

Abscissa, 343
Absolute value, 215
Abstract system, 71
Aleph-null, 20
Algebra, 206
Algorithm, 50
And ($\wedge$), 118, 213
Angles:
  plane, 179, 325
  trisection of, 24
Answers to odd-numbered exercises, 365
Antiquity, problems of, 24
Arcs, 195

Arguments, valid, 302
  conclusions of, 302
  premises of, 302
Arithmetic:
  clock, 80
  modular, 85, 86
  modulo 5, 86
Associative property, 73
  for addition, 149

B

Base, 41
  five, 45, 46, 55
  number, 51
  ten, 32, 45

413